HAS ANYONE
GOT A LIGHT?

Frank McDermott

MINERVA PRESS
MONTREUX   LONDON   WASHINGTON

HAS ANYONE GOT A LIGHT?
Copyright © F. C. McDermott 1996

All Rights Reserved

ISBN 1 86106 045 9

First published 1996 by
MINERVA PRESS
195 Knightsbridge
London SW7 1RE

Printed in Great Britain by
Antony Rowe Ltd, Chippenham, Wiltshire

HAS ANYONE GOT A LIGHT?

For Pouki:
the alpha and the omega
and everything in between

Ma tu, perchè ritorni a tanta noia?
perchè non sali il dilettoso monte
ch'è principio e cagion di tutta gioia?

Dante, *Inferno*, Canto I: 76 - 78

PART I

1

Nothing easier than pornography, said God, creating Eve from a rib of the sleeping Adam.

Surely he must have known then about all those erogenous areas, and where it would all lead.

What was he really up to?

2

Social problem.

Hand-shaking in France can be a practical as well as a social problem. It is not just a matter of when and where - the answer to that being almost always and everywhere - but of how, when you have a bag in one hand and newspapers, and a bunch of yellow chrysanthemums in the other. Now an amateur mathematician has worked out that time spent by French office workers in exchanging morning and evening hand-clasps adds up to one hour per person per year.

But think of all the time wasted breathing.

And all that duplication, triplication, fornication, multiplication and division.

- Oh, the dull rugby of it -

The social scientist was giving a serious of educational broadcasts, on television, on the modular evolution of the pataphysics. An aeroplane, he said, may be described as a vehicle that is not drawn by horses. He did not even have what you could really call a tvicious face.

- Suddenly electrified when a figure, in despair, goaded beyond endurance, emerged and, picking up the ball, ran desperately, galvanising players and public alike. It was, as you of course guessed, the referee -

Let us do some peace research, he resumed.

7

The squad had been idly killing flies by hurtling a flat soul at them instead of in the more conventional manner with a folded newspaper. Then they got their orders. Versailles, 1940. All day long they toiled to install the gun beside the river, digging deep. It was in place when the colonel arrived in the evening. "Get that bloody thing in immediately" he ordered, "Goddamit, it might rain." So the gun was clean, well-oiled and dry when the Germans collected it next day on their way to Paris.

"Pedals" he said, "have to be pushed hard to get you up a hill."
(Unless of course you've got an engine behind you)
(But he hadn't yet heard of the internal combustion engine)

Asked about the evolution of warfare since Dunsinane, he did an even more impossible thing.
What?
He became even more ludicrous.
What kind of grin did he then manifest?
A sheepish grin.
They are always made by intellectuals, revolutions?
Always.
But you know who goes on turning the treadmill,
afterwards.
Who?
Us.
We, the experimental animals, bred and fed for higher purposes,
God help us.
They treated him contumeliously and put him to death.
Can you cut off life in the middle as well as at the end?
Trees would be fine if they didn't cut off someone else's view of the sea.
- The route through the sea
is open and free
said the girl in the cavorting speed-boat
streaking hop skip and jump for the harbour mouth -
In a game of catch-catch in which you never catch up
contemplating your navel
in naval contemplation
all at sea

wisdom from here
or organs lower down
- the feet for example
(goin' to walk all over God's heaven)
took Adam everywhere
Key to everything, indulgences, said Luther.
Aggornamento. Catching up. Eternally. For two thousand years.
Can eternity catch you up? Pass you out?

Who do you think you are anyway?
One over nought.
Infinity
Nought over one
Naught over one
- bit atheistic that, really
The Reformation (at last.
But don't forget the peasants' revolt, is now, and ever shall be,
world without end)

Ah men, oh men, woe men, women
Women?
Oh, women.
Ee, women.
Why didn't he read Strindberg before that sermon on marriage?

Indulgences
said Luther
key to everything
married a wife
nun better
if you've never done it how do you know?

It was Christmas Day in the madhouse (But why does it always
have to be in the past tense?) The dinner was jolly, with a jolly good
party afterwards, everyone playing lutes and flageolets, goblets and
gold for golden goblets (hendiadys is no disease of poultry), and
singing, and so on and so on. In one corner there was Johann
Sebastian, churning away on the spinet when, catching sudden fire, he
sailed away on the ecstatic wings of a lyric such as no man has heard

from the beginning of the world, nor shall henceforth, ever. But old miserere couldn't leave well enough alone, and had to get up and recite, a little thing of his own composition, he said, something like this:

But man, proud man
dressed in a little brief authority
most ignorant of what he's most assured
his glassy essence like an angry ape
plays such fantastic tricks before the high heavens
as make the angels weep

to which a Prince of the Church replied, on the same Christmas Day a few centuries later, "For Christ's sake, napalm them".

What sort of Remonstrance did they address to the Most Holy Inquisitors of Spain and Portugal, their Most Eminent Excellencies?

A Most Humble Remonstrance
(based on the Penny Cataclysm).

Vat vatch?
Eleven vatch.
Such much vatch?
Metaphysics is strictly for...
Well, what is it for, exactly?

Lady Macbeth gave it as her considered opinion that it was not alone the spot, but the very damned spot.

It could perhaps be filled in with metaphysical plasticine.

The two-roomed flat, when she went to see it, had one room on the first floor and one on the sixth. One foot on the ground and the other in the stars.
A schizophrenic goose-step.
"Assassins," she screamed, "be ye accursed." And so they were, so they were.
The rumours about her husbands were entirely unfounded.

Why do the well-grieved Achaeans
look back in anger
at Helen of Troy
too lovely to die
when their names shall be remembered for ever?
without cryogenics
the modern way
immortality
- when the time comes
and science knows -
and a glorious resurrection
through deep freeze
if you can pay
ask for a FREE illustrated brochure TODAY
(who said the poor wanted it anyway?)

Penelope (wherever did she get the name) sat down in a field of clover.

In the centre of the fire, a bright incandescent cube like an old-fashioned gas-mantle. A cat shaking after a drop of water has fallen on her, the burning wood blushes, a gust of wind passing over a cornfield. One piece, charred black, a Japanese gateway; another, away now from the centre, turns up at the edges as if it were burning cardboard; ash in front like a potato on which the mud has long been caking in the sun.

A car loses its smell of new and rubber.

It's still there, that incandescence, the cube intact. Something in the wood. The horn of a unicorn, the nail off the big toe of a dinosaur, a flake of ash, delicately balanced a moment on air, a hatched-out bird soon swallowed up in the flock.

The radiator is a distant stream pushing its way, passing, obstructed, through rocks and stones, pebbles, sand, strong, stopping, hesitant, off again, finally indefatigable; except that it will cease upon the midnight, with no pain.

It is more than a cube. It now has facets, it glitters like a diamond.

A snowflake drifts by, melting on the breeze.

Tomorrow may drift in and go as easily on the carrying tide not knowing what the port beyond the harbour holds.

"Well, you know" said the judge, "there is this curious and almost palpable moment that comes in a dispute that may have started as a joke, when one of the two feels hurt, defeated or humiliated, and is not quite sure whether to go on treating it as a joke or turn really nasty. The rules are not clear."
There were seven people present, and a woman.
Turning to the witness, he asked courteously:
"Do you think it worse to be burned with a cigar than with a cigarette?"
"I don't know, Sir. I don't smoke."
"You killed him with nineteen blows of the axe."
"Did I? I hadn't counted."
(The eve of a new life is a day like this)
"You know, today I condemned a man to death."
"Was it interesting?"

There was great radioactivity everywhere.
Of course, everyone knew it was just a Kafka Beatlemania, a mutation of jeans, and anyhow Khrushchev had said Stallion told him you should never swop horses in midstream, especially in Hungary, where they are all great horsemen, and who are we, the faithful, to say him nay? And then, singing in unison, in those solemn base voices, for he was a jolly good fellow, they all carried out Stalin together. Pure Eisenstein (Poor Eisenstein).

By the evening of the first day, his left hand had grown just a tiny bit longer than the right. Oh nothing very serious. But work it out for yourself. You can imagine what it was like at the end of three hundred and sixty-six (it happened to be a leap year, worse luck). Beckett foretold it all, so there. The Chinese expert said he might have been able to do something maobee if they'd got him working in

12

time on the feet; for it's a long march to Tipperary, but my heart's right there.

There is someone on the phone who wants to know how you spell apocalypse.

And a certain man going down from Jerusalem to Jericho had a revelation. An aggornamento, he said, that's what we need, an aggornamento.

But he fell among thieves.

Metamorphose odieuse, said André, picking up the scrubbing-brush again. La condition humaine, he added as an afterthought. It's time I sat down and wrote my antimemoires. Hanging outside the Shop Anglais, a flitch of exclusive bacon fluttered in the breeze. Cut off, delicately flavoured with Johnson's Baby Powder and roasted separately, the rinds go deliciously with le whiskey (it's an old Vietnamese recipé).

Is your coca-cola very strong?
No, but it's very powerful.
For, after all, all that can happen potentially exists
skulls all or skulls prospective
celestial skullduggery
a ripple on the waters of eternity
glug glug.

What comes before and after? In between, the pattern is clear. Or is it? A man is born, he lives, and dies. A woman is born, she lives, and dies. A child is born. A man and a woman live. And what dies?
Night dawn morn noon evening night
night into night
in between
a little light
for even when the sun is hottest the cool of evening comes.
Rain beats down. The covering snow. Ground cracking under the frost.
A stone embedded.

Implacable.
Unmoving and unmoved.
A child sits near.

The stone stays put. Picks another, throws it idly. Plop. Ripples spread out concentric, spread, fade, deconcentric. Another. Another sinks, disappears, a new subaqueous life. The stone's still there. Unbudging. Challenge. A free edge, after all. Prise it up. Dirt under the fingernails. It's budging. Edge it up. Loosening. A little more. There. Turn it over. A worm, half in two.

Slugs, white slugs, moist, sunless, unnameable. Curious. A twig. Look, it clings. Pitch it in the water. Twig hits water. Slug lost in grass. Disappeared. Can't find it. Lots of others. Plop. Put it back. No need to crush them. Back again, all loosened edges, fits. And now, down, down, how far down, how far around in and out, out of the light of day, wriggling, crawling, boring, breeding; living and dying.

The child is God.

3

Flying around the table lamp, a very tiny fly, first this year. Struck at it, missed. Irritated. Struck again. got it this time. A bit of life snuffed out. Life?

Where has it gone?

4

Words. Sperm of the intellect.

5

They all love it.

Including the moralists, who need to read it a second time to be sure they are being scrupulously fair.

Exactly every fifty pages or so would have been too mechanical. More cunning than that, the programme fed into the computer had arranged the culminating sex passages less mechanically through the text.

Still, when you think how difficult it is to say anything original on the subject, it was admirable.

And you can't blame the author. How is he to get his manuscript published otherwise? Or even read?

Alexis laid down the book.

A snowflake drifted past.

He could hear the radio across the corridor. He concentrated, but could not identify the music, muffled by the intervening door. She had always loved music, Christine. It was at least something the twentieth century had brought that, as she lay there, dying (it must be faced), she could command, and all the great ones from the dead were conjured living out of a mechanical box.

The phone rang.

Let it ring, he thought.

It insisted. From the end of the corridor, beside the front door, its measured nag exulted, an unimaginative and metronomic virago, browbeating the sound from the room opposite into a mere murmur of almost mutely persistent but ineffectual protest. As he reluctantly made to stand up, it stopped, leaving a silence palpitating with relief, and the sound of the music became semi-audible again. Some friend of Jacky's no doubt, not yet conscious as I am of the accumulating empty Sunday afternoons of a lifetime.

Dumb, infertile, inarticulate.

A noble epitaph if I should die tonight.

Alexis Dolan. Alexis. Fancy name chosen by plain John, whose name was from his own father John. Spoiled pianist, spoiled artist. Perhaps. John and his seven sons, all potential swans, and now all, the five who survive, solid men of sense. Well, perhaps not altogether all. His seven reduced to my two, mixed, a daughter at last. Jacqueline. Shall I compare thee to a summer's day.

This morning I audibly heard birds, the first this year. Strange little bundles. Life fluttering on two wings. Harbingers. In your hand, so frightened, panic eyes and ruffling feathers, darting head, liberty itself touched with a monstrous sacrilegious hand, innocence outraged, like a little beaten and uncomprehending child. Bully, brute.

Spring is not yet. Will the snow fall from the hard blue sky?

A twinge in the knee. A tuberculous knee, and my life was different. My brilliant first year at the University that opened up all the ologies. Only to choose. Aquinas a cross between a passion and a pose, but the odd casually dropped reference or quotation had served well. Even cut pieces out of my hair in front to make my forehead seem higher and larger but it remained narrow. It starts as a whim, affectation or a small vanity and grafts imperceptibly on. Affectation becomes personality. Clothes maketh the man; clothes, naked the man. Shaw without the knickerbockers. Stalin clean-shaven. Hitler unquiffed.

18

But the knee was no affectation, and the limp that went with it had become a permanent adjunct. It even partly explained why he was living here in Paris. A question of climate, hoping to avoid the damp.

The music came to an end. He got up and crossed over to the other room.

Christine was sleeping. Must have dozed off as she often did, listening. Her hair had come loose and was partly unwound on the pillow. She stirred as his dragging leg scraped slightly on the floor, woke and looked shyly and a little guiltily at him. His nurse that was, a conventional story. He had been so thin then, so bright, so foreign, and being foreign exotic, and being exotic, attractive, different. His industry had astonished her. His affectations had taken, giving him an air of self-confidence he was often far from feeling. Nearly always, in fact.

She had been born in Paris, mother German-Swiss, father French-Swiss, he working in the Paris branch of a Swiss engineering firm. Having gone to school in Paris, she was French-speaking but had passed several long holidays in her mother's home and learned the local Swiss-German patois. One of his first memories of her: called to the phone in the clinic. He had thought first it must be bad news, thinking, was she crying, then realising it was only the accent, talking to a Swiss-German girl friend.

The ludicrous schoolboy French he had brought with him enabled him to understand a word in twenty, but he persisted doggedly, and refusing to talk English, unless absolutely lost, helped to force the pace. A first turning point one evening with his introduction to the aperitif, a curious yellow liquid that turned white when water was added, tasted of aniseed balls (ten a penny), and let itself be drunk without resistance. At the second, he felt that his speech was getting thicker, but what fluency, if nothing else, it introduced into his French. At the third, he was prepared to take on the Sorbonne in metaphysical disputation in their own language on their own ground.

Nothing of the fluency remained next day; only the memory, and a head. But the obstacles were what the seas had been to the Conquistadores and, once conquered, the rewards were unimaginable. And the sea is immense, but not infinite. A child can paddle, an adolescent swim, and it is long since man built his first boat. Somewhere south and east from Killiney and the much-loved wintry seas of his own childhood lay El Dorado, France, Italy, Spain, Greece, the Mediterranean and the Golden South where men drank wine into which flowers of jasmine might fall from the scented trees.

Ironic that his first taste should not be the yellow gold of the sun but the white which the Swiss by ingenuity and hard work had turned into a gold of their own, the snow which made sunshine into something hard, brittle, metallic, and the clear night sky of winter into a perpetual night-life that lasted until a dawn that was always accompanied by the sound of voices of people already up and about their occupations, so different from home, where people blandly said it was unlucky to go out in the morning until the streets were properly aired.

She was assigned to his section shortly after his arrival. Speaking much better English than he spoke French, and impelled by a determination to practise it that seems to be almost a patriotic instinct in the Scandinavians, Dutch and Swiss, she tried to make it the language of communication. But he was adamant, imposing his cacophonous approximations, even attempting puns which failed utterly to cross the language frontier and left her bewildered; it took him quite a time to learn that it was not her sense of humour, different as that might be from his, that was at fault.

His illness had been more to him than a physical shock. His arm was affected as well as his leg, and any hope of what he had ambitions to do with the piano was ended. He would never do more again than just play, when his hope had been, one day, to be able to play superbly; even if the cure was complete, he knew his right arm would never again give his wrist the strength and suppleness it needed. His medical studies were suspended, for how long he could only surmise; books he could read, of course, but that was rather different from the camaraderie of the lecture hall and the dissecting room.

20

And then, Maureen. In the abstract, shoulder-length auburn hair sounded as if it could not avoid being slightly vulgar, but her face was cool, oval, aristocratic, eyes grey-green, and she carried her hair with an actor's panache and conviction. He had seen her several times, despaired of ever getting to know her. One day he spoke to her, discovered to his surprise that she had not been unaware of him; more amazing still, the haughty goddess of his imagination had a soft voice and a sense of humour. But was no doubt capricious. She could afford to be. She accepted his invitation. But, obviously, she had not gone unremarked. And the first result of his relative success was jealousy. He had never actually seen her with anyone else, but the others must undoubtedly exist and, seeing the sort of person she was, they must be more sophisticated, more assured than he was, in every way at an advantage. Her interests, too, were no doubt different and his poses and his little learning were not only irrelevant, but slightly comic. Jealousy is as difficult to dominate as any other kind of acute pain.

He was passionately convinced she would not turn up on the Saturday afternoon. Thoughts of it came back as persistently as a bluebottle: the fourth time you go for a newspaper to swat him, come back, and he has disappeared, you lay down the paper and, immediately, the little-shrieking whiny flight is mockingly and impudently audible again. He had been trying to revisualise her face. It obstinately refused to come back into focus. She was already late. He was idly looking into a shop window when she was suddenly beside him, the sun shining full on her. He noticed a few freckles, and was grateful; they somehow made perfection human, almost accessible. The beautiful distant oval dissolved into a smile. He looked at it enchanted as they shook hands: the compliment he should have paid occurred to him later.

"Shall we go to the sea?"
"Let's." She smiled. "But I've got to be back early."
"Killiney, Dunlaoghaire, Howth?"
"As you wish."

They got a bus, went on top. The front seat, with an unimpeded view, was vacant. Soon they were out along the coast road, the park at Fairview stretching out to the sea on the right. Flower beds were already full of colour with early flowers, and the trees in leaf.

"Not long ago, that used to be the sloblands. In fact we had a review at College with a song that went ' ...for we're heading for the sloblands, with its mystical allure, I can smell it in the air, said Sherlock Holmes'."

"There's a touch of it even still," she commented.

"Only seaweed. There are always accumulations of it in places, from the Liffey mouth round to Clontarf. Especially along Dollymount and the Bull Wall. It was out there, I think, that there was a great project to make a Blue Lagoon."

"Covered in, I hope."

"It would need to be. But apart from the time when Oliver St John Gogarty presented the swans for the Liffey, it provided the only occasion in history when Dublin Corporation went poetic. One Councillor in a frenzy of imagination suggested that they should import a real gondola from Venice. Another had an even brighter idea. Why don't we import a couple, he said, and let nature take its course?"

She laughed.

"What a splendid idea" she said. "Can you imagine how marvellous it would be, in a few years, with gondolas' nests in the dunes along the coast?"

- "And little butty men in caps and uniforms going round with walking-sticks and a steel point at the end for spearing up litter, trying to prevent Dublin chisellers from pinching the eggs -

- "And troubadours with mandolines serenading: Santa Lucia in a Dublin accent under the May moon."

22

- "Under an umbrella, more likely. And little gondole disporting in that dolphin-torn, that gong-tormented sea."

"Who is that?" she asked.
"Yeats."

"All I know of Yeats is the Lake Isle of Innisfree. I learned it in school. I had to, in fact. 'Give the poet's thoughts... ten marks.' How glad I am to be finished with school and examinations."

"'And pluck till time and times are done, the silver apples of the moon, the golden apples of the sun.' Did you also learn that?"

"No."

"Not even 'for the world's more full of weeping than you can understand'?"

"No, I was never very much interested in poetry. I like it when someone quotes something, like you did just now. But poetry in a book... I don't know. It looks boring. I couldn't bring myself to open it and read, in cold blood, so to speak."

"It has to be personal?"

"I don't know. I am really very ignorant, you see. But sometimes, oh very very occasionally, like - what was it you quoted about dolphins?"

"That dolphin-torn, that gong-tormented sea."

"It has something strange and mysterious. Even I can feel it. That word dolphin is mysterious in itself."

"Where do you think Dolphin's Barn got its name?"

"I never noticed the name. It's funny how words that are familiar change into something different. Dolphin's Barn. What a mixture. It sounds like a kind of garage for non-ocean-going dolphins. Is there a

23

bus garage there? Maybe the buses are dolphins. And is the barn for one dolphin or for a whole shoal of them?"

"Even so, why a barn? Maybe the dolphin was originally something else. They say the Elephant and Castle in London was once upon a time the Infanta de Castilla, Catherine of Aragon. That was where she lived when Henry VIII got rid of her."

"Dolphin's Barn," she said, "Bachelors' Walk. The Nag's Head."

"The Boot."

"The Magillicuddy of the Reeks."

They both laughed.

"Anyhow, gong is a lovely word too. It kind of..."

"Reverberates?"

"Is that the word. Gong, dong, Chittagong. Do you know, I have an uncle in Chittagong. What a lovely name. Gong, gong, Chittagong. It re... what was that word again?"

"Reverberates."

"It's no good. It doesn't ding-dong enough. You are turning me into an intellectual. Do you know, this is the first time I ever talked to anyone about poetry in my life?"

"Would you like me to write a poem for you?"

"Could you?"

"No."

"I bet you write poetry."

"What makes you say that?"

24

"Something about you."

"Do I really look like that?"

"Like what?"

"Scruffy. Long hair. Lost look."

"You know well what I mean. Well, do you?"

"Well…"

"I knew you did."

"But awful stuff."

"I'll bet you don't really believe that. Anyhow, you don't have to show it to me. Unless," she added mischievously, "it's about me. In that case I have a right to see, haven't I?"

"If I were Yeats you would. But I'm not. I'm only me."

"But Yeats was only Yeats when he became famous. All you have to do is to become famous. Well, is it a date?"

She held out her hand.

The touch of her hand sent a thrill through him. He tried to hold it, then felt by an imperceptible but unmistakable pressure that she wanted it back. He let go in confusion, feeling he had done the wrong thing and spoiled everything. But, engrossed in talking, they had not noticed the miles slipping by, and the bus was already in Howth.

"We're there," he said.

She nodded.

He preceded her down the narrow winding stairway and, turning to help her off, slipped on the metallic bars of the platform. His ankle twisted slightly but painfully. She was beside him, a look of concern on her face.

"It's nothing," he said, limping a little, "it will be all right in a minute."

They sat on a wall. The harbour was crammed with boats. The smell of fish from some boxes mingled not unpleasantly with the sea-tang, the worst of it carried away by the wind. The smaller boats were hornpiping, frantic cradles on the little choppy waves. The hill rose up, awaiting them. He glanced dubiously at her fashionable shoes and, following up the line of her stockings, decided she was definitely not the hearty hockey-playing type. Anticipating him, she said:

"They're solid enough for all the walking I propose to do."

"You don't want to follow in the footsteps of Tristan and Isolde?"

"What's that? I thought that was an opera, Wagner or something."

"It is. But it was here, at Howth Castle, that Tristan came to fetch Isolde, and take her back. In fact, Chapelizod is called after her."

"Really?"

She wasn't much interested.

"I don't even want to see the rhododendrons, even if they are in bloom, which they probably aren't. I just want to see the sea from the top of the hill. Can we?"

He got down from the wall, offered his hand, but she was already down also. A boat was pulling in to the quay, and they stopped to watch it being brought skilfully alongside.

"Funny to think of it," he said, as they made their way up the hill, "Tristan coming in to perhaps that same spot, down there where that boat came in."

"But I thought that was only a legend?"

"Will the skipper of the boat be any more real than Tristan if you come out here tomorrow, and find he is no longer there? Tomorrow, he won't be. Or even, probably, when we come back here later. Tristan, legend or not, will always be here. There must be a moral in that, somewhere."

She did not reply. Why should she care about scraps of guide-book information? That aloofness that so easily settled on her rendered them ridiculous, prattle of a child in the presence of adults. She looked absurdly frail and out of place on the stony path. A gust of wind blew her hair across her face. As she tossed it back into place he realised he was already hopelessly in love with her. The path grew steeper. He went in front and held out his hand. She took it and they advanced hand in hand until the path levelled out again. Thinking to gain some good marks, he then let go of it. They sat down on a bench, overlooking the sea.

The seat was in a little clearing cut into the bank, shaded from the wind, and the sun concentrated a pleasant warmth. They stretched out their feet in front, savouring it, and let the light and warmth play on their faces. He saw kaleidoscopic images on his closed eyelids which the sun turned into a dull-red screen. She was beside him. For how long. The future lay before them, and the great world, out there beyond the horizon. Some day perhaps, she might be someone who was always as near as she was in this blessed moment beside the sea, no longer removed when a used ticket idly dropped at the end of a journey.

The headland was bare. There should be olive trees, silvered, their leaves shimmering, the land rising gradually to the hills. Two goats ate with concentration, the black one, like a lunatic weaver, pulling strands of ragged bushes right back over his head. Suddenly it

27

stopped, looked over at him with that knowing awakened lecherous eye of a conspiratorially randy old man. Pan. Losing interest, it clambered over some rocks, leaped down again, and disappeared.

Above, the sky was blue and empty. Only out to sea was there life, a lone seagull, incredibly single, fishing, wheeling back up each time into the silent air after banking in a great wide circle round. Watching it, he felt the weight of his body, its remorseless attachment to the earth, the earth to which it would return. Never would man have the freedom of a bird, never raise himself higher than the ludicrous height of a jump. The blue up there would remain inviolate. Jove alone could see what was beyond the little cloud he now noticed in the shape of a chariot. Icarus. Even he, myth as he was, had not really gone up but only come down. And the wax had melted in the sun. Blood oozing from a shattered body. Only the melted wax was smooth. I am a Greek, he said to himself. My mind can soar, my body will remain on earth. Flying is strictly for the birds.

He looked at her. Again the wind ruffled her hair, drew a few strands across her face. Her hand went up of its own volition, moved the hair back from her eyes.

"Usually I go south when I come out to the sea" he said, "Dunlaoghaire or Killiney. The only time I ever came out here was late at night, after dances."

"There is a gull down there," she said "the big one on his own. Watch him."

It was the same gull, well to the left of a squabbling group that seemed to have gathered out of nowhere.

He was a real lone bird, ignored and ignoring. He seemed whiter than the others, hovering motionless, then tacking slightly to left or right, treading air, before peeling off down at some target in the water they could not see.

"He would make a good photograph" she said "if he did not come out too small to look like anything more than a blemish on the print. I've tried. I tried with aeroplanes."

The gull rose very fast from his last dive and came up in a great wide arc over the sea through the horizon and then against the sky in front of them, braked, hesitated, and then flew inland over their heads.

"Was that intended as a salute?" he asked as it passed.

"I don't know that I want to be saluted by a gull. Like swans, they're fine in their own element. When you see a row of them standing on a sea-wall, with their flat feet, their country-mug walk, their bickering, their mean little beady eyes... and that awful squawking."

She shivered.

"Cold?" he asked.

"No, I was thinking... that lot down there. I don't know what they're after. Fish, I suppose. But gulls are scavengers. If it was the dead body of someone who had drowned, they'd be at it just the same. Just like they are now. You are right, though. It's getting a little chilly. It's a bit early in the year yet."

He looked at his watch. Three hours already gone.

"Perhaps we might have something to eat out here" he said.

"It's hardly worth while. As I told you, I've got to be back early."

"Sea air is good for the appetite. Let's go and see."

They left the gulls behind, a noisy committee on a discussion that had ceased to interest anyone but themselves - not that, in the manner of committees, that mattered. A few small yachts moving back in

29

towards the harbour accompanied them like friends across the opposite side of a great wide meadow. Others were setting out, late-comers from an office perhaps, or a doctor, free at last on even the Saturday afternoon begrudged him. Coming round the last corner before the path led downwards again, an old man was playing a tremulous "Bard of Armagh" on a fiddle, with a cap hopefully on the ground in front of him, and the tune came up thinly, chopped by little gusts of wind.

The first real afternoon of spring; and going so quickly.

It would be nice now to have a pocketful of money, to stroll negligently into the best hotel or restaurant in the place, to descend with a look the most condescending of head waiters. Like in a film. She is cut out for the part. He made a mental calculation of his student finances.

To be fair, where he did take her did not look bad from the outside, and by the time the proprietor, smiling at the door, had welcomed them inside and got them firmly seated at a table by the window, it was too late to escape - for him at any rate - without being downright rude and hurtful. He sensed that she would have had no compunction about walking out, and was miserably conscious of his psychological cowardice. The menu was the bacon-egg-and-sausage variety.

Nothing wrong with that except that it was all wrong. She cast an ironic glance round, then unexpectedly said:

"I'm hungry. If that's real home-made brown bread, I could eat a plate of it."

In gratitude and relief, he could have died for her on the spot.

As the sun was shining on the window the room was warm enough for the door to be left open; just as well, as it meant that only a trace lingered of the unmistakable smell of boiled cabbage. She did not seem to notice. Fascinated, the proprietor treated Maureen like visiting royalty, anxious only to please. A horse-drawn cab clattered down the roadway outside, a nice old-fashioned note, soothing,

30

tranquillising; time suddenly became plentiful again. But his sense of inadequacy maddeningly remained and, even though it meant they would soon be parting, was almost glad when they were outside again, on the way back to the bus.

Littered with the discards of yet another daylight of living, the day looked worn as they drove back into the city. They did not say much. He did not know how to broach the subject of their next meeting, and they had almost reached her hall-door before he finally did so.

"Yes," she said, "but not for some time. I'm going to London next week. Good-bye for the present, Alexis."

She had already opened the door. She held out her hand.

"Good-bye, Maureen."

He hesitated, then kissed her. She made no objection. As he tried to kiss her again, she caught hold of a lock of his hair in front and pulled his head sideways with an astonishing mixture of force and gentleness. She held on for a second, smiled mischievously, and had disappeared behind a closed door before he recovered from his surprise.

The remainder of the week-end passed in alternate elation and depression, but mostly dominated by a wild lyrical joy at the gentle savagery of her farewell.

It was twenty years before he saw her again.

6

He had strange pains in his leg. As it was the one he had twisted getting off the bus on Saturday, he paid no attention at first. When it persisted, he got worried and finally went to a doctor. The doctor ordered x-rays. A few days later he knew definitely he had bone and joint tuberculosis. As there was no history of the disease on either side in his family the blow was all the worse and the more unexpected. He was in his second year of medicine but, having more or less got over the stage all medical students go through of imagining they are suffering, successively, from each disease they read about, disease, sickness and death had become external abstractions, raw material, clinical realities, something that concerned others only. He mentally panicked. His life was ruined. His class would pass on, qualify, leaving him behind. If tuberculosis had already attacked his bones and joints, why should it stop there? "Galloping consumption" had always seemed a slightly absurd expression he inanely associated with the tide at Mont Saint Michel which is said to come in faster than a galloping horse. Now the Four Horsemen themselves were perhaps mounting.

He was soon busy making travel arrangements. The specialist called in recommended Switzerland. Was there a grim significance in his insistence that treatment should start as quickly as possible? Anyhow, he promised to write immediately and arrange for a bed.

To his surprise, Alexis soon found himself almost enjoying his new role. The family, shocked as he had been, were solicitous, venerating a martyr who had already more or less risen from the dead. The prospect of going abroad for the first time was exhilarating in itself. France, unfortunately, there would not be time for, and Italy was far away to the south. Switzerland he had thought little about, seeing it rather as a turntable in the middle of Western Europe, partaking of the

32

qualities of all its neighbours and keeping out of their lunatic wars, a country of mountains, glaciers, lakes, international organisations, good administration, cream, watches and chocolate.

And money. He looked at the strange banknotes, trying to visualise, and the same series of images came back, mountains, glaciers, lakes... The travel brochures did nothing to alter the images; but there were trains in mountain passes, immense bridges the Romans might have built, white steamers on blue lakes with the inevitable white cross on a red ground trailing behind, vineyards, sunny lakeside swimming-pools with bronzed handsome men who would no doubt know masterfully how to order sophisticated drinks for the nymphs negligently distributed around in the sun, one with a knee crooked, another tossing back over her shoulder her long, damp, newly-combed hair...

But Maureen. He would be gone before she was back. He did not even know her address in London. The nymphs and the pools and the wine in sunny lakeside cafes were for others; he would be lying on his back, tied to a bed and a routine frustrating and imbecile as a soldier's, rooms and corridors reeking of ghastly orderly hospital smells that was their insulation against life, against muddle, against people, normal people, against the warmth of living, against honest dirt even. Operations perhaps. Knives, scalpels, catgut through the eye of a needle, and you're sewn up like a bag. The financial burden on the family. And his mother's grief.

7

They were civilised people, the Swiss. The red flowers transformed the sterile room. Sterile, sterility. At home, the room would not have been so sterile. He remembered hospital wards, the drab rows of beds, horseplay with other students in their relief at getting outside again. The flowers would have to be brought; they would never have been provided.

The light was still on when he woke. Last night, reading, realising he was falling asleep, the radiator had sounded quite differently, pulsing remotely with surges and occasional little sighs, almost as if he were on the deck of a ship halfway between two Greek islands. Between two states. The ticking of a clock grows louder too at night. Or even a watch. The sky was brilliantly blue outside, the crisp cold air almost tangible. Maybe it was that which woke him. Anyhow, everyone woke early here, or seemed to. Traffic was audible from the road beyond the clinic grounds. The pipes now only purred, almost imperceptible.

For a medical student, he ought to be better at identifying flowers, plants, fish, trees, but he could seldom put a name on them. Roses, lilac, asters, nasturtiums, wallflowers, sweet pea, woodbine, dahlias, begonias, pansies, violets. Mostly from seed packages. Anyhow, they'd be called something else here.

Pity it was so impersonal. The price of efficiency. He hadn't even seen them brought. They had come while he was having yet another x-ray. Were they meant as a surprise? Even surprises fitted into a schedule? Someone had told him before he left that, in Switzerland, everything that is not forbidden is compulsory; that planes flying into Geneva do not have to land into the wind as elsewhere, there being only one runway, everything is so well-ordered, even the climate. Was order and cleanliness, for a change, all that unpleasant? There was something beautiful about the austerity of the room, with its solitary splash of red.

That was looking out from the bed. Beside it, on either side, papers, books, magazines, newspapers were piled, resignedly put back into place, each time the nurse or cleaners entered, from where they had dropped, fallen, or simply been carelessly placed. No reproaches. Only the silence. The curved back was becoming reproach enough, resignation coals of fire heaped on his head. He leaned over and picked up Gray's *Anatomy*. No wonder he had fallen asleep. A good quarter of the pages were bent over in the heavy spread-eagled book. He looked at its bulk distastefully and sighed; yes, no wonder he had fallen asleep, trying to read that. He could not even remember what chapter he had been at.

Yet even the attempt to read it indicated that he had reached a certain stability and was settling down.

The familiar journey as far as London had passed unnoticed. Once the farewells had been said, he had gone below, met an acquaintance, and postponed thought. There was little more than enough time to change stations from Euston to Victoria, the romantically-sounding "gateway to the Continent" looking almost as glamorous as Westland Row in Dublin, where his journey started.

Alone in the taxi, he thought of Maureen, hidden somewhere here in this monstrous conglomeration of people, still perhaps the largest on earth. He half expected in some mysterious way to see her, some miraculous coincidence when he came out of Euston, or was passing along the streets, or even, to the last moment, before he boarded the train. The platform was crowded as it pulled out. Melancholy for those present and those who are not. To leave is to die a little. But we die anyway, and except for the ultimate destination, the rest of the itinerary is guessable but unknown. And even the guesses are sometimes wildly wrong.

France he saw for the first time, literally, with a beating heart, knowing with a conviction for which he had no reasonable or logical justification - and above all now - that it would play an important role in his life. It was like the first day in school, or the first day, so different, in the university, itself so different from what the reading of a syllabus had led him to expect. Calais was, and was not, as he had foreseen it. For the moment, he wanted to see no more: it is often better to wait until there really is time before opening a book or putting on a record that is a real acquisition. He would be back. Any worries he might have about his health were quite irrelevant to that one, cardinal conviction. There were glimpses of an intriguing land and another life from the train. Villages that looked so different. The thrill once of seeing the word Paris in large letters on a siding: the way towards, or from. But he slept almost until the train entered Vallorbe and Switzerland the following morning.

And he had his first experience in the station buffet of Switzerland's fresh rolls, croissants, butter and marmalade in their silver-plated containers, the hot coffee and the hot milk in theirs. After a night in a train, who could withstand that?

Sunshine. Even backyards here look clean. Flags. Everywhere, the red invariably brilliant, as if immune from sun and rain alike, and ageless. Did anyone ever see a faded Swiss flag?

And vineyards. He looked lovingly at them, believing he was now seeing the universe for the first time. Bread and wine, sacrificial, eternal. He had an atavistic recognition, coming back to the winelands, from which his Celtic ancestors had set out to the remote western isle where, wineless, their descendants have been melancholy ever since. Or so de Madariaga says. No wonder.

But his direction was east rather than south. And the mountains grew higher here than any he had ever seen. Inconsequentially, he thought so small a country should not have such high mountains. Or so much snow. As if having to walk ten miles when you missed the last bus in Ireland (unless you got a lift) should not be as far as in a huge country like Canada, or Australia. Or Siberia. When the train stopped at a station, the ground was icy. People were stamping to get the circulation going again in numbed legs. A long wet trail passed down the dry platform, with here and there a fast-melting lump of

36

snow that had been carried in on a boot. The tinkle of cowbells was so expected that it almost sounded familiar. Under the snow, he could distinguish the landscape known from childhood on triangular-shaped Toblerone. The chocolate with the little flakes of white in it. Three isosceles triangles in one lump caught awkwardly in the teeth but left a delicious after-taste when you had swallowed the lot greedily down. Not too sweet. Not too rich. Tempered by those mysterious little almond flakes.

Skis. Endlessly sailing with no visible means of support up hill and down dale. Jump, float, land, weaving again, crouched, perfect, skid, skew round, over, dishevelled matchwood. Eh, Mercury, what's it like to be human again, limping on a baton-crutch? Icarus feathers after all, your ankle wings.

Horse-sleighs did after all exist outside Russian novels. There were two at the station. No troikas they. Heads hanging patiently. He left his bags down on the pavement. Little knitted caps on their heads, boys and girls on skis passed with insolent disdain through the traffic, skimming in front of plodding cars.

Out of a café doorway as he passed came the lilt of "Pigalle" - surely not the most appropriate name to associate for ever with a first memory of Switzerland.

There was a glorious whiff of roasting coffee. Why not leave his bags at the station and take a last breath of freedom in this new world? There was a touch at his elbow. Of course, he was being met. A car was waiting. His bags were already taken. As they passed, one of the horses threw up his head, snorted, and looked him straight in the eye. Almost accusingly, the great soft round brown eye, except that the rest of the face seemed to be laughing. A soundless horse-laugh. Normally a horse looked back, if you insisted - by rubbing his nose, for example - but he did not take the initiative. And this was supposed to be a practical, prosaic, efficient country, with no time for nonsense. Tout qui n'est pas interdit est obligatoire, they had said.

8

The clinic, at first sight in any case, was copy-book efficient, untouched by human hand. Unobtrusive reception. He passed over the medical records he had brought, was shown to his room, noted as he passed through that his address was now at 21. The room was predominantly cream coloured, offset with a very light pastel green. There was a small balcony, a view of the garden, mountains (inevitably), the sky blue but shading now in the late afternoon sun. Almost as if he had been indexed by some physico-psychoanalytic electronic machine, he had finished, having unpacked and had a wash and change, when there was a tap on the door. Would he please come along to the doctor's office?

"I see you are a medical student. I hope it will make you feel doubly at home among us here. My name is Jaccoud."

He spelled out the name.

"I am the assistant in the surgical section. Quite a number of us on the staff are old tuberculosis patients. I was a chest case myself. It helps. Although, when it happened, I did not see it like that."

"I can appreciate that," said Alexis.

"I tell you this because it will help you when you get depressed. And you will get depressed, at times. It's inevitable, and it's natural. But it is bad."

"How long do you think I'll be here?" Alexis asked.

"It's very difficult to say. I don't believe in fortune-telling, or not in medicine anyway. I don't know how much you know, or how much your own doctors have told you. I won't hide from you the fact that your condition is fairly serious."

"I guessed that much."

"We have got to the paradoxical stage that bone and joint tuberculosis is now more difficult than pulmonary, which people still fear more because it used to be fatal so often. I should say a year, at the very least. But it need not be time wasted. Try to think of it, not as it may seem to you now, as an interruption of your life and your career, but what it will seem like in twenty years' time, when you look back."

"If I live that long..."

Jaccoud looked surprised.

"You do not really think your life is in danger?"

Alexis blushed.

"Of course," Jaccoud continued, "none of us can guarantee we shall be here in twenty years; or in twenty days, for that matter. But apart from that..."

He played absentmindedly with a small letter-opener shaped like a Toledo rapier.

"One thing I've been thinking about, Doctor. Will it be possible for me to keep up with my medicine?"

"Well I don't know if you have the same proverb in English, but here we say – how shall I put it – it is by smithing that you become a smith. Here you will be actually living in the..."

"Forge."

"Is that the word?"

"By forging you become a forger."

"I beg your pardon? Well, we shall no doubt be able to help you to some extent. We have one of the most celebrated epidemiologists in Europe here, on the staff. And of course, if you are interested in languages…"

"Passionately. Incidentally, may I ask where you learned your English?"

"Two years, post-graduate, in London."

"Well, if I can learn French like that, I shall consider my wasted time well spent."

Jaccoud smiled.

"You are, I am afraid, too indulgent. But maybe I had better remind you that you are here, first of all, as a patient. It is good that you should have interests; so many patients let themselves go, like a plant without water. But you must rest. You must not try to do too much. Your illness is physical, but the mind and the body are one, and the brain is a very important part of the body. If you overtax it, it can also affect the rest. We are a clinic, you know, first of all. Now perhaps I had better explain the routine to you, and tell you what we are trying to do."

9

A week passed. Routine had already been established.

There was a certain amount of physical pain, vague fears also, wondering whether and how far he might be permanently disabled. Loneliness was recurrent, but during the first few days there was little time for it. Everything was new, and much was happening, tests, formalities, examinations. There were none of the vast expanses of time he had imagined: the day was chopped up by meals, by cleaners, by washing, by nurses, by doctors, by the arrival of mail, by an electrician to replace a blown bulb. Civilisation. Only the evenings stretched, and then too much. He was too nervous and fidgety at first to prevent his mind from wandering before he got to the end of a page.

The other life already seemed remote, except when falling asleep, or awakening, with all the metaphysical uncertainties of the unconscious as he sank into or emerged from it, and habit and accumulated memories predominated over novelty and incident. He still looked for instance, on waking, to where the window had been in his bedroom at home, was momentarily puzzled that a washbasin should have replaced the fireplace.

Then days began to take on their new pattern and rhythm. He knew when his time would be his own. Reading became possible, became in fact a necessity. He made a real start on his medical books. He asked for French and German magazines and newspapers, was delighted when he could understand most of the headings and part of the text but found himself just as often staring in maddening frustration at a page on which not one sentence would yield up a meaning.

41

He wrote to Maureen during the first week, telling her of his illness, giving his impressions of the journey and of his new life, trying to keep the letter interesting without allowing it to become too personal. Referring to their Saturday afternoon, he introduced the word "we" a few times as a kind of talisman.

He had almost ceased to expect a reply when one arrived. He had never seen her writing. It was more childish looking than he would have expected, and yet was curiously firm.

A letter from someone loved is a miracle. Which is just as well, as the contents so seldom are. There wasn't much to read into or take out of hers, after he had taken a rapid glance at the signature to make sure it was really from her. And yet it was exactly the kind of letter he would have expected her to write. She had only just come home. She was very sorry to hear about his illness and hoped it was not serious. He must let her know from time to time how he was getting on... Feeble as it was, he grasped at that straw: it was at least a line of communication open. But if only it were a little less stereotyped, a little bit personal. Had she really pulled his hair when he had kissed her? Absence makes the heart grow fonder. Or perhaps farther. Out of sight, out of mind. Take your pick.

Something to make an impression on her. That poem she had asked for. A joke. And yet. No, she had said so, no interest in poetry. It would be worth the value of the paper it was written on, and the ink, and she would not be a collector of pieces of used paper or go in for the chemical recovery of ink; a poem never won a woman's heart unless it was not already won. Poor old Beethoven and his ferne geliebte. He had his mortal happiness posthumously: we love your memory and revere your shade.

And yet

At least she had written. That meant he could reply, but not too quickly. Reply, and then another agonising week, fortnight, month, wondering. And then at the end of it all "I was glad to get your letter and to know you are not feeling too badly (could she not have made it "too lonely"). One of my uncles lived in Lausanne/Zurich/Lucerne.

42

There was a lake, I remember. But I suppose that is a long way from where you are. Will you be able to ski? I should love to. You are lucky. The weather is ghastly here, cold and wet. Well, I must end now. I have been to three dances this week, and I must go to bed early for once. With best wishes." He probably would never be able to dance. He would spend another week thinking of her going to dances, wondering who with... What's the use? Better let it drop. Now.

His decision taken, he felt regretful but better.

Two hours later, he was so lonely and depressed that, almost without lifting his pen, he wrote twelve pages of a letter to her. It tired him, but with a relieving fatigue, the convalescent fatigue that follows seasickness. He did not remember the address off-hand. The envelope must wait until he did, or could find the piece of paper with her address. An unclosed letter leaves the subject open. He knew he should read over what he had written, but could not bring himself to do so. Staring out of the window, he thought of her. Us. Not so much an absence; loneliness, deeper-wounding is her active non-presence, she whom I love. The day was fading. The flowers had been renewed again that morning. One petal had fallen, red like a blood droplet on the white under-mat. He took out his writing pad again and wrote:

A petal falls
drawing the others closer round her
the wounded rose
shivers in the wind.

One day he might send it to her, his first real poem ever.

10

The following morning he found her address, and had the letter posted, without the poem.

In his shy way, Jaccoud became friendly. Apart from his professional visits, he would occasionally drop in and talk in that too-perfect English that he managed like an expert on skis, locomotion perfect, never a foot wrong - but it's still not your own feet. He was French-speaking but knew German almost as well, and found Italian easy. One day he said:

"I have never been to your country, but I should like to go. I had a friend once, when I was a student, who had read your famous Sinj..."

"Synge?"

"Excuse me. Is that how you pronounce it? Synge. Well it made such an impression on him that the only ambition he had in life was to go to the Aran islands."

"And did he go?"

"No, he was married before he was twenty, and he has now got three children. But I met him last summer, and it was still the same. I am sure that some day he will do like Gaughin and throw up everything and just go."

"That's a lot to do on the strength of one book."

"It's not as unusual as you might think. We do not produce many great names. The French rather look down on us, and if we do produce someone like Honegger or Corbusier, they just annex them. They automatically become French. But you may not know that, apart from the major powers, we have the biggest consular service in the world. Not because we have any illusions about Switzerland's importance but because we have nationals living in all of these countries. And they are not all travel agents, or bankers, or commercial travellers, or working for the Red Cross. A lot of them are, of course. Some are scientists. A lot are anthropologists. But there are always a few others who find Switzerland too organised. Some, like my friend, have read a book and imagine they have discovered their spiritual home. I really believe that one day he will simply disappear and go."

"By the way, thank you for the books" said Alexis. "I found *La Porte Etroite* fairly easy to read. In every sense of the word. I never read Gide before."

"I thought you would like it. Being Irish, I suppose you are religious."

"I suppose I am. At home, everyone is, in the same sort of way. It's part of the natural order of things. What are you, Doctor? Protestant?"

"Officially. I don't really believe in anything. Maybe that book appeals to me for the same reason as it appeals to you. For me it is a kind of link with my childhood, when I did believe, intensely. And a book can be moving if it strikes a chord that once sang true. He writes beautifully, of course."

"I could sense that. I'm afraid I know very little about French literature. There is so much in English, which is always easier to read. And anything you read in school, in a foreign language, tends to be or to become or to seem fossilised. Which is a pity."

"I envy you being able to read Shakespeare. You can't translate him. Is it true that he is difficult even if you speak English?"

45

"I would not say I could tell you the exact meaning of every word in, say, *Hamlet*, for instance, but the meaning seems to come by a kind of instinct. Especially if you read for pleasure, and do not have to answer some stupid pedant of an examiner."

"That's precisely it. I shall never be able to read Shakespeare like that."

"Well, your friend can apparently read Synge, and in a way, he's almost more difficult, since his English is taken literally from the Irish in an idiom completely alien to English."

"Jean-Pierre was a real specialist. Mine, you remember, is medicine, not literature. And, anyway, with him it was a kind of mysticism, a man who had discovered his Shangri-la."

"Did you ever see the Flaherty film *Man of Aran*?"

"No. I've heard of it. Perhaps some day, in a cine club. You can't imagine what a romantic place your country, and its ocean, seems from this little continental island, with all its mountains and its lakes and its scenery. For us you belong to Edgar Allen Poe and *Wuthering Heights* and Walter Scott. That probably sounds completely silly to you."

"I'm afraid the reality is quite different. I mustn't allow myself to bore you stiff about a tiny, poverty-stricken little island lost out there in the ocean and talking as much about itself as if it were the centre of the universe and anyone was interested."

"Every place is the centre of the universe. And, anyhow, lots of people, given the choice, would go to Tristan de Cunha rather than Texas, or to the Hebrides rather than to Hanover."

"The trouble is, if you get three Irish together and they're feeling generous, they may allow the English Shakespeare; the rest, from Swift down to Synge, Shaw, Wilde, Yeats and Joyce, are all ours. America is its biggest piece of land off the coast of Ireland, our largest colony in fact."

"Well, it's time I was leaving," said Jaccoud. "If there is anything you need, including books, let me know."

"Thank you very much, Doctor. You know, I often had a foreboding of something like this happening – so much so that, in a kind of perverse way, I almost looked forward to it, a time out when I could concentrate on a lot of things I would never have had time to do working full-time for a medical degree. I didn't say so at the time, but you may remember, the day I arrived, you recommended just that."

Jaccoud got up to leave.

"Don't forget, I also warned you not to overdo it!"

"No danger," Alexis answered, "my natural indolence will look after that. One of the most maddening things of all is the way I can fall asleep with a book I'm really interested in."

"Our bodies are often wiser than we are," said Jaccoud. "Goodnight."

11

There were other English-speaking patients. He met one, in the laboratory, one morning. The American was friendly, obviously longing for company, and seemed pleasant and intelligent. But Alexis refused the opening. To get into an English-speaking group, so easy in that kind of closed society, would have seemed like going from Ireland, not to France but to Brittany. His mind was an inchoate mass of ideas and vague ambitions and he knew much better what he did not want than what he did. Apart from Jaccoud, he had few contacts. The chief doctor was cold, reserved and very professional. His dignity was somewhat frustrated by an enormous unruly seal-like moustache and very round spectacles that looked too comical to be anything but friendly. They proved to be a mask. He was positively sour, the only person in the place Alexis took a dislike to.

The nursing staff were mostly elderly, serious, efficient, conscientious. And dull. He longed to see something a little more Latin, from Italy or the Tessin. One morning his breakfast was brought up by a maid who was unmistakably Italianate and who was obliging enough to trip and drop the whole trayful on the floor. She was so comical in her surprise and confusion that he burst out laughing. She looked helplessly at the mess and then started laughing too. They were both hilarious when the door opened and a sour-puss poked a stern face in. The little maid did not appear again; only a faint coffee-stain remained on the floor to mark her passage and the liberating memory of a little anarchy.

Soon after he had one of his worst periods of depression. It came on him unexpectedly. He had been reading quite contentedly when the hand holding the book became uncomfortable. At the same moment, the central heating seemed too hot and he got a smell of sweat from under his armpits. He moved position, and the change gave him a feeling of tiredness across the small of his back. He dropped the book and lay flat, with a sudden loathing for this body he had been allocated and which was no doubt now at only the first stage of the frustrations it would inflict on him for the rest of his life. Our bodies are often wiser than we, Jaccoud had said. Yes, doctor's raw material, laboratory specimens. Provided we accept their terms. But, married to them, there is no alternative but to accept their terms.

And that meant being stuck sticky in a bed, immobilised in one spot, a derisory way indeed of starting to travel in foreign lands. Earth hath not anything to show more fair. Bronzed bodies hurtling down ski-slopes, nonchalant girls lying round in deck chairs on sun-balconies. A life I will never know. Going round a lake in one of those big white boats. Setting out early on Sunday morning, stopping off at some little port a few hours later, to take breakfast on a terrace just in from the lake-side. And Maureen, sitting opposite, sitting next to me, looking out across the water to the mountains opposite. She had not replied. Not even the stereotype he had imagined. How idiotic to send off that enormous, silly letter. Three weeks ago already. Twelve pages of his pseudo-intellectual posturing. He tried to remember what he had written and could not recall anything that might justify, let alone forgive it. Self-condemned without the evidence, he felt his cheeks grow hot with shame. He picked up the book again, could not concentrate, pitched it in disgust into the far corner of the room, startled himself by the noise he made, listened, but no sound around protested, got out of bed, recovered the book, creased back the bent pages, and stood looking out the window. The air was cooler, but his head was throbbing. He struggled back to bed, lay down, with one foot lying over the side, too miserable even to straighten out the bedclothes.

Let us be logical.

Loneliness enhanced logic and logic bred new depression.

He was icily aware that Maureen was lost. Even that was an exaggeration. You can lose only what you once owned.

49

But logic is only a small part of the mind. So many get on quite well and much more happily without it, never bothering. Falling in love is not very logical to start with, but it's enough for a start. Now in retrospect, his one Saturday afternoon with her seemed even more idyllic. She became still more lovely, remote now in a new dimension... he slept.

A cold foot woke him but, half-awake only, he clung to sleep, coaxed it back as he brought his leg in, noticing that, unless he moved too abruptly, his headache seemed gone. This time he really slept.

But the depression woke with him, gluey on his consciousness, not to be shaken off. The second day he again tried a rational attack on it. His career was interrupted. Agreed. But I can create a frame for the life I want to lead. My brain might allow the success open to the professionally competent, but I've always wanted something more. I'm becoming pompous. It doesn't matter, no one is listening, and no one knows. I want something more. Maybe its what people mean by a vocation, following a vocation, and Maureen is somehow part. There is so much to learn, to know, to do. Europe alone. The fabled Mediterranean. Could any man, in one lifetime, explore it all, and yet find time to give something back, to add his mite to what would pass on and not perish?

His balance-sheet was getting satisfactorily near its final ruled double-line when he remembered Maureen again and all crumbled. For a second, her face came absolutely into focus, before he properly realised he was thinking of her, and then refused recall. The framework folded up. His schemes and ambitions of a moment before became as irrelevant as the scenery of another play.

12

Jaccoud had news.

"Bad news, I'm afraid," he said. "It will be necessary, after all, to operate on your knee. We took all this time to make up our minds, because there was always a chance we could manage without operating. After seeing the latest x-rays, it seems clear that, by operating, we can cut the treatment by a good six months, with every chance of getting better results."

Alexis was silent.

"The operation is not very much in itself," Jaccoud went on.

"When is it to be?" Alexis asked.

"The day after tomorrow. Not much notice, I'm afraid."

"If it has to be, I prefer it that way. Thinking about getting a tooth out is much worse than the actual extraction."

"As well as that, once it has healed a bit, we shall be able to let you out of bed, probably let you go out within a couple of weeks. The town itself is nice, you know. You haven't even seen it yet, I think."

"Only the evening I arrived. I almost went for a last fling, but your reception service was too efficient. It's curious, crossing the threshold into a new world. It has always fascinated me, that threshold. I remember my last day in school. Everything was already a bit changed. To the masters – one in particular – we were almost adults; at least, no longer quite the same."

"They probably realised, too, it was the end of another year."

"There was a sort of fraternisation. And going out the gate, I said to myself, this is the very last time. If ever I pass through again, it will be the same gate, but everything will be changed. And coming here, crossing the last frontier between the world of healthy people and hospital, it seemed more real than the one between France and Switzerland."

"The womb and the tomb" said Jaccoud "although that doesn't seem very complimentary to my own country."

"One frontier is the way in, one the way out. Our own little bit of individual national territory, sliced off from eternity."

"And as arbitrary and irrational at one side as the other with no say at all in your coming, and little more in your going. Even suicide is only a choice in appearance. Did you ever think about suicide?"

"I can't say I ever did."

He looked curiously at Jaccoud, the well-groomed hair, the perfectly-creased trousers beneath the white coat, the impeccable Swiss professional correctness. Thirty-seven or thirty-eight, probably. The eyes were always thoughtful; now they were sad as well.

"You were in Ireland during the war?" he asked.

"Yes, Ireland was neutral you know."

"Your eternal quarrel with the English?"

"Largely. Even now, part of Ireland is still included in what is called the 'United Kingdom'. The generation who fought for independence found it difficult to see any difference between that sort of occupation and Germany's occupation of Czechoslovakia, for example. And then, no one in Ireland believed about the concentration camps until they saw the photos at the end of the war. English papers were ludicrously anti-Irish, with the most ridiculous stories – German submarines refuelling in Irish ports, for example, when there was hardly enough petrol in the country to fill a cigarette-lighter. If they could make up that sort of propaganda about us, what must their propaganda against their real enemies be like? Most of the time, all Great Powers seem equally odious to small countries. Then, it was only a question of whose turn next."

"The concentration camps were real enough."

"I know – now. Although if I had known earlier, I'm not so sure I would have done anything very heroic. Perhaps we are all glad of an excuse to keep out of war. Finally, the Germans were the only ones who entered it voluntarily. England and France did to save their skins: it was obviously their turn next, one way or the other. The Americans stayed out until they were kicked in hard, by the Japanese and Pearl Harbor. The Russians weren't given much alternative either."

"We could actually see them across the Rhine, at Basle and Schaffhausen," said Jaccoud, "never knowing what morning we would wake up with the invasion tanks rolling down our streets, and the bombers overhead."

"During the first couple of years it seemed impossible that we could escape. Until the Germans attacked Russia, I could not imagine any way in which they could be defeated. They seemed invincible. And inevitably, they would swallow us up too. After all, part of our population is German-speaking and so it was part of the sacred duty to liberate them."

He was silent a moment.

"We lived in daily fear. You may find it hard to believe, but I am sure I was not the only one who almost wished the Germans would attack. I remember coming home in the evenings, reading a paper at my evening meal. Always the same story. I often wondered if we would ever again see the day when an airliner would crash, killing fifty people, and that would again represent a major tragedy. I remember the day the war broke out, thinking it would be like – the

53

Seven Years' War, I think it was – that it would end when Germany joined with England and France to fight the Russians. It has almost come to that. And, since there are two hundred million Russians and seven hundred million Chinese, it would mean all joining up with the Russians to fight the Chinese, in the name of some new -ism. There is no limit to human lunacy."

"Orwell wrote somewhere about all the smelly little orthodoxies contending for our souls," said Alexis.

"One evening I was sitting at home. There was a Dürer woodcut on the wall opposite. Saint Jerome in his cell, writing, a kindly lion on the floor in front of him, lying with his tail between his hind paws. I put on a record, and tried to concentrate on the music. And I remember thinking to myself: I sit here listening to Debussy, looking at a Dürer woodcut, as bombers go out to blast innocent people to eternity. At this very moment, whole households of people are writhing in agony. I have sat here, evening after evening, listening to Brahms, Schumann, Mozart, as bombers rain down death. How can I? The answer seemed to be, I can, and I do. I became obsessed with the idea. Perhaps I should have joined some army. But as I once said to you, the French rather despise us; they think we welcome wars because they make us rich, that our attempts to relieve suffering are a form of conscience money. Anyhow, there was no longer a French army. And I suppose I'm really very Swiss at heart. We are all automatically in the army here, and to volunteer for another during wartime is as good as high treason. So I volunteered for the International Red Cross."

"Surely doctors were more needed than soldiers – there were more than enough enrolled to kill."

"That would be true if the world were a rational place; if it were, war would be unthinkable. Did you ever notice, by the way, how much more final the German way of death is than anyone else's? Life is a Totentanz. People talk about the Spanish preoccupation with death, but their word for it, at least, is soft compared to 'Tod'. It is crude death. It almost smells of the earth. It physically stops the breath when you utter it. And 'Tod' is accompanied by Vernichtung.

Nichts. They reduce you to nothing, not even a memory in someone else's mind, while that lasts. Anyhow my problem was a personal one. Disease and illness are evils if you like, but they are natural, in a sense even accidental. As a doctor you can more or less cope with them. You know what to do. But this mad, indiscriminate slaughter of one another is an evil that is terrifying. If I believed in the devil, that would be diabolical. If I believed in hell, I was already living in it. It is, I don't know how to put it; maybe metaphysical evil is the word. You are a privileged spectator who can look on, safely."

Jaccoud took out a handkerchief. There were beads of perspiration on his forehead.

"Well," he continued, "for six months I went out on inspections of prisoner-of-war camps. It sounds paradoxical, but it almost made me feel that war wasn't so bad after all. There was always a tremendous lot to do and take one's mind off the worst – reports, travel difficulties, and so on. And if adults insist on playing this silly game, being a prisoner-of-war was just a logical continuation of it. I did not see them as I see you, prevented from doing what you want to do and should be doing. With a routine job you accept the routine. You have to. But I don't know if you can ever do a job rationally that has moral implications and altogether stifle them without at the same time stifling yourself. Perhaps I was lacking in imagination. For the moment, I had had enough of imagination, and was glad of a routine which seemed like doing a duty, and not having to think any further. I had done my military service. Prisoners-of-war seemed like we were when we went to barracks first, professional complainers. They were so matter-of-fact about everything that they seemed as well off, at least, as risking their lives somewhere else.

"Then, after about six months, I was sent on a special mission to Czechoslovakia. The Germans had always pretended of course that the stories about Jewish massacres were just Allied propaganda. They wanted us to see for ourselves how Jews were really treated. I was met by a group of German officers, and introduced to the Mayor of this all-Jewish town. It had its own Town Council, its own police, even a bank. People looked well, especially by war-time standards. There was a clinic. They had an orchestra which gave a concert. The

55

music seemed pathetic and yet, in some way I can't explain, one of the bravest things I could imagine. In a kind of square there was even a football match. It seemed almost like a peace-time town. People strolled around. All the officials I met were Jewish. They answered my questions. Their answers about food seemed particularly reassuring. There were always a few Germans near, but the town had well over a thousand people. I was suspicious, of course, but no one made any attempt to protest, or slip me a note, or anything like that. It was so different from, say, some of the prisoner-of-war camps full of Cockneys I visited, which were one long complaint from the beginning of my visit to the end.

"I completed my inspection, and was about to sign an inspection book before getting into the car to leave, when a man suddenly burst out from a small group who were standing there, watching, and shouted at me in German: 'Don't believe them,' he shouted 'it's all lies, lies. They are all murderers, swine, swine.' Something like that. Two sergeants rushed forward immediately and took him off.

The major turned to me.

'You see what we are up against?' he said. 'Even when we accommodate them in a model town, there still are provocators.'

"He had the book in his hands, open for signature. He handed it to an aide. Seeing my hesitation, he turned to the others who were still standing there, petrified. He called them over, singly, one by one.

'This gentleman is from the International Red Cross. Tell him: is there any truth in what that man has just shouted.'

'No.'

'Swear it.'

'I swear it.'

56

"There were eleven of them. I counted. I remember counting them. He took the book back, still open, and held it out.

"I signed it.

"I signed at least one death warrant at that moment, although these gentlemen had no need of death warrants. I had been taken completely by surprise. Up to then, my work had been routine. Our position is extremely delicate. We know that the Geneva Conventions are cynically broken by all belligerents when it suits them – with the same cynicism as our laws are broken by the people who are there in our name to see they are respected. The Red Cross can do a limited amount of good. Our first duty always is not to compromise the little we can do. I should have insisted on an enquiry. I realised that fully afterwards. But I also realised that, even if by doing so I succeeded in getting a semblance of justice for one man, the others would have paid bitterly for it. But can you suppress every generous instinct that you may have as a man, the revulsion at injustice, in the interests of some hypothetical, higher good? Anyhow, it was too late. The Germans had given me lunch in their mess, a good lunch, with excellent wines. By then I had relaxed, half convinced by what I had seen. They had been highly civilised in their mess, and once you have broken bread at someone's table, it's difficult to remain as suspicious as before.

"Going back in the car, the incident began to hammer in my brain. I had done nothing for the one man brave enough to have no doubt committed suicide – in vain – for his community. The only thing now was to make a full report. This I did when I got back. My superiors did not seem to think I had done anything particularly wrong. Any power for good is more dependent on goodwill than a power for evil, and none more so than the Red Cross. The incident was significant. The proof had not been made that even one town – which could not be representative in any case – was above suspicion. The man might be genuine, or he might be a trouble-maker. The second was unlikely, as few trouble-makers are prepared to risk their lives for the pleasure. The case was unfortunate, but one of many, an enigma which might possibly have a good side – and that was true of so few where the Jews were concerned.

"To me it was different. More and more evidence was accumulating about the gas-chambers. I remembered the eleven who had sworn. The man himself made twelve. That left me thirteenth. Judas. I was sure he had been murdered, as I was becoming more and more sure that others were being murdered also, by these cultivated gentlemen who had entertained me to lunch. I could not go on. I resigned as a delegate. But then I found I was even worse off, in an oasis, cut off from the suffering, rewarded for my own cowardice and incompetence. I had a nervous breakdown. I tried to commit suicide. That failed. One day, some time afterwards, I saw a photograph of the Nazi occupation of Vienna. The whole population was called out to watch a new spectacle: old Jews, of both sexes, down on their knees, scrubbing the roadway. In this capital city of a Europe with two thousand years of Christianity behind it, was there one priest, or one Catholic or one Protestant to leave the ranks, to come out and take the scrubbing-brush from an old man or an old woman, and go down on his knees in their place – even if it was useless to protest, and the Nazis had a grim way of dealing with people who interfere with their sport? I know from my own experience that I would never have the faith or the courage to make that gesture. But there are people who have. Like the man who protested in the model Jewish town. And it is people like him who enable us others to face life, even if we are not worthy to live."

Alexis found he was unable to speak.

After a while Jaccoud said: "I do not know why I told you all this. Perhaps it is because you still have the choice, you can still do all I hoped one time to do with my life."

He moved towards the door.

"The Russians have a proverb," he said: "To live one's life is not just like crossing a field."

13

Jaccoud's story reminded him of the greater tragedy all round, beside which his own problems were infinitesimal. The extermination camps had been closed – but for how long? How would the wrecks who had survived start a new life again? Millions, literally millions of people, families broken up, mangled, maimed, blinded. Despair. And guilt, for which shining uniforms were no longer an adequate cover. The great crop of conscience-easing phrases. Like "Displaced Persons." Millions of them alone. And another Brave New World.

That same morning, a new nurse appeared. Young for a change. Even with her hair severely done up in a bun, she looked pretty. Thank God, at last one who does not look solid or motherly. She was, however, very efficient and professional. It still seemed exotic to be greeted with a "Bonjour, Monsieur," but he had by now heard it often enough to recognise that her accent was distinctly not Swiss-German. She had come to take a blood sample.

"Will it hurt?" he asked.

"No," she answered seriously, "just a tiny cut in the finger. It is nothing. It will not hurt."

"Are you sure?"

"Yes," she said, a little impatiently.

"You see," he continued, "I'm very thin. I've given so much of my life blood for Switzerland already."

She remained perfectly serious.

"I am sure Dr Jaccoud will have taken account of that."

He wondered who was pulling whose leg.

She took his hand. Hers felt soft and feminine. She swabbed a finger, gave an expert jab, and the operation was over. The finger did not even bleed. She inspected it.

"I cannot foretell what the doctor will say, of course, but I think you will survive this," she said.

"Thank you," he answered, "I feel relieved."

She turned to the table with the phial. Gray's *Anatomy* was standing on the top of a pile of books. He gave it a slight push. It toppled and fell exactly as he hoped, flat, with a shot-like sound as it struck the linoleum. Startled, she let the phial drop, and it smashed.

"Oh, excuse me, I'm awfully sorry," he said, innocently.

She stooped and picked up the pieces of glass, her professional pride ruffled. Then she looked at him. Would she smile at last?

"You are going to lose some more blood," she said impassively.

"If it's in a good cause I don't mind," he answered, "but I must admit it's the first time in my life I've been asked to let my blood be shed twice within the space of five minutes."

"You did it on purpose, didn't you?"

"What?"

"That book," she said.

"Yes," he answered, and stared her in the eye until suddenly she let go and smiled. She picked up the syringe again.

"You must remember, a hospital is a serious place."

"Gold is where you find it," he answered irrelevantly. "They say life is a serious place too. Depends on how you take it." He held out his hand.

"The other one," she ordered.

Again the short, expert operation. This time she took no chances, and did not turn her back. Then she went over, removed the flowers from the vase, emptied it into the wash-basin, rinsed the vase, refilled it, put the flowers back, and expertly arranged them. They looked refreshed.

"Thank you," he said.

"I will be back in the afternoon," she said, as she prepared to leave.

He repressed a facetious compliment he was on the point of making and which, he realised, would now seem misplaced and vulgar.

She looked back from the door. Her smile seemed somehow joined in conspiracy with the flowers.

14

It was decidedly a full day. He was still thinking of her when there was another knock and the post arrived. Maureen's writing on the envelope gave him something closely akin to a feeling of guilt. Absence makes the heart grow fonder. Out of sight out of mind. Be vigilant about your ideals: you know not the day nor the hour.

His twelve-page letter, about which he had such doubts, had pleased her. She was almost enthusiastic, commenting on various things he had mentioned. A couple of sentences at the end set his heart beating faster. "There is a chance that I may be going to Paris later in the year. I suppose even that is only about half way to where you are. But who knows?" He could scarcely believe it. Even if she did not come, she was interested enough to have thought of coming, on her own initiative. And she had now written twice, the second time less a duty letter, almost a real one. The world was suddenly gay and bright. He momentarily forgot about the operation. Even glaciers move, imperceptibly.

15

Characteristically, the clinic had checked his file before the operation and asked if he wanted to see the chaplain.

He did. One never knows.

Father Robertson was from Bristol, a heavily built man of about sixty with a very complicated lung condition who was a more or less permanent resident.

"Well," he said, entering the room, "it's nice to see one of ourselves."

Not knowing whether this was meant in a religious or a racial sense, Alexis bristled anyhow. His visitor's next remark clarified the issue.

"You're British, aren't you?"

"Irish," said Alexis.

"It's the same thing. I've never understood all this nonsense about Free States and Republics and all the rest of it. The last time I had a parish – a long time ago it was – three quarters of my parishioners were Irish. Good people. A bit given to drink perhaps, but good Catholics."

He looked hard at Alexis.

"You're not one of these Sinn Feiners, are you?"

On the spot, Alexis decided to add a few new names to the martyred dead. In a proud, sad voice, he answered,

"My father was executed by the British in 1916. My eldest brother was shot by the Black-and-Tans, and my mother's sister was run over by one of their armoured cars in 1920. What do you expect an Irishman to be?"

"If he's a good Catholic, I expect him to forget all these old stories. A lot of good it is to them, with their independence, and half of them starving. Look here, my boy. When you are as old as I am you will realise that all that talk is only talk, and evil talk at that. And I am not talking to you only as a priest. I am talking to you as a man who has lived in this little country here for the last fifteen years. It's not a bad place in its own way. But an Englishman – or an Irishman if you wish – could never get used to it. The way they eat, for one thing. All that lettuce and rabbit food. And making tea with those dirty little bags on a string."

"But don't you think some things are better here?

"What's better here?"

"Well, coffee for instance."

"Coffee? Never touch it. Bad for the heart. Do you know, they couldn't make a cup of tea to save their souls. And God knows, it's not hard to make tea. Well, I suppose I'm lucky to be alive at all, with the way my lungs are. You are not a lung case, are you?"

"Bone and joint. I am having an operation on the knee tomorrow morning."

When it came to hearing confession, Alexis found him unexpectedly liberal, much more so than their conversation would have indicated. He found himself almost liking him.

But hoped he would not call too often.

16

The new nurse attended at the operation, which turned out to be longer and more painful than expected. The surgeon worked on it for almost two hours. Alexis was brought back to his room, still under the effect of the anaesthetic. The nurse was left to watch; the evening before, he had discovered that her name was Christine.

She was sitting beside the bed when he came to, with a fierce dumb pain all along the side of his body. Gradually he remembered where he was and what had happened. For one awful moment he felt that his leg must have been amputated. His hand went instinctively to find whether or not it was still there. She moved over quickly.

"Does it hurt very much?"

He nodded.

"Dr Jaccoud asked me to let him know as soon as you were awake. I shall be back in a few minutes."

In the world apart of pain, he was dumbly grateful for her presence that seemed to communicate across vibrating walls of isolation. He felt maimed, doubtful whether he should ever be able to walk again. Why should it happen to me? Perhaps I should have turned back that day of my arrival when the horse laughed. We walk on when we could still turn back. What is the compulsion: fear, courage or simply afraid to be seen to be afraid? He had not fully realised it beforehand; now he knew, felt quite sure, that his leg would never be the same again.

Jaccoud was along a few minutes later.

"It was a more difficult operation than we had expected from the clinical examination and the x-rays. For the moment, what you most need is sleep. I am going to give you an injection."

Alexis was too tired even to show any interest; feeling worse than a seasick passenger longing for land. He was dimly aware of Christine and Jaccoud before they receded into oblivion, and were succeeded by four men in step resolutely walking down a road. He followed them. The road inclined upwards and for no reason he was standing on the top balcony of an immensely high building. Before him stretched a beautiful city with its blue-watered bay. Far below cars passed. In an open space was a school playground, children playing basket-ball. I would not be tempted by the kingdoms of this world or the glory thereof, he said, for finally they are composed of poor sots like myself, their inhabitants, feet falling off from too much walking in the sun; it is enough to walk around in my own atmosphere and feel an odd lunatic pull from the moon or the sea.

But why had no one told him he was being married? It was too late now. He would have to go through with it. It was awful, this irrevocable step, why, he did not know, except that it was catastrophic, the end of everything. And then he remembered. Maureen. But what had she got to do with it? Anyhow, she had gone to England and he would never again get a drinkable cup of tea. He distinctly saw her in a Lyons' Corner House, with an apron. But when he tried to approach, she set a poodle on him, and walked out haughtily, now dressed in a fur coat.

The images disappeared, and he was quite unconscious.

He lost a lot of weight during the week that followed, but the worst of the pain was past. The stab of knowledge that came when he first woke after the operation was correct. His leg would never be quite the same, although it was hoped that the disease was definitively stopped, and he was now to some extent convalescent; in other words, a long period of non-radical treatment, for both arm and leg, lay before him, but he would have a limp for the rest of his life. It was hard to accept, this first permanent diminishing, a definite stage in the gradual process that for most people is imperceptible. Mortality

66

raised its ugly head, became tangible. Twenty years is a milestone; the twenty-first birthday, majority, has an almost superstitious significance, the combination of mystic numbers, three and seven. A welter of fears and uncertainties oppressed him as soon as the pain eased and made way for other thoughts.

Having written home, he set about writing to Maureen. There was the vague chance she had mentioned that she might come out to Switzerland; he remembered it again with excitement. The operation was an event that, at a distance, gave him a certain distinction, meretricious if you like, but real. After all, it was a happening that lifted him out of the ordinary, and life is generally so humdrum that a happening has its value, as a talking point if no other. No worse really than the blackmail of a child who has a cough or a cold or a toothache. His mind went back to the image of the glacier he had been thinking of after receiving her letter. She had at one time seemed to him as immutable as one. Sun shines on the great sullen masses, but the transformation does not go deep. The sun goes down. Night. Stillness, fastness, death playing will-o-the-wisp in the shadows. All the patients who have died here, never again to see the spring, the solitary crocus in the snow, the rivulets on these hillsides when the snow melts at last, lilies of the field, the grass that is today and tomorrow is cast into the oven.

Where the worms diet not.

17

For the moment, his letter to Maureen remained unwritten. He tried, but what he wrote always seemed wrong.

By the time he was allowed up, Christine had become extremely important to his universe, and more than just professionally indispensable. His ambitions, for which he was theoretically prepared to sacrifice everything, became pitifully inadequate when he had to look to them for moral support. The free time available could have been spent on Gray's *Anatomy* or one of his language books but went much more agreeably if Christine happened to be around. And by mutual consent, she happened to be increasingly around, a good deal more than her duties would strictly have warranted.

She told him about her parents.

"My mother is a real Hausfrau, but an excellent one. Apart from professional chefs, you wouldn't find a better cook anywhere. She is one of these Swiss-Germans who think Lausanne and Geneva are dirty. But she's kind and good. She's blonde of course, and she's still a natural blonde. At least, I never saw any dyes around the house – she does her hair herself always, like everything else, and makes nearly all her own clothes.

"My father is her opposite, in everything. There is always a half-smoked pipe around the house. I suppose he must have married my mother because she was beautiful. It seems he is a brilliant engineer, anyhow, he has patents for several inventions. But at home he hardly ever opens his mouth. He just sits there. Sometimes he reads. But more often, he just sits there. Marie-Claire – that's my sister – and I often used to try to make him laugh. When we were both small, he was wonderful with us, always making things that none of the other children could ever hope to match. But now, when we come home, he hardly ever speaks to us. My mother suffers a lot, and it's specially lonely for her now that we are both away.

"I think it's partly that he just can't stand her chatter. She is like a lot of women in that part of Switzerland, whereas he is unlike nearly all the men they marry. They must have been very much in love one time. Maybe he still loves her in his own way. I remember one time, before Maire-Claire was born, down in the Engadine (a most beautiful place you must visit, full of flowers, especially in summer). They had taken me out on a walk. I suppose they thought I was too young to understand, but it's one of the most vivid memories I have. I can see them now, arguing, whether it was all right to swim there naked. Then they took their clothes off and dived in. After that they came back for me. The water seemed terribly cold. But I still feel the surprise of seeing these two strange people, so different from the mummy and daddy I knew. It's sad I shall never see them free and happy like that again. Do you think marriage must always end like that?"

"I don't see why," said Alexis.

"I don't either. But it seems to. Perhaps people marry each other for the wrong reasons."

"Most likely, it's the people themselves who change. If you continue two almost parallel lines they grow more and more apart."

"Maybe they should be continued in the opposite direction in that case."

"Or be perfectly parallel and meet in infinity," said Alexis.

"It's too far to go. How do you ever get there?" Christine asked.

"Die, I suppose. It doesn't sound like much of a solution."

"My father has a bad heart," Christine continued, "that is part of the trouble. One time he was always off climbing mountains. His heart is worse to him than a death-sentence."

"A bad heart is nothing. One of my friends had to stop playing football because of his alleged bad heart. He then took up rowing – and you've seen photos of crews at the end of a race – and became a sculling champion."

"My father is unfortunately not like that. He knows he could, literally, drop dead at any time. So do we," she added grimly.

He took her hand.

"And until he dies, he will go on hurting my mother. He is hard and cold and impatient and bitter while she is soft and sentimental. She loves him. I can see that for her he represents all she remembers from a wonderful period in her life when they were both young. Nothing of that remains. And yet I think I feel more sorry for him than for her. She got something at least, but he feels cheated of what he might have been or might have done. Even physically he feels crippled, although he looks perfectly normal, and his heart is only a threat, but a threat that is there all the time. Do you think it's just?"

"How, just?" Alexis asked.

"The way life treats people."

"I'm not particularly privileged myself, you know."

"No."

She looked at his hand, holding hers.

"God, religion, and all that," she continued, "can you make any sense of it all?"

"I was brought up to."

"So was I. So were my parents. My mother goes regularly to church and is as happy to take it as she sees it, without complications, as she would have been to take her marriage. My father, on the other hand, no longer believes in anything. Religion is something to edify someone with the brains of his wife, and he is Swiss enough himself to resent a God who could create an expert brain and make it depend on a piece of machinery so poorly made and badly serviced as his heart."

"And you?" Alexis asked.

"Suppose you were all-powerful and all... you know everything, past, present and future

"– omniscient –"

"– all-powerful and omniscient, and you decide to create a world. Would you include illness and age in it? Would you include death? Above all, since you are all-powerful and omniscient, would you include evil?"

"The obvious answer is no. But the trouble about all talk is that so many of the conclusions depend on the way you put the questions, just as the ability of a speaker is often a good deal more responsible for convincing than the truth of what he says."

"I'm not a speaker," Christine retorted, "and I'm not trying to convince anyone, least of all myself. You asked me a question. I asked you another. Maybe words are always traps. But surely there are questions which invite a clear reply, or even a qualified reply. If I ask you, how is your leg, you can say it's good, or it's bad, or it's not too bad, or it's hurting, or it's hurting very much. The other question I put to you is one that has been forced on me, not one I would ever have wanted to ask myself"

"Why not?"

"Because I would have been quite happy, in that respect, to remain like my mother and never ask questions. But the centre of Christianity

71

is the Redemption – you know, God sending his Son... I don't know how it goes in English..."

"'God so loved the world that he gave up for our redemption his only-begotten son'..."

"That's what I could never understand. That awful, cruel death. God could have prevented it, as well as the causes which are supposed to have made it necessary. I would probably be married today if I hadn't started thinking about these things and deciding that if they were true as they are told to us, it's also true that some of my descendants at least will be damned. If you knew that a child of yours, or one of his children or grandchildren would be damned, would burn in hell for all eternity, would you ever dare accept the responsibility? And if even one person was damned for all eternity, even one of all the millions who have lived and will live, do you think the world should ever have been created, by a God who had the choice and could have done otherwise? You are an intellectual. You should be able to answer."

"Who said I was an intellectual?"

"You are. You are always reading or studying."

"In English, you have to be something more. In fact, you have to be a bit of a crank to qualify as an intellectual. It is always a doubtful sort of a compliment, when it's not actually a term of abuse. It implies that you may be pretty busy keeping your brain occupied, but that you are not much good for anything else. Whereas in French, the word usually seems to be used to distinguish between those who are and those who are not interested in..."

"Thinking?"

"Yes, I suppose so," said Alexis, "and books. In English, it always sounds a bit pretentious. But I haven't answered your question. I'm afraid I never thought about it. Religion in Ireland is not a question of intellect but of loyalty. It's not philosophical or metaphysical. In a way, it's pure politics. By and large, Catholic

72

equals Irish, Protestant equals pro-British, when, in other words, you regard the others as 'natives'. Even today, I could tell you at a glance in the street whether a person is Catholic or Protestant."

"I didn't know it made people look different."

"It doesn't. But centuries of treating others as 'natives', or of being treated as 'natives' does. So you see, religion is a very simple business, like having your Communist Party card. Someone knows. It was all written down in a book originally, and it's been certified through the centuries. Someone knows the truth, teaches it, tells it to you as a child, and tells you what will happen if you don't obey – it's pretty terrible when you learn all that can happen to you. But someone knows, and knows what's best for you. So you grow up a good Catholic. Like me."

"But surely there must be more to it than that?" said Christine.

"Yes, I think there is. A revolutionary thing called love. At least, it was revolutionary to start with. The trouble is that, to make themselves more efficient, revolutions become institutionalised and then the institution swallows the revolution. Christianity to start with was gloriously revolutionary. Love. Love everyone. Love your enemies. If you cannot change them, pray for them. There is a power greater than anything your poor derisory human efforts can imagine, much less achieve. Co-operate with it, and have faith. Be perfect as your heavenly father is perfect. Own nothing, and be free. Share all you have, and be rich. You own nothing. You are just a custodian, for a few short years; so give what you have, and you shall be rich eternally. But if you have anything against your brother, go first and be reconciled with him.

"That was the beginning, the hard beginning, the persecutions, the struggle to survive, and the miraculous victory of what no one had ever thought of using before: non-violence, love in exchange for hatred. And the beginning of an institution that swapped the boundless love that preceded it for a series of doctrines to defend. You can see it starting already in the Acts of the Apostles: the day when time that could be spent preaching the gospel becomes too precious to be spent

73

serving at table like the rest, and the organisation men stepped in. Like the pigs in Orwell's *Animal Farm*. You can trace the rot back to there: the fishermen who became Popes and Eminencies and lived in the biggest palaces in Italy; the ineffable reduced to dogma, formulae to satisfy the makers of formulae; the institution itself splitting into East and West and, a few centuries later, into Catholic and Protestant; the Inquisition: if your brother scandalise thee, burn him at the stake: that'll larn him, and stop the scandal; until religion reaches its finest flower in Glasgow, where God is the rival mascot of two soccer teams, and Belfast where everyone knows that every time the Catholic team loses a match, a Cardinal is sacked in the Vatican o' Rome."

"But you still believe?" asked Christine.

"As I told you, that's the way it is in Ireland. But I believe that something of the original has managed to survive, in Ireland as elsewhere, in spite of the organisation men for whom the organisation is always more important than the man, and the manner of doing more important than the goal. In spite of all that stranglehold of prelates and palaces and purple hats, there must have been millions, in that two thousand years, who gave up everything and became the faceless servants of the sick and the poor and the homeless and all the unfortunate in their own and other lands. In a couple of centuries, they provided free education in Ireland, hospitals and hospitality for wayfarers and visitors, although everyone now seems to think that was all invented by Lenin and Karl Marx, and kept learning alive in a Europe overrun by barbarians. If you have any doubt about the sacrifice, think of the implications of vows of perpetual poverty, chastity and obedience. But that is still not what I wanted to say. I seem to be discussing the issue instead of explaining. Perhaps, in its simplest terms, I mean that I've met and seen good people, that something called goodness exists and is positive and tangible... no, it's not that either. I really don't know how to explain. All that hasn't necessarily got anything to do with Christianity. It should, but it hasn't. And there are always those who destroyed so much of Roman and Greek art because it was pagan, or burned all they could find of what the Incas and the Mayas had produced, and put fig-leaves on statues, and burnt African art because they had never seen anything like it, so it must be bad. Not to mention the American Jesuit paper I

74

saw recently which, in an article on the numerical forces of various religions, looked forward to the increase in the numbers of Catholics as soon as 'modern convert-making techniques are brought into play'. Nihil obstat. Did you ever hear such blasphemy – and from the intellectuals of the Church, God help us!"

"You are not very convincing," said Christine.

"I know. I'll have to think about it. Or maybe, better not. Belief is like beauty, essentially irrational. Or love."

"We've got back where we started. Or rather, where you started."

"Without advancing very much further."

"I've often wondered what a clergyman means when he talks about love, I've never heard a sermon yet where it didn't come up. But it always seems as abstract as everything else they talk about: without any relation to everyday life – except money – the repairs to what has suddenly become *your* parish church, for instance."

"You know the story of the Jew who went to Mass with his Catholic friend? He watches carefully to make sure he does everything right. There was the ordinary collection for the clergy, then a collection to help put a new roof on the school, and a collection for the repair of the organ and, coming out, a collection for the old peoples' home. Having matched all his friend's various contributions, he asked: "Wasn't Jesus a Jew?" His friend nodded. "Well", he said thoughtfully, "I wonder how did we lose the business?"

"It could also be said, of course," said Christine, "that the contributions were all part of a non-official communism."

"'From each according to his abilities, to each according to his needs'?"

"Yes."

"A rather imperfect one" Alexis commented.

"Do you know a perfect?"

"Frankly, no. And I can't see it happening voluntarily. People have to be forced to be 'generous'. Unfortunately. But perhaps that is why Christianity has outlived all the political systems. Even in the purely human sense, the ideal of Christianity may be as impossible as the Communist ideal, but it is based on something more attractive and, in the long run, more practical: love of one's fellow-men, especially those in distress, rather than hatred of class enemies. Hatred is no doubt easier, and certainly more voluptuously satisfying... "

"– Let me think," said Christine, "no. I don't think I ever hated anyone in my life."

"In the case of individuals, hating requires a genuine effort. But it's quite easy to hate in the mass. Look at the way Americans hate communists, or the way a rioting mob can hate its victims. It's always lying, and always destructive. When it becomes a doctrine and a way of life, it's horrifying, bestial and terrible."

"Nazism?"

"In ways I think the Inquisition was even worse – the perversion of an ideal, whereas the other was a perversion to start with: burning you at the stake to instil a belief in the mercy of God, the propagation of love by torture. But it can happen any time the organisation men take over and enthrone things like efficiency. Did you ever see anything more horrible than a typing pool in a big insurance company office? Talk about respect for the human person... what the world needs is a little enlightened anarchy... "

"And love?" Christine queried.

"And love," affirmed Alexis, "if only we knew what it means."

"I don't know how it is in your church, but in ours, people are always talking about love, but always as if sex didn't exist. In fact, it's only since I went through the nursing school that I dare mention the word without blushing. Yet I know that that time I told you about when I saw my parents bathing naked, love really did exist between them. Whereas now..."

"There are moral theologians who can tell you with the accuracy of a calliper screw exactly where sin begins in sensuality. Some are even more sweeping. Any touch between the sexes, outside marriage, is sinful. What happens within marriage, we'll tell you the night before. I have been holding your hand. Did you notice?"

"I pretended not to."

"It's no harm if you don't enjoy it."

"But I do."

"Then, if I were a moral theologian, I would start measuring. Even to shake hands might be an occasion for illicit touching. One Archbishop of Seville holds that all modern dancing is sinful. To touch your knee is pretty risky. As my hand has been lying in yours in your lap since I last moved it, there should by now be a smell of sulphur. We had what was known as a 'penny catechism' in primary school, and a fuller version in secondary. You got so much to learn by heart, questions and answers. If you didn't know them, so many biffs on the hand with a cane or a leather. As a result, I'll probably be able to recite on my death-bed 'Unchaste thoughts are always very dangerous and when entertained deliberately and with pleasure, they defile the soul like criminal actions.' What I don't understand is where the artist comes into all this. One of the reasons art is so dull is that it's no longer interested in the human body. All this abstract muck. As far as I'm concerned, the most beautiful line in creation is the line from a woman's shoulder to her breast.

Theoretically, as a good Catholic, I shouldn't know of its existence. Fortunately, there are evening dresses, and bathing costumes, and bikinis, and if I were to keep my eye modestly averted all the time I'd end up with a moral squint. But, as far as I know, it's all right to look at that line on a statue or in a picture. Perhaps not too

77

long. Anyhow, you can see priests and nuns bringing groups of schoolchildren round art galleries. But the artist who produces the statue or picture, and who uses the real thing, all of it, undraped, where does he come in? It's a rather dangerous profession of course, to be taken up at your risk and peril. Like acting. But apart from the fig-leaf episodes, the Church saved most of the Greek and Roman sculpture that survived, while Michelangelo, to name only one, hobnobbed with popes, and went in for fig-leaves only when it was necessary like a theatrical prop. It's all very mysterious.

"There was a great deal also, of course, about the Sixth and Ninth Commandments. I think you number yours differently."

"What are they?" Christine asked.

"'Sixth: thou shalt not commit adultery... Ninth: thou shalt not covet thy neighbour's wife.' You will notice that in both cases, the injunction seems to be addressed only to the male – woman being an inferior being – has she really a soul – and that it refers only to the married. So when I go to confession, what do I tell? Personally, I think it's mostly a lot of nonsense. To be honest, most priests would say the same. They would tell you that, after all, sin is something serious if you can be damned for it. On the other hand, they would be afraid to say so: they could hardly encourage you to hold hands. Since it might lead on to something warmer, a dangerous occasion of sin they would say, a positive encouragement to debauch. In fact, if you don't intend to marry the girl, what are you up to anyway? And if you do intend to marry her, why don't you get on with it... As they are not fools, it's not put quite as crudely as that (although in Ireland, especially at what are called 'retreats', there is always the 'Hell-fire' sermon when the visiting preacher thunders about the dangers of the 'long roads and the lonely walks'). But they are forced into the dilemma by the institution of confession. It's like a court. In fact, it's referred to as the 'tribunal of penance'. Except that you accuse yourself. But by going, you are submitting to the rules. And when neither judge nor accused believes in the relevance of the rules, where are you? Of course, it is said that conscience is the ultimate arbiter. But that's one of the many things that's never plainly stated in the penny catechism. In a way, it's much worse when you have to accuse yourself: a prosecutor can at least make it plain to you what you are alleged to be guilty of – much to your astonishment perhaps. But how can you really decide what you are guilty of, and how far? Curiously, the only people who make the effort, in deadly earnest, are novelists, and ironically enough, the ones who have been most serious about it down the ages are precisely the ones the Church has banned. Under a different law of course, the one about not giving scandal. Let thy right hand not know what thy left hand is doing..."

"But I've always heard it said that Catholics are lucky – they get their psychoanalysis free. Everyone seems to agree that you can get rid of a terrible weight of guilt by confessing it."

"That seems to me to be the most dishonest argument of all. The resemblances are purely superficial. The psychoanalyst or psychiatrist is trying to find out what is blocking you psychologically and encourages you to talk freely. He has no preconceived ideas in all this of what is right and wrong, and he no more wants to change you than a doctor. In confession, the rules are laid down, and the object is to change you. 'The surest sign that our confession was good and that we had sincere sorrow for our sins is the amendment of our lives.'"

"It seems an admirable purpose," Christine commented.

"In the abstract, yes. Except that Galileo is only the most famous case of thousands and perhaps millions of people forced to acknowledge some offence against dogmatic teaching since proved – proved, mark you – to be wrong. It's fine to confess and get rid of the load of guilt; I know from experience it can be wonderful. But you have no idea what an impressionable child can go through with all these big and terrible words about sin and guilt, especially when he gets to puberty and doesn't know whether he is morally in the wrong, and if he does, doesn't know how to confess it. There again, the pudic veil is drawn precisely where he is most in need of enlightenment. I believe that's one of the hidden reasons why half the Irish never marry. And why there is so much emigration – not so much for economic reasons, important as they are, as to get away from the stranglehold of things they are forced to accept without being able to accept them with their reason, or in their hearts and minds."

"Perhaps that again is only the intellectual talking. Would you abolish confession if you had the chance?"

"Certainly. Apart from anything else, there is nothing in anything Christ ever said to justify its existence. If I said at home it was simply a way of keeping control over people, I'd probably be called a communist. In fact, people were executed as heretics by the Inquisition for saying precisely that. I'm a medical student, as you know, and we have the reputation of being a pretty foul-mouthed lot. There is a good deal of talk between students, but hardly ever when the company is mixed. I've got enough of my Irish upbringing in me to have been a little shocked, even still, a while ago when you mentioned the word 'sex.'"

"I'm sorry," Christine said.

"Sorry?" exclaimed Alexis, "no, I mention it because it's so idiotic. And yet it's carried to such lengths that it is the proud boast of some clerics that literature in the Irish language is free of all impurity. Like pasteurised milk. Homogenised also."

"Is it true?"

"If it were true, there would be no literature in the Irish language, or precious little. What happens is that the literature exists, but is not reprinted. But that's enough about that blasted country. It can't be of all that interest to anyone else. You said just now that you might be married if..."

"The reason I told you," said Christine slowly, "is only partly the reason. I suppose the real reason was that I was also afraid of other things."

"Of what?"

"Robert himself, I suppose. Or maybe it was simply that things were just too easy. The parents on both sides were in favour. Even my father, so far as he is in favour of anything. We were at the same school, and we were always in and out of each other's homes. He was soon to qualify as an architect. He is handsome, very handsome. Maybe that is the real trouble. I saw the success he had with other girls and I knew that, sooner or later, he would be unfaithful. And I could not stand that. It's not so much that I am jealous by nature as that, I don't know, I imagine it would break something in me. We were more or less engaged. I broke it off. We had terrible scenes. He swore he would never love anyone else. And he meant it. He would appear at such odd times, my father would be angry but say nothing. I wanted desperately myself to go back on my decision, but it took such an effort to make in the first place that I could not bring myself to do it."

"You are sure it's all over?" Alexis asked.

"Quite sure. He is married."

"I'm sorry." Her answer did in fact make him feel unforgivably tactless.

"It's better that way. I'm not beautiful. She is. She is just the right type for him." She said it without apparent bitterness. "Italian, with long black hair. They look right together. He is very Swiss in his attitude to women. He always refers to her as 'my wife', never as Lina." She paused, and added: "And she loves it."

"You wouldn't?"

"In principle, no. With him, I'm not so sure."

"Women are complicated."

"How?"

"With all the talk of equality between the sexes, and questions of salary apart, the last thing, it seems, most women want is to be treated as an equal by a man."

"Maybe we haven't got used to it yet," Christine answered, and looked at her watch. "I didn't realise it was so late, and I've still got a thousand things to do."

She stood up, hesitated, and then bent down and kissed him.

18

Lying on the bed after she had gone, he realised that one of the things he had missed most without noticing it since he had been abroad was talk, the sort of talk that started after a meeting of some College society and might range over every topic under the sun without ever coming to any conclusion on anything, talk being an activity in its own right without anything so base or degrading as a purpose; like physical exercise, nothing left after a hard evening's talking but a pleasant sense of fatigue.

The company had been mostly male, and he was something of an exception as a medical student. Talk with a girl, alone, was different, less an intellectual steeplechase than a kind of dance and, if she is attractive, necessarily a kind of courtship. He did not know how much he really meant most of what he had said, but he was very much aware of the different flavour of their talk, as a meal takes on a different dimension once the wine is there.

Some days are flat, flat as old beer. Some froth over, like champagne. And what if tomorrow you have a hangover.

A new stage had happened in their relations, and as the glow her presence lent began to fade, he felt uneasy about it.

Logically, his position was perfectly clear. There was the life he envisaged, felt he was somehow destined to lead, and of which Maureen was essentially part. So he must not let Christine fall in love with him, even if she wanted to. He remembered her spontaneous parting kiss. Unfortunately for logic, there was a solitude in face of another solitude, as she had quoted to him once from Cocteau. He knew that, whatever his plans and ambitions, there would be times – most times when she might be free – when he would gladly let everything drop for the pleasure of her company. He hoped rather doubtfully that this did not imply any disloyalty either to his ambitions or to Maureen.

He had been a member of the Saint Vincent de Paul Society in College and knew from visiting Dublin tenements that poverty was more than a question of statistics or standards of living. And it was not uniform either. Nothing was more amazing than the courage and cheerfulness of some of the people he had seen living in squalor that for others would represent unimaginable misery. He had seen old people, resigned and serene, nothing of stoicism in their resignation, something warm, positive and confident: if religion is the opium of the people, what is wrong with opium anyway? If it makes you happy...

But now he began to wonder if any pattern could be pieced out from the infinite variety of human behaviour. Following the example of the lives of the people who plunged seemingly arbitrarily to their deaths the day the bridge collapsed in *The Bridge of San Luis Rey*, would it be possible to learn anything by collecting and comparing newspaper reports on crimes? Perhaps that was what storytellers had always been, consciously or unconsciously, attempting to do: to get at the living reality behind conventional morality – and the utter banality of statistical deductions, quantification, only too often, of what seemed relevant but somehow wasn't. But can anything more be learned about the lives of others than from one's own experience? Is it too vicarious to be significant? He decided that his grasp was too small. His ability to imagine characters, motives, situations was depressingly restricted. He would make a very poor god, create a very limited universe. He decided nevertheless to see about collecting the raw material he had just been thinking about.

Men are forever laying down rules, drawing up plans for ideal societies, defining what is normal and so by implication what is abnormal. And men are forever giving them the lie.

That very morning, the newspaper reported a murder trial involving a peasant family that, theoretically, could not possibly exist in contemporary Europe. They were not so much a family as a clan, a matriarchy, living on a farm so remote that it was almost an

84

independent state, and it kept its contacts with the outside world to the minimum of buying and selling and the unavoidable intrusions of officialdom. They were afflicted, however with not one but two old grandmothers, a situation that demanded a pragmatic solution, and some statecraft to prevent outside interference in their internal affairs. The first old lady was very competently disposed of, with no suspicions aroused. The second proved more of a problem. Her going hence was engineered through a plot and in an atmosphere Atrean in its gloom and complexity, involving incest, moral blackmail, jealousy, greed, unbearable guilt, confession to an outsider and the final denunciation.

The same paper carried another story of a man, apparently not mad, who shot his son and his wife, went down eight flights of stairs and shot his eighty-year-old mother, and then attempted to shoot himself.

Part of one day's harvest of happenings on a god-fostered earth that, nearly two hundred years ago inaugurated the worship of the Goddess of Reason (in the person of a demi-mondaine with doubtful qualifications for the honour beyond her exposed upper reaches, but let that pass). Now and at the hour of our death. Phenomena phenomenonically statistical. Ten, fifty, a hundred have died since Christine went out of the room. Some on the roads, others in prisons, hospitals, clinics. Some in their beds, as if it were the most natural thing in the world. Perhaps in this very building. Crashes. Obscure lives of obscure people, a brief notice in a newspaper the only fame they ever know. A few months ago, the sombre beginning of November, a dormant piety hibernating through the summer brought them in thousands to the graves of parents, children, friends, those they loved or should have loved. Chrysanthemums on dumb graves, the golden flowers.

Loved?

Tears are only so much water and a little salt; or so, O my late love, all my friends will have it.

Did I ever love?

Maureen's image appeared in a flash with absolute clarity, and vanished. He could not bring it back. Think of breathing, and breathing becomes an effort. Her hair, her features one by one, her eyes, that smile of hers, he could see them individually, but they would not fuse. He had not yet written. Writing, with its curious unwritten protocol. Sometimes a letter cannot be too quickly answered, sometimes too quick an answer seems as wrong as an out-of-place compliment. As varied as conversation. Different people and different situations demanding and producing radically different styles. Matter-of-fact letters home; his account of his operation, for example, had minimised the whole thing, and especially his disappointment at its result. His eye fell casually on a paper he had half-read, a poem with an ending he found painfully apposite:

...like pollen on a bitter wind
fertilising weeds that fertilise corruption
the years pass
and love, cancer'd
awakes malignant;
if only her heart were steadfast
or mine sincere.

('Shall I compare thee to a summer's day')

"My dear Maureen," he wrote to her, "the operation is over. I don't know if I revealed my inmost thoughts under the anaesthetic. If so, I must have said a lot about you. In fact, it has been over some time, it could have been worse, and it could also have been better. Or did I tell you at all that I was going to have an operation? I wrote so much rubbish in my last letter that I'm not quite sure what I included. My first reaction after waking up was fright. If you just drop off to sleep, you wake up and are quickly reassured that nothing sensational has happened to you meanwhile. I knew at once that something had happened to me, and for a terrible moment, I thought my leg was gone. You can't imagine how glad I was to find I could still touch both of those two primitive means of locomotion. On the other hand, the operation has been less successful than they had hoped, and it looks as if I shall have a limp for life. Of course, it's always possible to exploit one's disabilities. I don't think I should ever have the nerve to wear a monocle. But how about a silver-topped cane?!

"I have been allowed out of bed and am even allowed little walks in the grounds (with an ordinary walking-stick). Did you ever realise how full of life the world is, even apart from people and animals? Usually it's very quiet. There are squirrels which, theoretically, we should be able to find wild at home but which I for one have never seen. Have you? They get particularly tame in winter, when their natural sources of food get scarce. In some parts of Switzerland they are a positive pest, but even if I were a farmer I don't think I could ever regard them – or rabbits – as that. There was a story recently in the newspapers here of a lady who went off for a week-end leaving one window of her flat open. When she returned, her bedroom was absolutely littered with silver paper from liqueur-filled chocolates (they are delicious, I must bring you home some!) In the middle of the eiderdown a little ball of fur was rolled up: a squirrel, dead drunk on liqueurs!

"Hens, however, I would cheerfully classify as pests for extermination (we can always make omelettes from egg-powder). The word 'cretin', I am firmly convinced, was originally written 'cret/hen.' The clinic has a whole battery of them. All is peaceful. Then suddenly that shatteringly ugly high note rings out and continues, a raucous engine turning over on the self-starter and won't 'take', until you think the skin on its throat must inevitably tear. And it goes on and on. Is it so wonderful to lay a bloody egg? Even if I felt as proud of the achievement, I hope I would at least express it otherwise.

"Another one of them goes on like an irritable grandmother in a sort of interminable petulant keen.

"One plays the drums: guh guh guh guh wheeagh guh guh, low down; another follows the same pattern in saxophone, syncopated rather than in counterpoint; a third, a little farther off, does a piccolo obligato, capped occasionally by an idiotic falsetto-ughghug gugu gug ooo AGH – from the cock. Ugh!

"From now on, I write the word, 'concathennation'.

"I would hate to die to the sound of a cawking hen or a barking dog, or the sound of a certain language...

"Pigeons are in much the same category. Jaccoud – he's one of the doctors here – tells me that, every time he gets his car washed, a pigeon can not only score a direct hit on the roof, which would be too easy, but with the same shot, can splash the window and side panel of a door. And yet – I must be reading the papers a lot – there was an extraordinary story of pigeons in Vienna, where the authorities (they probably all own cars) decided the pigeons were becoming too numerous, and endangering all kinds of public monuments, from cathedrals to statues. Poison was laid down with the food. One old lady had her private contingent. She put out food as usual on the window sill. The pigeons gathered suspiciously on the roof opposite. After a lot of palaver, one flew over, tasted some food, waited, swallowed some more, waited again and then apparently gave the all clear, as the remainder flew over and started eating. Does it mean that birds – even pigeons – can reason? Hitherto I had always thought some people might think them beautiful – at a fair distance – but that they were in any case dumb.

"Except perhaps when they are white.

"Someone at the clinic breeds white pigeons (with my usual ignorance, I thought first they were doves). They have a cot in the trees, which it seems difficult to get into. As many as six will alight on a nearby roof. Occasionally they all take off together, fly upwards tails fanned out, incredibly beautiful against the green of the trees and the blue sky. Imitating Matisse (Oscar Wilde says nature imitates art). I should love to get that shot in colour. They fly awkwardly, as if they had only recently got their wings. Sometimes one will make for the cot while the others watch, decide half-way down that the angle is not right, fly back up again, fluttering over the head of another, standing impassively in place, to get back on the roof, and then leave again almost immediately in a despairing, straight dive back. This time it stops like a helicopter, seems almost to reverse, and finally disappears in, whereupon all the others follow, and utter confusion results until the beating of wings dies down at last and the chattering and the cackling and they go back to that mysterious blinking communion of theirs. What really fascinates me is the little extra last-minute jump on to the roof over the bird already occupying the place where it wants to land. Some day I shall get that marvellous photograph.

"The gardener told me that the place beside the cot is full of sunflower seeds, which they love but haven't the gumption to take themselves: he has to carry them over to the cot.

"Did you ever see a bee big enough to land on a sunflower and bend it over with bee-weight? Or a worm with claustrophobia? – very dangerous psychologically, given its living conditions. Better be a caterpillar – if your existence is to be ephemeral, then at least have the consolation of being a butterfly for a day.

"What is the latest fashion for mushrooms? Coolie hats?

"Have you ever meditated on the uglitude of braces?

"On pudgy men?

"Thin men?

"Skinny men?

"Malingerers?

"The horror of brassieres and girdles? In a blinding flash of inspiration it occurred to me the other day that even so mediaevally accoutred, you would still be fair, lovely and graceful. And men have said less, and it has been accounted unto them as a declaration of love...

"There is a cat too, very wild, looks at you with hostility and suspicion. Unlike the pigeons, its eyes are unblinking, filled with hate. You begin to think of witches and changelings and unmentionable things on dark mountains on moonless nights. You make a move towards it, proffering friendship. It decides you are

89

already too near, gets quickly away to a calculated distance with the feline ease of a black athlete, stops, and begins with elaborate nonchalance to lick its paws as if your contemptible self had never existed. But it is all the time watching and that, I think, makes its lordly indifference phoney – difference between a lord and a pseudo.

"A white feather from one of the pigeons, neatly sheathed as if fixed there on purpose between the wall and a trailer from a vine.

"Have you ever seen a lizard from close up? If they are really cosy in the sun, you whistle and their heads will cock sideways – you know how a puppy will, in a puzzled way, if you make dog whines, or bark – or don't you do vulgar things like that? Anyhow, I find their taste is rather highbrow. I've had most success with Schubert and Mozart – whistled – although they are not averse either to a little saccharine – Noel Coward, or musical comedy. I saw a slightly larger one this morning, sitting on top of some steps under a shelter because a few raindrops had started to fall. Not so damn silly. Then the sun came out again. I moved and it disappeared, but its tail remained visible over a stone for nearly half a minute after the rest had gone. Tread on the tail of my shirt... Even if you succeeded in capturing a lizard, with a fish net for example, how long would it take before you could really make contact with it – a little one, or one seven or eight feet long, as they apparently have in places like Mexico?

"Somewhere not far off, a train has just giggled hysterically.

"The crazy don't-give-a-damn flight of a butterfly. Landed on a big red-brown flower, flicked off a few loose petals in the process, seemed to nibble something – but it took me some time to decide where exactly its head was situated – ignored a wasp that came down on the same flower as if it were a creature of another species, and gently flew spastically off.

"With none of the ugly persistence of a fly or a bee's ponderous stupidity.

"Did it ever occur to you to ask yourself in irritation, with all Europe to land on, why does a bluebottle have to concentrate on me?

"Another bee, a bumblebee this time, big as a small bird, has weighed over the same sunflower. How big is a small bird?

"And a dragon-fly, like a conscious model aeroplane, has flown back and forth over me at least half a dozen times.

"Marvellous, this smell of lavender.

"But what's over the earth is only a fraction of what lies under it. I suppose I've never had time to watch before. But now... the variety of ants alone is terrifying... Do you know an insect like a tiny upturned currach? I think we call them "clocks" – did you ever hear that Dublin expression: 'It will fill you full of clocks' – a mock alarmist warning against eating or doing something or other? In French they are cloportes. Nice-sounding word, isn't it? There's a lot of them around. I saw one of them the other day going – rapidly for it – in the same direction as a maggoty thing, a long shimmering wormy thing articulated like a train but more closely articulated, insinuating its way along like a horizontal night-club singer across the concrete. Would it superstitiously avoid the lines? No, it went its own way regardless. Was it interested in a small fly? No, they crossed each other's paths, avoiding each with the preoccupied indifference of two motorists at a crossroads. That left the cloportes and the wormy thing. They too passed each other unconcerned as two boats in an open harbour. An ant scrambled busybodily over the cloporte's back. What do you think does either of them feel – as much as a citizen with the law on his back?

"Do you think I've turned into a naturalist or an entomologist, or something?

"Not at all, Maureen, not at all. I might if you were here and interested, but then I hope we should have better things to do than to watch insects. Most times I would just sweep them all out of sight with a bloody great brush. Do you think that's what happens when God loses his rag with the world and lets loose a cloudburst or a volcano or a hurricane? Or something? And if you are not here, why can't I be where you are, and the old trams running again, to Howth or Bray or Killiney. The sea champing around the base of the cliffs. How I miss the sea. A picnic somewhere. Those old trams, smelling of what, greased iron toasted in electricity, sparks when the trolley left the overhead wires, bump across the points, conductor jumps out with a kind of crowbar... spitting prohibited in and on the tram, penalty forty shillings. Passengers entering or leaving the vehicle while in motion do so at their own risk – did you ever leave or enter a vehicle without being in motion? – it struck me at the age of eight, the first great thought of my life and prelude no doubt to a great literary future...

"I would love to see you here, but don't really expect it: it would be too wonderful.

"Instead, I have been working on my French, and even written a poem for you:

Le vent rode, tombe encore la nuit
ferme les volets, amie,
contre le temps

"If that is not enough, and as you did once accuse me of writing poetry, I also offer you this:

Days lengthen
the bud becomes a rose
what if,
we two loving,
earth life and time
so soon foreclose?

"If I were a school examiner I would not award you ten marks for being able to give the poet's thoughts...

"Please write, when you can."

He did not give the letter to Christine, who posted most of his letters for him.

19

It is momentarily disconcerting, James Stephens once remarked, to have an archangel appear on the scene, but you make the best of it, and in five minutes he had his tinkers chatting with the archangel like an old friend. Alexis found after a while that he could live with his damaged leg and, for long periods, forget it completely. Pictorials in French and German might be good for his language studies, but he noticed they were becoming a self-imposed duty that could easily absorb an inordinate amount of time; a pleasant occupation enough but, as he was acutely aware, he might never have such freedom and leisure again. As everything in life is limited, choice is inescapable and he wanted, not just to pass the time, or still less to kill time, but to use it. The only exception – but he should allow none; and, inevitably, lacking the iron will that makes the great tycoon, a good deal of his day went in making arrangements that would be enforced tomorrow, or plain daydreaming – or simply seeing Christine on various pretexts.

When is one finally cut off from the loved and lost – which alone remains unforgettable?

He dozed, kept dreaming of a few words which were abstract objects, not words with meaning but absolutely pure and beautiful, with something in them of the graph, a line, curved, words in a silence but not in space in the extraterrestrial sense, yet wholly real, that gave him a feeling of well-being, relaxation, happiness he did not want to wake from. He kept handling the idea between sleep and waking. Then it began fading, getting farther and farther out of focus. He tried desperately to explain to someone who made a joke out of the whole thing: "You'll find your phrase" (but it's not a phrase, it's physically words, like a 'necklace' without the lumps) "one day." "Will I?" "Yes, but you'll be dead."

One morning he said to Christine: "I have something to celebrate. Jaccoud has given me permission to go outside the grounds at last, to go as far as the town if I like. Would you like to come with me?"

She nodded. "I'm delighted," she said, "it means you are really getting well."

"Do you know the cafes? I have only a very hazy idea of what I saw the evening I arrived, when it was all new and a bit frightening - not the place, but my reason for being there."

"It is small," Christine said, "but there are several cafes and restaurants. There are a number of other sanatoria and clinics besides ours, as you know, and quite a lot of people come here to visit relatives or friends, and do some skiing at the same time. The Mont Blanc is considered about the best. One part is a cafe, and the crowd is youngish and cheerful – a bit too rich sometimes for my liking; the other part, with a terrace that is closed in by glass in winter, overlooks the valley, and is used as the restaurant."

"Let's go there," he said, "it would be nice to eat somewhere else for a change."

"Do you want me to telephone?"

"Is it as popular as all that?"

"I don't really know. It's a habit I got into in my first job. I worked with a publisher, a marvellous man, from a very rich family. Publishing was just a kind of hobby with him. He has one of the best private collections of paintings in Switzerland. My main work, when I look back on it, seems to have been telephoning restaurants. A little different from now," she added somewhat wryly.

"It doesn't seem to have been a very exhausting occupation. Why did you leave?"

"After the break-up with Robert, I just couldn't go on living there."

"I'm sorry," he said awkwardly.

"The most interesting people used to come, artists and writers."

"Immensely rich, handsome and intelligent... just the opposite of me. As a matter of fact, I hardly know how to use a telephone. And anyhow, I hate the things. No, let's just go and see. You know, I've dreamt for years of this. A real continental meal, brilliant, amusing people -"

"Don't be too optimistic," she said.

"I'm sure they are brilliant, handsome, beautiful, witty and all the rest. It's part of the birthright I've been deprived of until now. And I go there, accompanied by a beautiful, witty girl -"

"I thought you were taking me?"

"You are developing what your countrymen - I don't know why, considering it's Irish - call a British sense of humour. And no more of this fishing for compliments -"

"You can't say I was fishing, when the fish landed unexpectedly at my feet without any intervention on my part"

"There is passive and active intervention. Some people call forth compliments simply by existing."

"Not guilty."

"You are not allowed to be judge and defendant."

"You are, with pleasure, if your verdicts are always as nice."

"How can a judge be just and guarantee in advance?"

"Forget about being just and just be nice. It's so much more pleasant for everyone."

"I really believe you've made a startling discovery that never occurred to anyone before."

"People are never satisfied with the simple and the obvious."

"Are you?"

"I think so."

"Then you'll love me," said Alexis.

"I don't think you are either simple or obvious. In fact, I think you are one of the most complicated people I've ever met."

"You sober me. It's not me that's complicated, it's life, that big complicated thing with the capital letter. It's the others –"

"Compared to Robert, for example. He was perfectly simple, and straightforward. He wanted to marry me. I wouldn't marry him. So he went off and found someone who would. I bet you would never take as simple and easy a way out in the same position."

"Positions are never the same."

"They are not as different as you might think."

"You sound like the voice of experience itself."

"No," said Christine, "it's just that I am simple too. But you're not. That's not a reproach," she added with a smile. "In fact, it's a compliment."

"In that case, we are quits. Can we meet at about seven? Good little patients shouldn't stay out too late their first night out."

"Or good little nurses either – any night. Let me hear you say 'au revoir'."

"Au revoir. Is it perfect yet? Is it still 'British'?"

"It's improving."

"You are a hard teacher."

"No teacher is worse than one who flatters."

"In Irish, we have a proverb: Praise the young and they'll progress."

"It's not the same thing."

"You are being Swisserious."

"I have to, to counteract your Celtic frivolity. It's Celtic, isn't it, not British?" she added mischievously.

"If you are not careful I'll give you the whole doleful tale of the dreary Hibernians again, in all its coagulated misery, from their expulsion from paradise to their qualified ascension with de Velera into heaven. You forget that I summoned you here to announce a celebration, the festival of the quick and the lame and the halt who are about to take up their beds and walk."

"I was only showing I had learned my lesson. Well, au revoir," she said, and waited.

"Au revoir," he answered.

She started laughing.

"Well of all the cheek," he said "wait till I record you reciting Shakespeare in a Swiss-German accent."

"Swiss-French," she connected, still laughing. "Forgive me. But it's so sweet, the way you pronounce it. You must promise me never to lose your accent."

"No need to promise," replied Alexis, "unfortunately. Anyhow, you will have to buy your forgiveness."

She understood. She caught him under the chin, looked him in the eyes, kissed him on both cheeks, and said in a low voice "au revoir".

"Au revoir," he answered.

This time, she did not smile.

20

"Un petit bistro, une station de Metro..."

"You know," he said, "that was the first sound I heard on arriving here. Just listen to the way it goes up on the word 'Pigalle'."

"Like a small boat on the top of a big wave, before it's thrown down on the other side."

"Or someone getting sick.   Throwing up.   Don't be vulgar. Anyhow, the two go together."

"Not in a small boat" said Christine.   "You only get sick in a big boat not, not when you are near the water."

"No, I know what it is.   It's exactly that sort of culminating sweep that comes after all those little shuffling bits in a tango – out into the open sea, but beware of the whirlpool.   What would you dance to it anyway?"

"It's a waltz, isn't it?"

"I think you're right."

"Dances are a bit like cocktail parties, making conversation with total strangers."

"I have a friend," said Alexis "who first of all exhausts all the usual small-talk about the floor and the band and the temperature and the weather and then puts in a strong finish by asking his partner 'what do you think of baby elephants as pets?'   Do you dance much?"

"No. I was never allowed out very much. Anyhow, Robert was so much a better dancer that I knew he would have preferred to dance with other girls. And that made me jealous. No, I never did enjoy dances very much. And you?"

"I was never very good, but I did enjoy myself. A few of us got fed up with being so awkward on our feet and went and had some lessons – and got our names in the gossip column of the College magazine. But I did learn to keep my feet off my partner's. I can manage a kind of home-made tango but the trouble is that everything I dance seems to turn into a tango. Or did" he said, looking at his leg. 'Now your dancing days are o'er, Johnny I hardly knew you.' I don't suppose you ever heard an Irish ballad that goes like this:

You haven't an arm and you haven't a leg,
Hurroo! Hurroo!
You haven't an arm and you haven't a leg
Hurroo! Hurroo!
You haven't an arm and you haven't a leg
You're an eyeless, noseless, chickenless egg
You'd have to be put in a bowl to beg
Och! Johnny I hardly knew you."

"It's horrible," said Christine.

"Horrible-funny, what we call gallows humour. 'Like a cod, you're doubled up head and tail, Och, Johnny I hardly knew you.' You remember it when you've forgotten the preachers. 'You're an eyeless, noseless, chickenless egg, you'd have to be put in a bowl to beg...'"

"But he's not really interested in the poor cripple, all he's really interested in is his own cleverness."

"It wasn't the ballad singer who recruited him. And the recruiting, don't forget, still goes on."

Christine was greeted by several people. A number were vaguely familiar from chance meetings at the clinic.

101

"Those two girls in the corner are nurses in the sanatorium above ours," she said. "They are supposed to be lesbians."

Alexis nodded. He was not sure what the word meant.

"There will be a certain amount of gossip tomorrow, now that I've been seen out with you," she said.

He looked at her in surprise.

"It's a very small world," she added "and a lot of people in it have no occupation except watching others."

"That's natural, I suppose. When I come to think of it, I'm interested enough in watching other people, but I can never imagine anyone being interested enough to want to watch me."

"You see how British you are!"

The waiter had promised a table in a quarter of an hour. The loudspeaker, having finished with "Pigalle" went on appropriately with "Boire un petit coup c'est agréable." Both tunes were with him for good, part of the dreamscape of first impressions that lies just below the consciousness always ready for service, outliving the changing body as it fritters away in nails that are cut off, hair that falls out, skin that is replaced, teeth lost – 'I am getting ghoulish' he thought to himself.

Through the doorway he could see a sled, stood upright against the wall of a house in a side street that sloped steeply downwards. Snow was gone for the year but the sled, too, reminded him of the day of his arrival. Time is a runaway troika. Can no one stop it? How many will it kill? How many will it most certainly kill? Destroy itself. One honest horse is the plodder in the middle...

"A troika in full flight is the most beautiful movement-in-action I've ever seen," he said.

"Where did you see a troika?" Christine asked in surprise. "I didn't know you had been to Russia."

"Nor was I. But I can use my imagination. Do you really think all those Italian painters saw Christ washing the feet of his disciples in a Renaissance palace?"

"No, but they had seen the palaces. They could get one model to wash another's feet. It's the only way. A painter has to keep his feet on the ground or else he becomes a mere decorator, and that seems to me to be something different."

"What do you mean by art? I often wonder myself what I really mean when I use the word."

"I haven't a definition," said Christine, "but I've heard a lot of talk on the subject. At that first job, with the publisher, I could go and see his pictures any time I liked. There was an enormous collection of books on art also that I could read when I had nothing else to do, which was fairly often. Of course, I don't really know anything, but I have heard what a lot of people who should know think, and I think I have developed some taste."

The waiter came to say their table was ready. He had placed them by a window which looked out at a different angle from the cafe, and from a higher level which gave a view, clear of the roof tops, of the mountains in the distance. Now they were mostly green, and the sound of cowbells came distinctly from the foothills. Wine, he discovered, was ordered open rather than in bottles, and she explained the mysteries of Fendant, Johannisberg and Dôle and of measuring in "décis"; brown pottery for the red wine, separate carafes for two, three and five décis, the latter looking as big as a jug by comparison.

"What a wonderful view," he said.

She smiled; people are always glad to hear their own land praised.

"But," he went on, "if you try to paint it – to go back to what we were talking about – you get such awful academic drivel. Not that I

103

wouldn't love to be able to draw as well as that, getting all those nice effects of perspective and setting suns and snow-capped mountains. But a collection of them anywhere – or even worse, of reproductions of them – in one of those big furniture stores, for example – is really one of the most dreary sights imaginable. Yet the scenes themselves are beautiful. Just look out. And the reproduction is accurate. So why?"

"Would you have the same objection to photographs?"

"No," he answered without hesitation. "In fact, one of the things I've been promising myself before I leave is to take some colour photographs."

"Before you leave?"

"Yes, I suppose I shall leave, some time."

They were both silent for a moment; her simple question, unpremeditated, set off a series of echoing implications that left them both surprised.

"It's a good point," he resumed "the sight is beautiful, the photo may be beautiful, why is the painting so awful?"

"Snobbery? What we've been taught to believe? Look how fashions change. Furniture your grandmother would have been glad to throw out is now selling for a fortune."

"That's where I get completely lost. Pictures are being bought and sold for fortunes, often by people who have fortunes and not much else. Bon. Let's say one is bought here, and put on exhibition before it goes to its new owner. I go to see it. Am I impressed by the picture, or by its price? If I'd never seen it before, and another was put in its place, would I be equally impressed? Probably. If the exhibit was a copy, would I know the difference? How could I, never having seen the original anyway? But would I be equally impressed? Honestly, I don't see why not."

104

"But you believe there is such a thing as taste?"

"In painting, to a limited extent."

"Don't you think that taste can be as subtle as education? After all, can you say at what point a person becomes educated? Or can you say on exactly what day he or she is an adult, or is middle-aged or old? And yet everyone agrees that there are illiterates, there are people who are better educated than others, and there are savants, just as there are children, adults and the old. You agree that some things are ugly and others beautiful. I think it's the same with taste. As I told you, in my first job, I began to see gradually what others could see in some of the pictures that were only daubs to me when I saw them first."

"But suppose it is only what they say they see because others, more famous, or with bigger reputations, said they saw before them?"

"You may be right, but I don't think so. I know I have learned something. I cannot explain to you how, but I know, I know it was so."

"I don't doubt it. One singer sings the same song better than another, or one girl knows better how to dress than another."

"Or one piece of chicken is better than another – mine was delicious. How was your steak?"

"A little bit too bloody for me, but good. You were talking so well, I hardly noticed."

"Me, talk?" said Christine. "I hardly opened my mouth!"

"Salad. No one in Europe must eat as much salad as the Swiss."

"C'est très sain!"

"That's an ominous phrase. Everything I hated as a child – especially cod liver oil – was always said to be good for me."

"You don't like salad?"

"No, it's excellent. And it always seems to be so tender here. I like things to be tender. Je suis un sentimental. I love Renoir, for example."

"You like those girls of his with the great rolls of fat round their middles, like motor tyres?"

"In his case, they don't seem to matter. Anyhow, they are all in a long tradition."

"Rubens?"

"And all the way back to that horrible little statuette like a round rhombus standing on its apex. Cro-Magnon or pre-German or pan-Celtic or something. As far as the women themselves are concerned, I'd prefer them Greek, Roman or Renaissance. But it doesn't seem to matter in Renoir."

"Isn't Renoir classical? I mean, they may be fat but they're normal. Not like Picasso."

"I know it can be explained," said Alexis "how you can stand under a monument, look up, and see it towering above you, but go a hundred yards off and your thumb is big enough to allow you to measure it off. The two sides of a long road meet in the distance, but they don't really – bad for traffic if they did. Or a man looks an ant to an elephant and an elephant to an ant, so what does he really look like? To me it's simple. He looks like what he seems to the eye when you look at him; if the angle alters, so does the picture. But if it amuses you, go ahead, put him in profile portrait back of the neck eating drinking singing sleeping yawning sneezing and blowing his nose all at once, with an eye for an ear and a nose for a mouth. If I get an old bicycle wheel, stick a pigeon's egg on top with sticking plaster, mount the lot on a new pair of handlebars (complete with bell and honkety-tonk motor-horn – don't forget that, it's important), and call the lot Pierrot, none of the art critics will talk of the subtle

106

relationships I have discovered between what were hitherto considered as disparate materials and the museums will not fall over each other offering me millions. That's the part I really resent. I could do with a few millions –"

"Of what? Pounds, dollars, Swiss francs... ?"

"Any of those disparate materials, which I would weld into an aesthetic whole."

"I heard a story about holes the other day," said Christine. "A man with a lorry is given a hole to deliver. It is a very valuable hole. As he goes round a corner he looks in his retroviseur –"

"His what? Oh, I see, his 'looking backwards see-r.' What a lovely word for a driving-mirror."

"And what's a 'driving-mirror'? A mirror that drives? Drives what? Or a mirror for use to powder your nose while driving? Doesn't seem very safe to me. Anyhow, he looks in his 'driving-mirror'"

"retroviseur –"

"– driving-mirror. He looks in his – retroviseur – and sees that the hole has slipped off. As it's such a valuable hole, he starts reversing in order to go back for it and on the way he falls into the hole."

"It's too unfair," said Alexis, "a writer has certain ticks which, if he isn't careful, turn into clichés and become a bore. A painter can cash in on his. They are his signature. They are his patented invention. They are his copyright and if he has a good publicity agent, he can keep on selling them, by the million. Because that's what the professional amateur of art buys – the signature, not the picture. Did you meet many artists?"

"Not so much in the office as at receptions my boss used to give at his house."

"The one with the picture gallery?"

"Some of them were at the house. As I dealt with the invitations, I was always invited too."

"Any great revelations?"

"No. They vary of course, artists, like everyone else."

"Are clothes always a pose?"

"As a Catholic, you might well ask that question – no one has ever attached so much significance to clothes?"

"With painters it's something sacred too?"

"I don't know. Ritual maybe. The sense of being apart."

"Isn't that in itself a pose? Or, at least, one you are entitled to only after you have demonstrated that you are a genius."

"I thought you were arguing that the only proof of genius is being able to sell rubbish for millions. But hasn't art always been sacred, or been associated with the sacred?"

"As well as with everything that is most profane libidinous licentious blasphemous and sacrilegious."

"But surely all that, too, was part of the sacred, in a whole lot of civilisations too? No, at these parties, there was occasionally the flamboyant type who looked and acted like an artist out of La Bohème. But most of them were quiet and modest, a bit distrustful of the other, successful money-making people – the ones who own cars and always eat in good restaurants. They spoke of someone who had succeeded in selling a picture with a certain envy, but generously. It was very difficult to win their confidence. They seemed to have made up their minds that outsiders would not understand."

"Did they resent that?"

"I don't think so, especially as, very often, they did not understand themselves what they were trying to do. But I remember one of them who committed suicide. People who take what they are doing as seriously as that deserve a certain respect. I had a curious dream myself the other night. I dreamt that I had made a painting. When I had completed it, I had an overwhelming longing to get rid of all the things that had contributed to its creation, the paints, the brushes, even the easel, so that my masterpiece – it was a masterpiece of course – could exist in its own right. Somehow their existence, now that it existed, seemed to diminish it."

"It's funny," said Alexis, "this craze to create. A child, seemingly by accident, may do something, once, that smacks of genius – at least in relation to what a child can normally do. If he can repeat it, he may actually have genius. Or it may just be his party piece and, in the end, become an almighty bore. Do you look at titles when you go to an exhibition?"

"Always?

"Why? By all the rules, you should be able to appreciate the picture in itself. What can a title possibly add? And yet you know it does. It tells you the artist's own summing-up, different from what you might otherwise have thought but, because it comes from him, final, unquestionably right, even if it is banal. But painting seems, too, often, to be an occupation which allows people who entirely lack talent to use their imagination to imagine they are artists."

"Surely there is bound to be a certain percentage of charlatans. But only a percentage," Christine replied. "Do you not look at titles?"

"Invariably."

"Well?"

"Well, if a painter calls his squares 'République', it at least tells me what he is supposed to be doing, even though I might have thought they were just interlocking squares – and painted them myself without any artistic pretensions. Look. This yellow plate, I place this red serviette on it. This work of art is called 'Ship at Sea'. You would agree if it were Picasso who did it. You would equally agree if he called it 'Mao', or 'Burning Galleon' or 'October' or 'Erupting Omelette' or 'Etna' or 'Beethoven'. You would stare and admire it with cowlike seriousness. A child would just giggle. You would consult your catalogue. Under '99. Ship at Sea. Picasso (1938)' you read: 'Here again, with his exuberant use of colour, we have another example of Picasso's uncanny gift of seeing beyond the outward appearance of things and, with a poet's vision, discovering hidden relationships that lie beneath the most commonplace of objects.'"

"Is that all?" said Christine.

"Well, this is No. 99. You expect me to go on inventing new penetrating comments indefinitely. Merde!"

"You are learning French much too fast."

"It's the ultimate comment."

"Do you know something?"

"What?"

"I can see that ship!"

"There you are. Exactly what I said. The title makes the picture. The pen is mightier than the sword – or the paintbrush. In the beginning was the word. The word contains the image, the picture just tries to follow. And you can't discuss it – or its price – without words. The title is the cork in the bottle."

"You don't really believe all you say."

110

"Does anyone? Do people who go out to kill perfect strangers in wars really believe what they say – when they don't know what they are talking about – or fighting about – in the first place? All adults believe in magic words more tenaciously and more passionately than any child. Just think of 'authority'. Invest anyone you like with authority and from then on, he has only to open his mouth and his will is done. He does not need to be a Hitler: think of some of these jack-booted policemen if you – you adult you – dare cross the road against the traffic lights when there isn't a car in sight. But then, I suppose, the composer of concrete music for concrete mixers may one day prove to be a Debussy for people with differently-attuned ears. Perhaps even the cackling of hens will be accounted music. If anything and everything goes, why not?"

The restaurant was emptying. The table next to theirs had already been cleared. Two tables away sat a melancholy man of about sixty, talking to himself, two empty wine bottles before him, and now drinking kirsch. As they stood up to go, they heard him, muttering. 'The city of San José. Costa Rica. When you come out of the Presidente, don't go left, towards the traffic lights, go right, down the hill, and you'll come to a gorgeous shop. Well, it's not gorgeous, it's an ordinary shop, painted blue. And inside it has lovely child coffins, with the lids off to show you, lovely white satin inside. Well, why shouldn't coffins be white? White coffins, with the lids off. Waiting to welcome you.'

The waiter brought the change. As they passed his table, the drunk looked up. His eyes were melancholy. He saw that Alexis was foreign, and said solemnly in English: "I'm dreaming of a white Christmas."

"Many happy returns," said Alexis, and smiled back. He felt a pressure on his arm, urging him forward. Surprised, he nodded goodnight to the drunk, and looked round at Christine as they moved on. She was pale.

"What's wrong?" he asked.

"I'm sorry," she said, "but drunken people always frighten me."

111

"But why?" he said, "he's perfectly quiet, and nice."

"I know," she replied.

"Jaccoud told me once that you have the biggest consular service in the world. That man is probably a Swiss consul. Or maybe some sort of agent. If he was sober, he'd be telling you how he exchanged a ton of coffee from Costa Rica against a cargo of nylon shirts from Hong Kong which he had sold at an immense profit to a new army in East Africa, and how much money he'd made and how clever he is. Instead, wine has made a poet of him, interested in maybe the only transcendental, metaphysical phenomena in Costa Rica."

"I know it's silly," she said, "but I can't help it."

The sky was perfectly clear. High up over the mountains the moon was in its first quarter, bright, but hazy along the blunt side. The walk, with his limping leg, was something of an effort. She took his arm.

"Poor Christine," he said, "not only do I talk my head off all the evening, but I reverse the natural roles coming back, you supporting me instead of me supporting you."

She squeezed his arm.

"It's been my happiest evening since I came here."

They did not speak again until they reached the grounds.

"Do you realise," said Alexis, "that we got one of the best tables in the restaurant, and I for one hardly know if I looked out of the window once after we were seated."

"Maybe views are only for people who have nothing to say or nothing left to say."

"I knew a Scot once who told me he had two grandparents living in the country. The old man sat at one side of the fire, the old woman at the other. The old woman would say, in a very long-drawn-out voice: 'Ay. Ay-ay-ay-ay-ay. Ay-ay,' to which the old man, after a long interval, would reply 'Ay.' I can see them, can't you?"

"Yes," said Christine. "I think it's terribly sad, your story."

"And beautiful, in a way."

"Yes. Nothing more to say. Resignation. Peace. I suppose so."

21

"We went to the pictures yesterday," said Marcella on Monday morning, "to see some horses we know."

Paddy Clery, spruce and clean-shaven on a Saturday night, still ploughing during the week, over seventy. How many years was it since he had been bitten by a mad dog, rushed (at the maximum speed of those days) to Paris, and been one of the first to be saved by Pasteur? Danny the postman carrying a bag of hay for the cattle into the 'town house' under the crossbar along the frame of his bicycle before putting on the cap that transformed him into an official of the State. Smells, and a Bunsen burner, your first contact with science, Corky, with his simian head, making sulphuretted hydrogen. Kit gaily singing in his flat Dublin accent, "She loves me not, she loves another" as the problem he is chalking on the blackboard obstinately refuses to work out; you know perfectly well he'll manage it, one of the best mathematics teachers in the country. Tracey with his more or less handsome worried face, older looking since he got the glasses, hair wavy but the waves not long enough, with his careful notes on English and the map showing how Charlemagne's empire split into three when he died. And a teacher called Moran, what nickname could he possibly be given since his class first heard of oxymoron but Oxy? Nicknames. The Block. Spider. The Don. Wee Barra. Big Barra. The Archbigot of Dublin and His Arrogance of Galway. Fly-in-the-tea-canister. The Weasel, Bull Murphy. "Different bleeding regiments in the same bloody army" was how Aussi dismissed all religious discussion: how did he acquire the accent after allowing himself just long enough in Australia to be able to say he'd been there, before he got out again? The Widgin who said it was a bloody shame to make the Prince of Wales King of England: they should have given the job to a married man. The d'Arcy who threw a stone and broke your front tooth, not much left of the French aristocrat who may have

114

originally contributed the name. The Bunion, who couldn't stop laughing in class at the idea of anyone being called John Bunyan, even if he did write the Pilgrim's Progress. Myself and Con and Joe and Joany.

A dance, and the blond who turned out to be a cousin of someone you knew and the sand-dunes afterwards and coming home to a sleeping home in the dawn of an August morning. Time for breakfast already. Why did not one always get up earlier...

A Civic Guard who had discovered an extraordinarily funny dirty book translated from a French author who was called, he thought, Rabeelis. One who wore plus-fours when he was not in uniform and was said to spend most of his time looking at lingerie in shop windows. And one who had a series of old cars, one car with the exotic name of De Dion Bouton written in brass, in ornamental lettering across the front of the open radiator.

Whist drives. The local concert. Miss Muriel Ryder will now sing "The Little Brown Jug".

The rugby match during the Christmas holidays that fell through and you all went up Nelson's Pillar instead and the day was so dull and dark and Decembric that you could hardly see O'Connell Bridge from the top.

The drill instructor picks you out as a possible boxer and in the first bout you get your nose knocked out of joint.

And a first, distant contact with death.

The light always burning at night in the next house. The old man, the father, eighty years old, immensely old, straight, with his silver-headed cane, who went vigorously for his walk every morning and stopped on the way back, with his old-man smell, and his big mouth and nose and a kindly smile as you wondered at the way nasturtiums were attached sideways to the stem, or tried to suck honey as you had been shown, or snapped the jaws of a snapdragon open and shut. And one day, he was bent, and tired. He still smiled at you, but the light no longer burned at night in the upstairs window.

And the boy at school who had lost his father and wore a black band on his arm and was an object of great interest to everyone, but who could smile and laugh. Would you have been able, if it had happened to you?

Did you ever think you'd see the day when you would watch a lizard as you are doing now, his body moulding to one, two, three – four creases in that rock? The best you could do was imprison a bumblebee in a jam jar and listen fascinated to the buzz but feeling obscurely guilty about it. It didn't matter about a wasp, nasty vicious things. Of course, a bee stung too, but only in self-defence. And you let it out of its glass prison when it got too tired unless you forgot about it and it was dead when you went back next morning. When you took the glass away it stood there dazed, until it roused, recovered and flew off.

A jam jar made a small glass house. You could make a bigger one with a cardboard box, cutting out the windows, cutting a rectangular strip for the door on three sides only so that the fourth could serve as the hinge. You put a candle in, a butt only, to prevent the house from going on fire, and the effect is marvellous. But even with a butt, there is soon a smell of scorching. A brown patch appears, and you have to blow the candle out. It is better to use a flash lamp, and even better to put a piece of red paper over the bulb, or cover the windows with red crepe paper. But you can't leave it on too long. Batteries soon wear out and they cost a lot. Anyhow, even when the light is on, you look at it, and it's fine, but you can't stay all night looking at it, can you?

It was more realistic when you borrowed the brush and made a tent with some old sacks. You could stay for hours sitting there, with a book, not much reading it, and the canvas had a strange dusty smell that was both pleasant and unpleasant. And after a while, especially if there was sun, and the light streamed a certain distance through the doorway and all the rest was a shadowed brightness, you felt drowsy and you remembered a perfume, and your body began to have uneasy stirrings that were pleasant in a frightening sort of way, like when you forced your thing into the neck and peed into a bottle, or peed behind a wall on your way to school when you didn't really need to, or that time in the country after you'd seen the cows being milked and you were in bed with your cousin and he said "let's play milking cows" and some of the adults must have overheard and came in and there was a terrible scene; or you slid down the banisters, or you climbed trees, edging your way up with your legs and it gave you the same sort of feeling and you felt guilty and you wondered if it were a sin. But even if it were, how could you describe it? There was nothing like that in the things you'd been told to say in your first confession.

One day your mind was put at ease. The kindly old priest teaching Christian Doctrine looked round the class and said: "I am sure none of you boys has ever committed a mortal sin"; surely he must know what boys did. But all your terrors come back with a rush the very next Sunday when the priest, after reading the terrible gospel about the end of the world, talked about confession and told a story he had read (he was a great one for pious reading) of a man who had just been to Holy Communion and had a heart attack and dropped dead at the altar rails. And his face was radiant as he lay there. But the priest (who had heard his confession the previous day) noticed that the host was still in his mouth, unconsumed, and removed it. Immediately the face turned black and there was suddenly a frightening stench of rot and corruption: the man had concealed a sin in confession and, as Saint Paul says, had "eaten judgement that is damnation in itself, not discerning the body of the Lord."

Had you too been concealing a sin in confession? But even if it was a sin, how could you possibly describe it to a priest? So you prayed and prayed, that God might give you the grace to make a good confession. And one Saturday afternoon, in desperation, you left your bike against the church railings and went in and tried to tell it all. And the priest understood at once and helped you get it out. Then he paused, and you waited, shaking with fear. "You realise what a terrible thing mortal sin is?" So it was a mortal sin. "Yes, father" you muttered, humbly. And he explained to you that, by sin, you lost God's friendship, but that God was infinitely merciful, and you must not be afraid: God would help you to overcome these weaknesses.

117

Purity was so pleasing to God. You must learn to respect yourself and keep yourself pure, and pray for help, when you were tempted, to his most pure Mother, the Blessed Virgin, and she would not fail you.

And you were resolved never, never to repeat that fault again and, knowing from your catechism that the surest sign that our confession is good and that we have sincere sorrow for our sins is the amendment of our lives, you came out of the church and jumped on your bicycle and it had wings.

But after three weeks' peace, suddenly it was back again. He prayed, and sure enough, was given strength. But it came back in sleep, and he woke to find a small wet stain on the sheet. He felt unclean, defiled, yet there was an undeniable feeling of pleasure. Surely he could not be blamed for what happened in his unconscious mind? But he was now awake. So he prayed, and went back to sleep.

And lead us not into temptation. What did that inexplicable phrase mean? If sin was so hateful to God, why did he "lead you into temptation?" The point was duly explained, ecclesiastically, but the economy of grace remained incomprehensible and irrational, Saint Augustine's felix culpa, the happy fault of our first parents which led God to show his immeasurable love for men, even to the sacrifice of his only Son.

Alexis remembered Christine's question; he had never thought to push it as far back as she had: if God is all-powerful and omniscient, why sin, why pain, why suffering, why death? Why the Crucifixion?

...The smell of books. The characteristic smell of bookshops. Second-hand bookshops and their mustiness, musty but not sour. New textbooks at the beginning of a new school year, their association with a childish helplessness in this first constriction he is really conscious of. That Russian book and its unmistakable odour. The book of Chinese short stories, with its grey cover, poor paper, red titles, pleasant lay-out. This piece of paper has been where I never was and probably never shall be. I can palp its texture with my hands. Peking. Chinese. Six, or is it seven hundred million of them. If all the guichets were laid to end. If all the geishas were laid end to end. Do they too have confessions, communions? Consciences?

Strange lands.

The fear you might have the first time you saw rain falling out of the heavens.

Or snow. Hail. Lightning. Thunderbolts. Meteorites.

A great red cloud suffusing the northern sky, aurora borealis.

Eclipse.

End of the world.

Apocalypse.

The sun was darkened, the earth trembled, and the dead arose and appeared to many.

As a child, the Chinese author was sent, almost daily, to a pawnbroker's and a medicine shop. The counter in the medicine shop was as tall as he was, that in the pawnbroker's twice his height. He used to hand clothes up to the counter twice his height, take the money proffered to him with contempt, then go to the counter of his own height to buy medicine for his father who was sick. And so he learned, a small Chinese boy, what the world is all about.

Later, he took over a flat that had once been occupied by a woman who hanged herself from a tree in the yard. Now the tree had grown so high that one could no longer reach its branches, but the flat remained a long time unoccupied, until he had at last moved in. He would sit under the tree, waving his fan and looking at the specks of sky through the thick leaves, while the caterpillars which came out in the evening would fall, icy-cold, on his neck.

From his seat in the garden, Alexis watched a cloporte on its back, struggling helplessly with all its little legs waving in the air, its radar out in front, equally helpless. Since he had become aware of them, he had noticed how dried-up they were. He had at first been horrified at the idea of standing on one and sensing the liquid squelch as it crushed. He found instead that, at a sign of danger, it folded up into a neat ball, a fraction of its normal size, and waited. A second one was now marching steadily down the path, all its antennae busy, going at its own pace. An insect has no need of machines to get it to its destination at an artificial speed, he thought sleepily, slightly dazed by the sun, and dropped into an absolutely horrible dream.

A café, a familiar crowd, people he knew from the university, couples forming, all on the point of leaving. He was about to ask where everyone was going when he realised that one of his lower front teeth was loose. He put his hand up to feel it and found that all the lower teeth in his mouth were loose and collapsing. He had a panic-stricken feeling of the terrible mess he would look: this, in addition to his leg, was the end. How could he ever face Maureen again, looking like this? The teeth all collapsed. He took one piece out of his bursting jaws and looked at it. It was a crude piece of concrete. Perhaps, he thought desperately, if I can get to the dentist in time, he may be able to do something, and moved towards the toilet where he knew there was a wash-basin and a mirror. But the pressure inside his mouth was choking him. He woke. A cloporte was in exactly the same position, struggling on its back. The same or another? How would you know one of seven hundred million Chinese from another? How many are born every second? How many die?

And, in spite of that, it was rather those who resembled each other who are unusual. Girls spent their time reading fashion magazines and trying as hard as they could – really trying – to look like one another – but different. As for men, with their absurd clothes: peas in a pod with the nostalgia not of the womb but of the aboriginal seed. Things that are equal to the same thing are equal to anything ("What proposition is that? Next boy? Tst, tst, tst, tst. Three weeks from the exam, and they know nothing."). All these new hairstyles, fashions, clothes, and still they look as unlike as even Christine and Maureen.

It had been so pleasant last night. Could he ever have had the same sort of evening with Maureen? He had been out with her once only and he seemed to remember that there had been no lack of talk. No, he was quite sure; one had only to remember that curiously detached air of hers. Sphinx without a secret – Oscar Wilde's boutades often had more wit than application. She was no sphinx either, no more sphinx than intellectual. She was no intellectual, but she was no fool either. But all this is irrelevant. One cannot particularise perfection. For she had a perfection he could not define except by imagining her in contrast to others he knew, unique as the one perfect bloom in a garden of flowers, what Maud Gonne had been for Yeats, or Heloise for Abelard. And the world well lost. If only he were a Yeats or an Abelard. His mind was too diffused on too many things, even if it had been endowed with that great driving power. Perhaps that was it: all that went to make up her personality, physical, mental and spiritual, fused and concentrated to the point of transmutation; once you have made the gold, the ingredients become as irrelevant as the flour to a cake.

Gold? Inappropriate. She was wholly feminine. The lustre of red gold perhaps. That glorious hair of hers. But something hard also, unapproachable, that if you tried to touch it, rolled up protectively like one of those cloportes, leaving only a surface visible.

The day had become cloudy. Vast eddies of vapour concealed and revealed the mountain tops, forming strange dragon shapes that abruptly changed as a patch of blue sky was uncovered, and the sun for a moment appeared. There was a sound of aeroplanes. Curious the way aeroplanes were suddenly there, large, well in view and audible, as if they had come silently just to that spot. It was not the first time he had noticed that they always seemed to become audible and hence, be seen, at just about the same place. This time there were two, a large one and a smaller, obviously faster plane, seemingly escorting the other, as incongruous together as a collie and a dachshund. Unbalanced. Up there in the heavens. Escort? If it was important enough for an escort, surely there should be more than one – one was simply an attendant on an invalid. They disappeared into a cloud. Who cares? Curse or blessing? The war would not have been possible without them. The cloporte goes at its own pace, as does the

121

eagle and the snail: man tampers. Perhaps he cannot do otherwise. Perhaps that is why he is different. Perhaps that is his tragedy.

The sky began to clear. One chalet on a distant ledge was startlingly visible for a moment, a vision in the mist, then disappeared again. Words were at times terribly inadequate. How to describe this changing scene? The words would first have to be written down before they could be properly controlled (mental arithmetic is easy only if the quantities are few and simple). But the act of writing implies composition, a certain arbitrariness of choice. And the words are still inadequate.

Perhaps that is one of the reasons why people want to paint, the urge to express something they feel and cannot put into words, or express inadequately by a photo-like reproduction, so that painting goes into abstractions in an effort to express relations the painter sees. If the result satisfies him perhaps he really is a painter. But the relations he has seen and succeeded in expressing may remain obscure and incomprehensible to the viewer, who goes to the expert, the art critic. Who may be a seer, capable of seeing both the relations and their expression, but he still has to explain – in words. And may succeed, like the second differentiation in mathematics... where the painter could not; or else produce one of those masterpieces of jargon that he himself possibly understands. Except that his function should be to explain – if he can – and not shroud in black light.

Perhaps that too explained a main difference between Picasso and his disciples and imitators: where he has tried out and succeeded in everything, even when the results are incomprehensible, he knows, whereas they are just making wild guesses.

He should have thought of that last night. Pity the best impromptus occur so long afterwards.

The white pigeons swooped by in uncertain, amateurish flight, swift sure passage abruptly changing into a halting carousel, some with tails fanned out as if air-braking, frightened of their own audacity in flying at all as a novice skier on too steep a slope. Were they really wild, pigeons, or did they always seek human help rather than fend

for themselves?   Pigeons in Venice.   Pity they could not be pre-
constipated.

Why bother with painting when nature exists?   What was Matisse
to these six white pigeons against a blue or even a clouded sky?   Why
bother with literature when life exists?   Why talk, when everything is
contained in silence?   Why bring into life, and torture eternally?

Christine was coming up the path, a letter in one hand, a torn
envelope in the other.

22

"It's from Marie-Claire," she said.

"Marie-Claire?"

"Yes. My young sister. You must meet her."

"Oh, yes, you did talk about her. You seem very happy about it."

"She is marvellous, Marie-Claire. You will see. She is passing through on her way to Zurich, and is going to stay for a few days. She is finishing a secretarial course in Zurich. Did you sleep well?"

"Wonderfully. And you?"

"I think so, but it was a very busy night; I had dream after dream, full of pictures – paintings I mean. In one, I was in my old room at home, but only after going to bed did I notice that all sorts of pictures had been added, including two that were superb. I knew it was my mother who had done this, because she has not much taste so far as pictures are concerned. As diplomatically as I could, I suggested that there were too many, and without telling her that the rest was tasteless rubbish, said I would be very grateful if she left me just the two. I've forgotten what, but they were genuine masters, perhaps Flemish, perhaps Italian. I also noticed lots of pieces of carpet on the floor, badly chosen. I was rather annoyed, because I had furnished the room myself, but thought philosophically 'Oh well, these bits and pieces will save what is underneath.' When I got back to the room, I wondered how I had not noticed the pictures when I first arrived, or the new addition, which started off by being a kind of statue in a frame. Then I got frightened, because it miraculously started to move, but I soon discovered it was mechanical. The only difference was that everything moved, head, eyes, mouth, lips, hands. As I came closer to get a better look, it turned into a horrible little man, still more or less mechanical, but sinister. And I think I thought it was God. I don't know if you have ever seen a statue of Balzac in Paris which is nude. It was like that."

"A couple of centuries ago, and you would have been burned as a witch! God as a nude Balzac! It really is a bit much."

"Isn't it? Do you think it was the devil at work?"

"It's what comes of talking of Picasso before going to bed."

"And eating too well. Thank you again for last night. It was a wonderful evening."

"Perhaps we can take your sister there when she comes."

"Oh, she'd love that. I hope she brings her record-player. I must ask her. Although it probably isn't necessary, she hardly ever travels anywhere without it."

"Isn't it a bit heavy for carrying round?"

"She doesn't mind."

"A record-player is bad enough, but it's not much use without records. How does she manage them?"

"She has a few she always takes with her. And then she goes some place - here for instance - and hears something on the radio, or at a concert, and buys the record."

"But that makes, say, four instead of the three she always carries. And five the next time it happens. Or does she shed records all over the place?"

"I don't really know. She has one Dinu Lipatti record that never leaves her. She has a Schnabel recording of the Schubert Impromptus

125

that she bought after falling in love with a pianist she heard playing them once at a concert (he of course never knew). She couldn't get a recording by him. The father of one of the girls she was in school with has a music shop, and knows a great deal. He recommended the Schnabel."

"That makes two."

"I forget what else she has. Oh yes, she has a Segovia."

"All very romantic."

"Is that a reproach?"

"No, no, not at all. Perhaps I should have said 'poetic.'"

"Do you play an instrument?"

"I used to?"

"Used to?"

He looked at his arm and shrugged.

"Before this happened. I was studying the piano very seriously. I secretly hoped to be a pianist. My father was glad to see me studying music, but would have been horrified at the idea of depending on it to make a living. Not serious. A nice amateur accomplishment, nothing more."

"I didn't know you were so interested in music. You never spoke about it. I thought your interests were painting, or literature."

"Both. But it was the piano, one time. Anyhow, that's all an academic question now."

"Why? Surely your arm at least will get completely well?"

"It's probably the cinema which has created the idea of the romantic artist – you know, Chopin, hair falling all over his forehead, a Dionysiac look in his eyes, coughing blood on the keyboard as he struggles superhumanly to the end of his concerto –"

"But it happens in real life too. Dinu Lipatti is a very sick man. I have not seen it myself but a friend of mine was at one of his concerts recently and told me it was frightening to see him."

"You know the usual conventions. The long slender fingers of the artist. Better still if they are tapering. What you really need is a pair of hands like sledge-hammers, but the precision of a Swiss watch. My own arm may get well, but never well enough. In ways I resent it more than my leg. In fact, I must be disintegrating completely. I had no dreams last night, but sitting here a while ago, I dropped off and dreamt first that one tooth was loose. This one here, I think. Then that all of them were loose. I put up my finger to see, or try and straighten them, and discovered my mouth was full of lumps of cement, choking me."

"Let me see."

He opened his mouth. She put a finger in and searched around. It accidentally touched the back of his throat and his teeth almost closed on her finger as the nerves reacted.

"Don't say 'ah' till the doctor tells you," she said. "Write this down on the patient's chart: no lumps of concrete, but a mad dog guards the passage to his inside. It bites!"

"Almost bites," he corrected, "and only when irritated. Did I hurt you?"

"No," she replied. "Anyhow, I'm no pianist. All I play is the gramophone."

"But you play that rather well? Don't you even yodel?"

"I don't even play a melodeon."

127

"A squeeze-box. And Marie-Claire?"

"She played the recorder quite well. Then she got interested in the guitar. But you can imagine what it is like travelling with a recorder, a guitar, music, a record-player and records."

"Female one-man band."

"So now she only carries the record-player and a few records."

"Pity," commented Alexis.

"Why?"

"You have to play something, I think, if you really want to appreciate music, even if it's only a mouth-organ or a tin whistle. Or a Jew's harp. Or a comb with a piece of butter-paper over it. Anyhow, I'm looking forward to meeting your sister."

"I'm sure you will like Marie-Claire. I must be getting back."

It was funny to imagine people you know only as individuals having relations, natural as that may be. It seemed to diminish rather than enhance them, diluting some vital element of the personality, temporarily at least, until a new equilibrium sets in. Members of families may resemble one another, but ugliness can resemble beauty down to some apparently insignificant detail that makes all the difference: it's a shock to meet the sister of the beauty who is so like her – but plain ugly.

23

Marie-Claire, fortunately, turned out to be one of those who enhance. A certain amount of baby-fat gave her face a jolly look. She wore her hair long and dressed in a way that unmistakably said 'student'. Perhaps because of her father's abdication, his withdrawal into an ill-resigned and irritated acceptance of his ill-health and disappointment, Christine had been in the habit of mothering Marie-Claire, and a good deal of the relationship still subsisted; it was accepted by Marie-Claire with an amused tolerance, a harmless whim which she found touching and slightly ridiculous.

"But why are you studying in Zurich?" Alexis asked.

"I did my degree in Geneva, which is of course French-speaking. I am going to Zurich so as not to forget my German completely, and also because my father got me some temporary work there that gives me some money. I wouldn't have missed it for anything. The secretarial course is very serious, but it is good – provided you work of course. The principal has a bun, and glasses. Sex-appeal, zero, but she knows all about comportment. You must always have your desk neat and tidy. You should always be in your place five minutes before time in the morning. The boss must never find you combing your hair when he comes in. He doesn't like that. Der Herr hat das nicht gern. You must never come to the office without stockings. Der Herr hat das nicht gern."

"Isn't 'Der Herr' also 'the Lord' in the religious sense?" asked Alexis.

"That's exactly it," said Marie-Claire. "Der Herr – any der Herr, is a very important person in German Switzerland. Lord, boss, husband, or male generally."

129

"You remember Uncle Heinrich in Basle?" asked Christine.

"Yes." Marie-Claire paused reminiscently.

"My mother's brother," explained Christine.

"His wife was our Aunt Emma," said Marie-Claire. "She was twenty years younger than der Herr Heinrich, and that made him twice as important since it also gave him the superiority of age as well as the natural superiority of the male."

"It must be admitted she was not very bright," said Christine.

"Bright!" exclaimed Marie-Claire. "She must have been out of her mind to marry him in the first place. As she was so immature, der Herr made her keep a notebook (which he bought – he wouldn't trust her to do even that much properly) in which she had to write down every centime she spent. He made up the account at the end of the week, and it had to balance."

"Were they poor?" asked Alexis.

"Poor? You should have seen the house" said Marie-Claire. "And the car. The biggest he could get. A Mercedes of course. Black and solid. He wasn't even mean. The idea was not to be saving with money. It was just Discipline."

"Woman's place is in the home?" suggested Alexis.

"Provided that is where her Herr wants her to be. Switzerland must be the only place in the world where women have not yet got the vote. And you know about our National Day?"

"No."

"On our National Day, the offices shut at five. Instead of six. That's what makes us great. Discipline. Hard work. Honesty. Ja."

"From the little I've seen, the results seem to justify a lot of it," said Alexis, feeling it was up to him, if only in politeness, to protest. "Look at me, for example, where else can I go, hoping to get cured, all the way from Old Tim O'Toole."

"But when you are cured, you will escape... No, I am exaggerating. It's not really so bad. But I find I appreciate it all the more from a distance. Sometimes I long for a bit of healthy French dirt."

"And when you are in Paris you long for your Swiss bathroom," said Christine.

"True. But you must admit. The men... My God, they are so slow and so sure of themselves and so right always and so smug and self-satisfied."

"You could hardly call daddy self-satisfied," said Christine.

"He's the exception. And even he – his Frau is also his Hausfrau."

They were sitting in Marie-Claire's room in a pension. She made tea from an electric kettle. It turned golden when she pressed a lot of lemon-juice into the three glasses.

"Christine tells me you are a great music enthusiast," Alexis said to Marie-Claire.

"Who knows nothing about music."

"What's the latest?" Christine asked.

"This," she answered, unwrapping a record. "The Arpeggione. Do you know it?"

"Schubert," he said, glancing at the cover, "no, I don't think so."

131

"We'll play it later. I hate trying to listen and trying to talk. One or the other. Poor old Segovia will have to provide the background music. Very popular this. I'm afraid I don't always like everything he plays. I admire it more than I love it sometimes. It seems to me a guitar should never be played in anything bigger than a drawing-room."

"If so, none of us would ever hear him," Christine objected.

"Anyhow," said Marie-Claire, "here goes. A portable gramophone is not ideal, but it's all right as a background. Albeniz."

"The neighbours don't object?"

"You can make all the noise you like, within reason, up to ten at night. Have you noticed the walls? Look at the window, and you will see."

For a room in a pension it was certainly quite something. There was about ten inches of solid wall on either side of the window, in and out, so that the whole was nearly two feet thick. The room was on the first floor, overlooking a road that led downwards into a park, and the French windows opened on to a little balcony enclosed by an ornamental, curved wrought-iron railing. The house, almost three hundred years old, had been modernised inside, combining all the advantages. Not alone was there central heating, but something Alexis had never seen before – central refrigerating: the refrigerator had no visible means of support and apparently operated from a central plant in the basement.

Between Alexis and Marie-Claire, the relationship was warm and immediate. He found her cheerfulness and gaiety immensely attractive while she, screened by her sister's longer-standing acquaintance with him, obviously enjoyed her bantering, slightly flirtatious role. She had spent four months in England and had been fascinated by one piece of native folklore in particular. The husband in the house where she stayed got up at seven every morning, made tea, and took a cup to his wife, his two daughters, his son, and Marie-Claire. He then went back to bed. She had been bewildered the first

132

morning by this solitary cup of tea instead of the English breakfast she had heard so much about at what, in England, was an unearthly early hour, and by this most un-Swiss behaviour of the husband. Only afterwards did she understand that it was a custom of the natives, a morning rite. "A nice cup of tea" became one of her catchwords. And she developed a passionate love of cornflakes, but not for the morning smell of kippers.

Alexis had seldom seen Christine so animated. She regarded her younger sister affectionately and without envy as more active and adventurous than herself, and her solicitude had something almost of deference in it. Marie-Claire seemed to accept this allocation of roles, her undoubted affection tempered at times by a slight impatience.

Christine had brought flowers – one of the first things she had thought of on hearing that her sister was coming. A ray of evening sunshine fell on them. What a picture they made against the white tablecloth and the golden glasses of lemon tea. . .

"What picture does a guitar evoke?" Alexis asked.

"Spain," replied Marie-Claire at once, "Carmen, flamenco, flounced dresses, hipless men, bullfights, earrings."

"Why not the eighteenth century?" said Christine, "small Court orchestras, and candlelight."

"Which reminds me," said Marie-Claire. It was growing dark. She opened her case and took out a squat red candle which she lit.

"And a carpet," said Alexis "what does the word 'carpet' suggest?

"Persia," replied Marie-Claire.

"Why not Turkey?" protested Christine, "or Afghanistan – those warm, brown-squared carpets."

"Well, Persia?" continued Alexis.

"Apart from carpets," said Marie-Claire "Persia means only one thing to me: medical students in Swiss universities. Millions of them. And they are all princes or princesses. A few exceptions do law or dentistry."

"Tell Alexis about your trip to Naples."

"With Elvira?"

"Who was she," asked Alexis, "a Persian princess?"

"Of course," answered Marie-Claire, "except that she was as broke as I was, so we had to live and travel on the cheap. On the way down, there was a huge Italian family in the compartment. The father and mother were both enormous, but they had five of the most adorable bambini – you know, those fantastic, great black liquid eyes: the father, a great hulk of a workman, simply melted in his corner when he took one of them on his knee. And, of course, they got hungry. So the food was produced. I've never saw so much salami and cheese and fruit and chocolate. And a great fiasco of chianti. In the intervals of looking after one or other of the five bambini, we had been talking, and they were amazed and delighted to have a Persian with them. So when the food was produced, we were invited to join in. We refused politely at first, but it was no use. If the truth were told, we were both hungry. So we had a marvellous picnic. And then, just before we reached Rome, the father and mother earnestly beseeched us to be careful and to be sure not to speak to people we did not know in trains in Italy!"

"Italy will have to be my first stop as soon as I get out," said Alexis.

"We went on down to Naples afterwards, and everyone was astonished that I was the one who spoke some Italian: no one would believe that Elvira was not a Neapolitana."

"It will soon be time for me to be getting back," said Alexis. "Could we hear a little of your new record?"

"The record-player isn't worthy of the record, unfortunately," said Marie-Claire, rising to adjust it. She went back to her cushion on the floor as the music started, and they listened in silence in the candlelight; it had grown quite dark outside. If only it were Maureen who was here, he thought, in the should-be impersonal room which Marie-Claire has somehow transformed, made intimate and personal; and immediately felt ashamed, disloyal to Marie-Claire, so unreservedly friendly, disloyal to Christine who had brought him here and eased him out of his loneliness. As the 'cello played on, he saw her in a new way. It was as if, only now, did her various confidences about her own life suddenly cohere into a picture of a girl, young, uncertain, basically afraid of life (if that expression means anything), regretting the love affair she had feared, regretting her parents' failure, pathetically fond of her more confident sister and, above all, alone. Her 'solitude en face d'une solitude' took on a new meaning, and thinking of his own father and mother, remote at this moment and far away in more than just a physical sense – as far away as Maureen – and of the author of this music, dead before he was thirty, he felt an overwhelming sadness, an almost cosmic sense of human isolation and loneliness.

The record was changed to the other side. No one spoke. It played to the end.

Marie-Claire got up again, still silent, switched off the gramophone and put on the light.

"We've all grown very silent," she said. "Have you ever noticed, when someone sings for a group of people, and they all applaud, the kind of embarrassed silence that then follows? Perhaps we always need a breathing space before we can get back comfortably to ordinary banality again."

"It's a beautiful record," said Alexis, "your little sister certainly has taste, Christine."

"You did not notice it before?" asked Marie-Claire banteringly.

"No," replied Alexis, "you have yet to learn how ignorant I am."

135

"They say that to know one is ignorant is the beginning of wisdom."

"Sad to think we must pass all our lives discovering just how ignorant we are. Even somebody like Schubert."

"Perhaps he died too young even to have realised," said Christine.

"If only I had his kind of knowledge I would cheerfully forget the rest," said Alexis, "all of it. Well, enough of Deep Philosophic Thoughts."

He held out his hand. It seemed the most natural thing in the world to kiss Marie-Claire on both cheeks as if he had known her for years.

"Thank you," he said, "what a nice sister Christine has got."

"Me too" she answered. "Isn't that right?" she added with a grin, giving Christine a tomboyish thump on the back.

"I'll never make a lady of her," Christine said to Alexis. "Till tomorrow."
"Till tomorrow."

24

Lizard on the wall, beautiful s-curve. Whistle to it. Just whistling. Then Santa Lucia. Head slightly towards me, three feet away on the wall in front. Really listening. Not quite certain where his eye is. Sound of water falling into a cistern, continuous, no interruption. Sudden flurry of white pigeon wings. Change position slightly. Absurd, why should he remind me of a sea-lion. On wall. No sun, it's not far away, but still behind clouds. Now the shape of a bent pin, stiff gracious, legs practically invisible against the wall. How long would it take to gain its (his/her) confidence. Friends. Take what form. Dog too much. Cat too interested, garce. Don't like crawling or slimy things but love lizards. Don't want as prisoner, even if possible to tame. Stop whistling. Head turned back and sideways now, again seems watching me, very occasionally moves, rest of body immobile. No, moved at last. Now not looking at me. Flap of wings again, scrape of pigeon legs on roof. Back in s-bend. Watching me again, head changed slightly a couple of times. Was that a tongue? Straightened out now, straight line with curves, legs out. Yes, definitely a tongue. Scrambles up wall. Whistle, as to a dog. Stops – definitely, I think whistle did it. Starts to move away. Whistle urgently. Stops again. Five minutes. Climbed rapidly up wall, tail left hanging over for a half-second. Disappeared over top, went along top, stop, looked down. Whistle again. No effect. Gone.

These ants. These bloody ants. Not enough for them to use my body as a thoroughfare without wanting to turn it into a snack-bar as well.

Odd blossoms are scattered on the ground and they are blossoms of Bougainvilliers.

137

Fallen leaves are fine, that used paper handkerchief among them horrible.

A procession of ants, up and down the wall. Eye follows to find the source. Invisible as source of a crowd in a great city or source of a great river from any of its many bridges. Right up the wall, down into the ground, into and under, whence and whither, who knows.

Are things under glass dead, or only sprouting?
Thoughts in an ivory tower
Hot cross buns
All things part of experience are part of ourselves
even the most painful
separate from only with a sense of amputation
if thy right hand scandalise thee
The great hungers
hunger
youth life love survival love
the wind across the river
harvest moon
first fruits of autumn.
But death is a living force stronger than life
shiver down the spine
and one day it's for the last time
this is the servant
morning nears
birds awakening
and spirits in the Inferno whose tears froze in their eyes before
they could fall
of all away-going the ineffable sadness
even from what is hateful
premonitory of the last
if it's all only a story anyway
fear on the other side of all involving
the plant can outlive the friendship that inspired it
a procession of ants...
lizard on the sunless wall, enigmatic,
chameleon.

25

It was the maid with the breakfast tray who brought the news.

"Dr Jaccoud was killed last night," she announced.

"It's not possible," he said, horrified.

"He was driving back here when his car seems to have gone over the side of the road at a bad corner. It fell twenty metres."

"When did this happen?"

"Some men on their way to work discovered it this morning. No one knows exactly what happened. It took hours to get the body up to the roadway."

"He was dead when they found him?"

"I think so. No one knows anything very much yet, except that he is dead."

Christine had some more details when he saw her a little later in the morning.

"People are wondering if it is suicide," she said. "He had a reputation for driving fast, but driving fast safely. Everyone says he was an excellent driver."

"Did he drink?"

"Never touched alcohol. He was a strange man."

"Did you know him well?"

"I worked more with him than with any of the other doctors. He hardly ever spoke, except when it was necessary while working. And he seems to have had no friends, nor to have wanted any. He could have had lots. Some of the nurses, for example, were crazy about him. How did you find him?"

"I liked him very much."

"He took his work very seriously. I know he was worried about your operation. Your leg did not react as well as he had hoped it would."

"He seemed to worry a lot about everything. He told me a story once about a kind of town the Germans had for Jews during the war as if he were personally guilty for what happened there. Too hard on himself. So you think it might have been suicide?"

"It's what people are saying. Someone mentioned that he had been treated for a nervous breakdown some time before he came here. I suppose you think suicide is wrong?"

"It's one of the Roman virtues, I suppose you could call it, that Christianity never approved of. Burial in consecrated ground was refused to suicides. I think it was to get over that that English law adopted the formula 'suicide while of unsound mind' – temporarily mad, so not responsible for your actions."

"You had to be mad before you could decide to end your life? Can anyone seriously believe that after this war, after the concentration camps, for instance?"

"Let me see, what did my penny catechism say. 'Presumption is a foolish expectation of salvation without making proper use of the necessary means to obtain it,' and despair is 'a loss of confidence in God's goodness'."

"Neatly encapsulated, to be kept handy like a box of pills. A Jew in a concentration camp, living in conditions which make it impossible for him to feel human or behave like a human being, knowing that his wife, his children – and probably his parents if he were young enough – have been massacred, and that he is only one of millions to whom the same thing is happening – is he to be blamed for 'a lack of confidence in God's goodness'?"

"Apparently."

"But it's monstrous."

"There is a let-out clause. The rules are formulated by makers of rules, not by people who have undergone these things and suffered them. A fundamental Christian tenet is that the mercy of God is infinite. So between the two there is a very subtle moral mechanism. And the corollary is equally important: Judge not, and you shall not be judged."

"I hate your rules," said Christine vehemently.

"So do I. But we have to live with them whether we like it or not. They are not necessarily wrong or untrue because they are unpleasant. Old age exists, waiting for us, whether you like it or not. You can't avoid it by disbelieving, any more than you can escape the ultimate, most illogical monstrosity of all, death; not even by suicide."

"'But do you really believe that if Jaccoud deliberately killed himself, he could now be in hell? That's what you've just said means, isn't it? That the remains they will bury with religious rites and no doubt some speeches – how he would have hated that! – are the remains of a devil. Poor Jaccoud!"

"All I know, Christine, is that Jaccoud was the first friend I made here, even before you; that while the rest of us will soon be talking of the Nazi massacre of the Jews as an episode of history, he was tortured by it, perhaps tortured to death by it. But those who ask questions are the ones who care. And those who care are the ones who love. Often it is not so much great deeds that move us as a man's depths of sincerity. I remember now that, after telling me his story about that village, I was so moved I could not speak, if I had tried I might have wept. As he left the room he quoted something to me, he said it was a Russian proverb, I think, something like 'To live one's life is not just like crossing a field'. To him it certainly was not. He was good, and I do not know any epitaph a man could desire from those who knew him than simply that. No, Christine, if you want to condemn Jaccoud to hell you'd better find another judge."

They spoke about it again later in the day, with Marie-Claire. The whole town was talking about the accident, people who scarcely knew Jaccoud now feeling they had always liked and respected him. But even before the dead go to their graves the remainder go back to their living, little pangs of remorse at their selfishness swallowed up in the knowledge that the same will happen when their turn comes: you cannot keep for long the ripple on a pond. But no Man is an Island unto Himself. Not even Jaccoud. It seemed typical of him to have been worrying about his part in the operation, as Alexis had only now learned from Christine.

To Marie-Claire his death was more of a casual news-item than to the others, who could hardly forget a body awaiting its autopsy. In a town that was well used to death, common as a commodity and part of its stock-in-trade, and so, discreetly handled and well managed, Jaccoud's end was lacking in that admirable discretion, and accordingly scandalous.

They finally had dinner together, as planned, in the Mont Blanc, still thinking about what had happened.

"Some deaths seem worse than others because they seem so wasteful, in people who seem to have so much to give," said Christine.

"On the other hand," said Marie-Claire, "there are women who can see a husband die without a regret but are broken-hearted at the sight of a sick poodle. You remember Lisabeth, Christine?"

142

"That was der Herr's sister," explained Christine. "But you'd better not say any more about the family or Alexis will think they are all mad."

"Well aren't they?" rejoined Marie-Claire. "This Lisabeth was married to another Heinrich, in name and in every other way. She was about forty-five –"

"More," Christine corrected.

"Was she? I didn't think she was much older. –"

"And he was sixty at least," Christine added.

"Swiss German husbands are always older," said Marie-Claire. "Even when they marry. Even when they are younger. They are born older. It's all that male responsibility... They had no children, but they had this awful dog. Not a poodle in fact, it was a Pekinese, a vicious snub-nosed evil-tempered ugly little wretch that would snap your hand off if you went near it."

"It wasn't really as bad as that," said Christine, laughing

"Wasn't it? I've got a scar on my finger to prove it. Look." She showed Alexis the mark on her right hand.

"Well," she continued, "there was no difference between Heinrich and Heinrich. But there was a big difference between Emma and Lisabeth. Emma was soft, and did what she was told. Lisabeth had the temper and the tenacity of a bulldog. In fact she bit. Maybe that's why she so loved her Pekinese. My God, how they fought. To make things better, Heinrich hated the Pekinese and was always trying to get in a kick at it. If her mistress was anywhere in the house, the Pekinese replied with the most unmerciful yapping. It was worse than a fire-alarm. If she wasn't at home, the Pekinese saved it all up until she came back, and then made it perfectly plain what had happened in her absence. Either way, it meant a fight."

143

"This went on until one day Heinrich had a heart attack and was rushed to hospital. It naturally happened the day neither Lisabeth nor the Pekinese was at home: she was taking it to the vet, probably to have its pedicure. Well, she mightn't love her husband, but she knew her duty, and off she goes to the hospital with a bunch of flowers like a dutiful wife to visit her Heinrich. Unfortunately, he said she smelled of dog and they had another fight and being a woman of strong habits, she slammed the door and left. Before wifely duty could get the better of her resentment and decide her to visit him again, Heinrich had had a second attack, and died."

"This wouldn't have made much difference, as Heinrich, who was congenitally lazy and whose most energetic action in years had been to aim a kick at the Pekinese, had never bothered to change the will he had made in favour of his wife, now become his happy and liberated widow. You might think the Pekinese should have been equally happy. But not at all. It looked as if Heinrich's hatred was necessary to its mean cantankerous nature, a kind of salt to its food. It fell ill. She spent a fortune on it. She took it to clinics in Berne and Zurich. She was getting ready to take it to London when she got held up by the quarantine regulations, and it died. She was, quite literally, broken-hearted. She died within the year, no interest left in living. And she left all she had to her brother, the other Heinrich. Maybe there's something Freudian in that, I'm not a psychologist, but it's queer. Anyhow, that made the other Heinrich even more rich, and made him even more worried because he was now even more responsible."

"Si non e vero e ben trovato" said Alexis. "I don't know whether or not it's true –"

"It's absolutely true," confirmed Christine. "Marie-Claire usually embroiders, but this time she hasn't exaggerated one bit."

"I've got a story to tell you which is even more unbelievable but it's not funny. It's so strange that you would say a story-teller who invented it was singularly lacking in respect for his readers' intelligence: it's too well rounded off, too perfect. I have it from a doctor who had a flat on the same floor as one of the people

144

concerned, and he's not the sort of person who makes up stories. There was an Indian in this flat who was getting close to retiring age and had worked for an international organisation in various places with a Pakistani of about the same age. Neither of them could stand the other, or say a good word about him; each thought the other an incompetent, stupid idiot.

"One day the Indian was not feeling too well, and decided to go along to a hospital for a check-up. The doctor who examined him discovered he had a very dangerous heart condition and ordered him to bed immediately, in the actual hospital. Hearing about this, the Pakistani began to feel remorseful. Here they were, two strangers in a foreign land, and if they no longer belonged to the same India, they at least were both from the same sub-continent. There was only one thing to do. So he went to see the Indian, and the gesture made both realise that the other was not nearly as bad as he had always imagined. On the way out, the Pakistani went to see the Indian's doctor. They chatted a few minutes about the Indian's health, then the doctor said 'You know, it was good of you to come and see your friend, but a few days under observation wouldn't do you any harm either.' The Pakistani demurred but the doctor insisted, and he finally agreed to stay.

"During the night, the Indian died. The following morning, the Pakistani asked about his friend; he died of shock on being told the news.

"That story is true, mark you. As I said, it would make very poor fiction."

"Incredible," said Christine.

"I must now tell you my black story," said Marie-Claire. "This time I don't know whether it's true or not. I wasn't there. It was just before Nero's birthday, and the master of ceremonies was in a terrible flap. He just couldn't think what to do to provide something new for Nero. Boiling oil, gladiators, throwing them to the lions – he'd done all of them. Fortunately, he'd been to a number of Hollywood films and remembered that one thing Nero could never resist was spectacle.

145

So he decided to put on a really super super show, in technicolour and, at dawn on Nero's birthday, he had five hundred carefully-selected Christians crucified at ten-metre intervals on either side of the Appian Way. From his white imperial charger, Nero advanced slowly down the line, savouring, having a wonderful time, marvelling at the ingenuity of the new forms of individual, personalised torture invented for his delectation and, being a musician, trying to identify the pitch of the different shrieks of agony. All went well until he came to one slave on his cross whose lips were moving, but no sound could be heard. Was the slave daring to curse his emperor? Nero got more and more angry. He had a ladder brought, climbed up himself, and put his ear to the man's mouth. Do you know what he was actually saying? 'Happy birthday to you…'!"

"I think your story is disgusting," said Christine.

"Then I'll tell you my Polish Jewish one. 'Where are you going?' said David to Samuel, meeting him in the train. 'To Cracow' said Samuel. 'Look here, Sammy' said David 'if you were really going to Cracow you would tell me you were *not* going to Cracow. Why are you lying to me?'"

"That would make good husband-and-wife dialogue," commented Alexis.

"Nothing more boring than people who go on telling stories. This is the very last. 'Daddy, how far is it to America?' 'Shut up and keep swimming!'"

"I feel it's wrong somehow to be so frivolous. Poor Jaccoud isn't buried yet," said Christine.

"I suppose the verdict was 'accidental death'" Alexis asked.

"Yes. The funeral is tomorrow."

"I don't think other people's good humour would have worried him," said Alexis, "or even interested him. Had he any friends? Or have I asked that question already?"

"None that I know of," Christine answered. "Certainly none here in the clinic. I still feel guilty about feeling happy. Not that I ever like mourning. They still go in for it – you know little girls dressed all in black, black shoes, black stockings, black everything. As if they had anything to do with it. But there can be a kind of reasonable balance."

"Poor Marie-Claire – that it should happen just at the time of your visit," Alexis commiserated.

"Well, I never knew this doctor," said Marie-Claire, "so I can't feel really affected. But I know what Christine means. What I find most awful is that everything suddenly goes into the past tense. The first evening I was here, Alexis might have said 'Dr Jaccoud is going to x-ray my foot next Monday', or take a blood test or whatever else they do. Now he never can again. It makes my blood run cold, that word 'never'. It is the most terrifying word I know. Even in the past tense, it means so many things have become impossible. I never learned to play the piano. I never loved someone as I ought to have done. But at least you are alive. You can change, you can perhaps make amends. But, in the future, it is a suffocating word. It's death, shutting you up in a box, when all you can do is rot, under the ground, sans eyes, sans ears, sans air, sans sun, sans sound, sans everything."

"No need to go from one extreme to the other," Christine said.

"With words you never know where you are going next," said Alexis.

"Especially with a little wine in," Marie-Claire added.

"Even without," said Alexis. "Think of 'Heil Hitler!'"

"They weren't just words. They were an incantation. Magic. Black magic."

147

"But still words. Think of fatherland, flag, country, enemy. All nice sensible words like the others in a dictionary. But they are really bombs, just waiting for the pin to be taken out."

"If it comes to that," Christine interjected, "are there any more potent words than 'yes' and 'no'?"

"'Let your speech be yea, yea, and no, no...'" quoted Alexis. "Everything beyond this... And my famous penny catechism says 'and every idle word that men shall speak, they shall render an account for it in the Day of Judgement.'"

"What's the 'penny catechism?'" asked Marie-Claire.

"Ask Christine," said Alexis. "As I explained to her, it's the way God is beaten into you in Irish schools. I can quote it like a gramophone, you've only to put the needle on at the right spot."

"Well, if it's true," Marie-Claire commented, "we shall all have a lot of explaining to do on the Day of Judgement. Meanwhile, maybe your gramophone could explain something to me. It's a parable about a woman who is not Jewish who comes looking for help, and Christ says something like, 'It is not meet to take the bread of the children and throw it to the dogs' (which never seemed to me to be a very Christian way of putting it) –"

"Perhaps a question of translation."

"Maybe. Anyhow, the woman answered 'Even the dogs come and pick up the crumbs that fall from the master's table'. Very cleverly said, and she got what she wanted. But with God too, has one got to be good at repartee? If so, I'm lost."

"Less than most!" said Alexis.

"And what happens to all the dumb and the inarticulate, most of the human race who would never manage such an answer? What's all this about it being your inmost soul that matters?"

148

"It's not the only example," Alexis recalled. "There is the famous answer to the trick question: 'Is it lawful to give tribute to Caesar?'"

"Yes, but that was, so to speak, on the other side," Christine said. "The phrase that always struck me was "Whosoever shall say to his brother 'Thou fool' shall be guilty of hell fire;" I've often called Marie-Claire a fool – you can imagine why – but it's really a term of affection."

"Maybe the original was something much stronger," Marie-Claire suggested.

"But the trouble is," said Alexis, "it's precisely over things like that theologians – what a bunch! – are most intransigent. Mahommedans don't worship God, they say, they worship Allah – even if they do mean the same thing as we do by God, or Dieu, or Deus. The Orthodox Mass is almost the same as ours, but it's all wrong, because the Mass can only be said in Latin. Someone in Rome dixit. And it seems that the first Jesuits who went to India barely escaped excommunication for heresy for daring to suggest (although they were the ones who actually went, and saw) that basically, Indian beliefs weren't all that different, and that we might have something to learn from them. The gospels are pretty strong on the subject of giving scandal. But by scandal, the theologians mean a girl showing a nice bit of leg –"

"And even the definition of that has changed a good deal since 1900," Marie-Claire put in.

"– But not Christianity divided into hundreds of sects, heartily detesting one another in the name of brotherly love. They've gone a long way from 'yea, yea' and 'no, no.' And anathemising Jews."

"Well, Christine," Marie-Claire asked, "are you satisfied that the conversation has been brought to a higher level? Remember, I started it all off with my little word 'never'."

She was leaving next day. They saw her to her pension and continued on back to the clinic.

149

"She's a great girl, Marie-Claire," said Alexis.

"I'm glad you two get on so well together," Christine commented. "If I weren't so fond of her I'd be jealous."

"Did you ever hear that expression 'A woman knows instinctively when she is right whether she is or not?'"

She paused before replying.

"It's the sort of thing either of the Heinrichs would say if they were clever enough to think it up. More likely it's the sort of thing they would never get tired of quoting if they happened to read it somewhere."

"Do you disagree?"

"Why women only? Did you ever see anyone more positive he is right than a man?"

"It's not quite the point. The man usually reaches his conclusion by some form of reasoning, right or wrong – and maybe starting from premises which are also batty. But it's a process of thought, not instinct."

"Sometimes I think you have as poor an opinion of women as a Bernese."

"On the contrary. I am a great believer in instinctive knowledge – for one great line of poetry – brightness falls from the air, queens have died young and fair – I'd give you all the philosophy ever written. Anything creative. The snag is you can't rely only on instinct: you need some check."

"Still, you must admit the phrase was not intended as a compliment."

"Agreed. I only mentioned it because it came into my head as I was thinking of some things I think I know. Instinctively."

"Such as?"

"Oh, nothing" said Alexis. "That I'm going to be a great man when I grow up, for example."

"That's not instinct. It's obvious. Everyone can see that."

"Don't pull my leg. Don't you know I'm a serious invalid?"

"How is your leg? Not too tired?"

"To tell you the truth, it is a bit tired this evening. Perhaps too intensive a social life."

"You mustn't overdo it."

"No, Frau Doktor."

"No, I mean it. Seriously."

"I know," said Alexis, giving her hand a grateful squeeze. "Did you think I don't?"

"Let me help you back to your room."

He sank back exhausted into a chair as soon as they arrived.

"Excuse my lack of manners," he said "sitting down before the lady. The accommodation is a bit limited. Wait a moment."

"Please don't" she protested, as he struggled to his feet again.

"No, let's sit on the bed. There's plenty of room for two."

She sat beside him.

151

"Are you sure you are all right? You wouldn't like a drink or something?"

"No, thank you, I'm perfectly all right. Just a little tired. Why are you so good to me?" he said, taking her hand "I don't deserve it."

"It's a nurse's duty to look after her patients, didn't you know?"

Sitting upright, his back in turn began to feel tired. He leaned backwards, still holding her hand. After a few minutes, this arrangement grew uncomfortable, and she leaned back beside him. He worked his bad arm round her neck where there was no weight on it, letting his other hand rest lightly on her breast. Neither spoke. He drew her to him and kissed her on the mouth. She smiled.

"You are nice," she said.

He kissed her again, longer and harder. He was handicapped by the encumbrances of his limbs, but one leg found its way between hers. Alarmed at the intimacy of the embrace, she tried to draw back, but realised that if she moved too violently she risked seriously hurting him. His mouth was still on hers. She let herself go and they remained locked together until she felt that the tension had found release. He was perspiring. She ran her fingers gently over his forehead but said nothing. He smiled a little uncertainly at her. At last she said:

"No one has ever done that to me before."

He looked at her in confusion.

"Are you angry?" he asked.

She paused a long time before replying, and finally said "no."

He kissed her again and they got up from the bed.

"Sleep well," she said. "You should rest your leg. If you like, I shall ask Marie-Claire to come along tomorrow to say good-bye before she goes."

"I should love to see her, but I don't want to take up her time. After all, it was you she came to see – she is not here on a round of hospital visits."

Christine smiled.

"You forget I am in hospital too. Don't worry. I don't think she will regard it as a penance. Good-night. Take care of yourself."

"Good-night," said Alexis. "Good-night and thank you" he corrected himself.

She smiled again, and left.

26

He fell asleep almost at once, but woke within a couple of hours and could not get back to sleep again. Maureen had not yet replied to his last letter. By the nature of things, she was almost an abstraction. But it is for abstractions that men are prepared to die – freedom, liberty, honour and the rest. It must be admitted too that, for an idealist, abstractions are also good to · live for: the number of communist millionaires living in non-communist countries cannot be counted on the fingers of one hand. Could he be honest about it? He knew he could not. Or rather, that honesty was too blunt a word. Maureen represented something as intangible as what he hoped to make of his life; abstract, if you like, in the absence of anything immediately perceptible or practical, but supremely important just the same. For Christine, he felt affection, a very deep affection, but it was something different in kind, and the difference was felt rather than definable. Instinctive? No. it wasn't quite that either; surprising how difficult it is to circumscribe with words something which so evidently exists. And now, this evening, things had gone a stage further.

Pleasant though Marie-Claire's visit was, he had been half-consciously worried to notice that it seemed implicitly understood between the sisters that he was Christine's 'boyfriend'. But if not, what was he? – especially after this evening. She was obviously half in love with him. Circumstances had brought them together and would ensure that they continued to meet; and the idea of their not meeting dismayed him beyond words. Was it fair to her? Obviously not. But perhaps that was the wrong question. Would she want their relationship to end? He thought not. Either way, she would be hurt. He felt an immense tenderness for her, which would probably never be love. Or was Maureen merely an excuse to enable him to shirk the issue? And so he was back where he started.

Towards six in the morning he abandoned all hope of getting to sleep again, got up, and wrote to Maureen, ignoring the fact that she had not yet replied to his last letter. He did not refer to the possibility of her coming on if she should go to Paris and, in fact, wrote a wholly different letter from what he intended, in which Jaccoud's death and Jaccoud's personality occupied a large place. With the contentment of having done something at least, he went back to bed and finally fell asleep.

27

Marie-Claire duly called and affectionately said good-bye. The following day, Christine started a spell of night-duty and he saw a good deal less of her, although she did manage to call every day. He got through a fair amount of books. Then, one day, the long-awaited letter from Maureen arrived, a beautiful, bulky envelope full of letter.

"I was very glad to get your two letters," she wrote, "and you must forgive my delay in replying, but I have been very busy. Your poems were not at all the sort of poems I should have expected – at least I can only speak about the second: I had to work hard with a dictionary on the first, since the French we did in school is like you know what. But it is certainly the only time anyone has ever made a poem personally for me, and I greatly appreciate the honour.

"As you did not mention your health in your second letter, I hope this means you are well on the way to recovering fully, and that horrible operation is now forgotten.

"Since receiving your nature studies, believe it or not the effect has been to make me open my own very amateur eyes. I have nothing to report about lizards; I suppose Saint Patrick mistook them for snakes and banished them too. Apart from the starlings (did you ever notice the amount of noise they make in the trees in front of the Gresham?) I have only one major piece of observation to report. It was a sort of black maggot about an inch long. Before I got your letter, I would have just stepped over it, disgusted. It was in our backyard. It was moving along as if it were an imitation snake – you know, lifting its back into a loop and then straightening it out – a regular Loch Ness monster. Well, I tipped it with the toe of my shoe and knocked it over on its back. You have never seen a better imitation of a hula-hula in your life. I was fascinated. Don't be

156

surprised if you hear of me going out soon with a butterfly-net, or a jam jar to collect frog-spawn and grow tadpoles in the bath, as my brother once did.

"Well Alexis, as I said, I have been busy. I'm afraid the trip to Paris is off. While I was in London, just about the time you fell ill, I met a doctor whom you may have known in College. His name is Bill Lenehan. He was back in Dublin on a visit recently and, to cut a long story short, we became engaged. The wedding is to take place in a couple of months. For the present, we shall be living in England. Later Bill may try to set up in practice in Dublin."

He dropped the letter, his hands shaking. It had started so well – the first time she had written something like a really personal letter – in order to announce this. He picked it up again and read to the end, but the rest was merely local gossip. He felt the same kind of shock as on first learning about his illness, a feeling that, suddenly and unexpectedly, everything had radically and irrevocably changed. She whom his imagination had so woven into all his dreams was to become – what was the name? – Mrs Lenehan. Missis: the awful, dull, prosaic banality of the word. She couldn't. She just couldn't. It was blasphemous. It was obscene. He stared out of the window, too dazed and miserable to move. The breakfast he had just eaten began to feel uneasy in his stomach. The feeling got worse until he was forced to vomit part of it into the wash basin. He sat down, feeling weakened and even worse, with nausea that was now both physical and mental.

157

28

With one part of his mind, he could see perfectly clearly that the black utter despairing misery of the days that followed had no rational justification. The romantic edifice he had built up had been built on daydreams that had no more foundation than a happy afternoon by the sea one Saturday before spring had yet warmed into summer. There had been no promise, no shadow of a promise, no implication of anything deeper or anything further.

– Except that logic is for paper, not for being. A tree does not think itself into beauty, but grows that way. A woman could slim by eating less, she knows she could. The logic is inexorable; but when the moment comes the extra food will follow the rest and remorse is for afterwards, be it immediately afterwards. Ash in a tray, smoke in the lungs, cancer of the chest. A man lights the match after he has put the cigarette in his mouth because it's the natural order of things, and all the statistical evidence in the world won't make his fear of cancer prevent him from smoking it. If men could but observe the Ten Commandments, there would be no need for police, governments, prisons, armies, bombs or napalm; no wars, hot or cold; no pride, no covetousness, no lust, no gluttony, no envy, no anger, no sloth; no martyred children, no blood shed, except by the merciful scalpel of the surgeon; sweetness and light, and no fear of death at the end.

Why not? Where do all our millions go?

Did I need those thirty pieces of silver?

I know it's wrong, and yet I do it.

I know it's right, and yet I can't.

158

Can't?

Sub specie aeternitatis. Sub Pontio Pilato. I wash my hands. But the stain remains. And they call it the field of blood, to this day.

If it was inevitable to start with. Inside you, is now, and ever shall be, now and at the hour of our death.

Would it have been missed out of the calendar, that night Hitler was conceived? Nero?

No sieve?

No mesh fine enough?

And the millionth infinitesimal sperm finds its egg.

And life is given.

And millions will die of it.

No sieve?

None.

Jaccoud. Already that grave eye no doubt has rotted, the precise tongue will speak no more. We joked the evening he was lying dead. Could you not watch one hour with me?

When I consider how my life is spent.

Doth God exact day labour, light denied?

He doth.

What am I? A live doll on the knee of God the ventriloquist? A puppet, and the devil at the strings?

I read Him in all the languages of the rainbow.

159

Ventriloquist.

Talking from the stomach, from the belly. The bowels move and are moved. The bowels of compassion and the fruit of his loins. The jaws of death and the gates of hell. Yawning open. Why yawning? Bored? Calibre. Of sufficient calibre. A calliper screw. A male screw and a female nut, giving and receiving, getting and spending we lay waste our powers.

Holy pew rotty.

She is beautiful. She is tall. Or not so tall. Only my size. Long straight legs where mine are forever maimed and crooked. One by one those hairs of hers were spun upon some unimaginable loom from dark copper old when Assyria was young by some Daedalus some artificer who looked upon them hoarded saw them in his dreams and wept that copper is not silken and worked until they flowed myriad but separate soft soft the vesper hush in an old abbey on a summer's night is not softer soft but impetuous challenged by a breeze across her eyes shook back into a curving wave a lazy curving wave through which an eye looked mischievous out and she was laughing laughing and incredulous dark brown freckles came out upon an almost alabaster skin alabaster even to one tiny vein blue visible and a mouth a laughing mouth a mouth for kissing that kissed me once once only I won't think on it lip on lip and mouth on mouth and the world well lost the outline of a breast two my love in her attire doth show her wit it doth so well become her no beauty doth she lack when all her clothes are on but beauty's self she is when all her clothes are gone poor Steve poor old celibate Steve vowed to celibacy incredibly reciting it in our puritanical school from Palgrave's *Golden Treasury* shyly almost shamefacedly and only I perhaps in all that philistine ready-to-snigger mob dimly foreseeing the revelation of your beauty yet to come and the mysterious beauty divine yet innocent of flesh on flesh curve of neck descending to rise of breast lewd only to poor tempted Anthony in his desert but beauty only nude innocent beauty if God indeed be love and premonitory and man be aught but flesh and this seraphic moment more than one more illusion on the long quest under the sun and moon for something more than each day's banal

160

share of life's unending idiocies I love you loved you love you. And you are gone and lost. For ever. Never, said Marie-Claire. Ever and never meet in infinity where God presides and mocks for ever and ever at our presumption and pretensions for ever and ever amen but never can ever take back what once has been. Eternally. Never shall my eyes forget or my lips cease to remember. But yours, o my love? So soon, already? God's in his heaven, all's right with the world. I am more lonely than the last lizard in a cooling universe where the sun too will soon be gone and stays only to mock at my diminished body. The music I would have made will be made by others and another will bare those breasts whose contours are in my imagination for ever. For ever.

29

How explain to Christine what he could not explain even to himself, but feel only? All the world knows – the world is so wise and experienced and has seen it all before – that there are better fish in the sea than ever came out of it. A perfectly good, logical and sensible philosophy, tested by time, proved workable, and the ultimate answer. Love is akin to hatred. Love withdrawn, and the beloved becomes mortal again. And life, indomitable, takes over. If the wound does not kill it cauterises. Suicide is only for the impetuous. Nothing lasts, not even despair. Nature abhors a vacuum and deliberately makes the void intolerable.

But sorrow is not dead, only gone underground, to reappear God only knows when and decides where.

And it was impossible to hide his feelings. The physical upset was nervous, momentary, and it passed. He slept badly or else fell asleep at odd moments during the day when he did not want to. His studies, which had acquired a certain rhythm, were completely disrupted; he could concentrate on nothing more serious than a newspaper and developed a voracious appetite for newspapers and magazines which he then usually found he could not read either, as soon as they were safely at his disposal.

He longed to tell someone, to talk. But Jaccoud was dead, not that it was the kind of subject he would have discussed with Jaccoud anyway. He had never mentioned Maureen's name to Christine: it would have seemed somehow indelicate, to both of them, to do so, and now it had become more impossible than ever. She of course noticed and, thinking it was just an ordinary depression that can happen to anyone and especially to patients, was discreet at first. Seeing it neither disappeared, nor even lessened, she grew worried, personally and professionally, but still hesitated to interfere or ask questions. Finally, she said one day:

"What's wrong, Alexis?"

He hesitated, and then answered "cafard".

"It's more than that. A cafard doesn't last that long. Homesick?"

"No."

She picked up a book, opened it, and idly turned the pages. He felt it was absurd, this inability to talk, and was afraid then he had already let the opportunity slip – that, believing him or not, she would not insist.

"I had a letter the other day" he said at last, "from... from a girl. In fact, from the girl. She is getting married. As you can guess, not to me."

She took his hand and pressed it.

"I'm sorry," she said. "Oh, I am sorry."

She said it and meant it. And at the same time, could not repress a feeling of jealousy, a resentment against this other, a sentiment of what she felt to be a mean joy. Such joy as it was faded, and she was left only with the feeling of meanness, that, and a boundless compassion.

He was equally uncomfortable. The words he had spoken seemed such a banal reflection of what he had been through for the last few days but, for a moment, he had the awful feeling that they were, in that, its true reflection, that his cocoon of self-absorption had inflated into an immense balloon that still enclosed him but needed only a touch of common-sense to burst it, and once burst, leave what all balloons leave, a shrunken remnant fit for the dustbin, its substance vanished into air. But if that were true, nothing was, nothing but earth and clay and matter, solid, palpable. Landscape was land, and

163

no more, music sounds. And tears, only so much water and a little salt.

"Tell me about it," she said.

He did not know where to begin. And she, he knew, must be on the side of the enemy, even she, despite the affectionate concern written on her face. But, lost in the desert, you will talk even to an enemy. Or the devil if necessary. And she was clearly neither.

"Tell me," she repeated gently, "is she very beautiful?"

Her question was less innocent than she intended. It struck at one at least of the chords of his reticence – his reticence now, and his reticence generally. She was not beautiful. She thought of her Italian successor who had married Robert; and felt jealous again, irrationally humiliated as if she could win only on a rival's defection when, after all, it was she who had refused Robert.

She had almost forgotten her own question when he answered: "The person you are in love with is always the most beautiful in the world."

"That does not tell me very much," she said, smiling.

"No, I suppose not," he replied uncomfortably.

"You know, it's almost impossible to find out anything about you, who you really are. I introduced you to my sister and, between us, we told you all the horrible secrets in the family cupboard, our parents, the uncle Heinrichs, and the rest. But you, you never once opened your mouth about your family. Perhaps we bored you?"

"No, no, it was fascinating. Some people are fascinated by their own families and their talk about them is fascinating too. It's like reading a book, except that you know this is literally true, not imagined. So, somehow, it's that much more live. But you can see them from the outside, and not get involved."

"You don't like getting involved?"

"It's not quite that. If I get involved, I want it to be by choice, my choice. Why should I have a lot of people arbitrarily imposed on me with whom I do not feel I have anything else in common?"

"It happens in a hospital. It happens to babies. It happens in school. It happens, perhaps worst of all, in homes for old people – I did a month in one once, when I was training."

"But all of these are different. You may be forced to be with them. But you can disown them even while you are with them, except perhaps when you are too old, and there is no escape to be hoped for. How horrible. You can't disown a blood relation. Or at least you can, but the relationship remains, unavoidable as yesterday. It's attached to you. Like being ugly. Or bald. Or," he added – "a gammy leg."

"So she is the most beautiful girl in the world?"

"Was."

"You mean you are no longer in love with her?"

"Do you know the most difficult thing in the world to answer, sometime?"

"What?"

"A simple question."

"Like 'Do you believe in God?'"

"No. Yes, that too. But I was thinking of yours. I suppose I must have been looking like the Sorrows of Young Werther in person for the last few days. If I try to explain why, even to myself, it seems ridiculous. But if it is ridiculous, so is everything. You asked me if I am no longer in love. You might also ask if I ever was, with a girl I was out with once, once only, for a few hours on a Saturday afternoon, when nothing whatever happened. Except that I realised I was already madly in love with her."

"Why only once?"

"She went away to London immediately afterwards. Before she came back, I was here."

"And that was all?"

"That was all, except for a few letters. Do you think I'm mad?"

"No. I know what it's like. There was Robert. But there is one thing that intrigues me."

"What?"

"What was the girl's name?"

"Maureen."

"Would you have been in love with Maureen if she was in love with you first?"

"For God's sake, Christine, no psychology. It has its uses, I admit. It would need to, to make up for its abuses. Like statistics, that touching faith in the mechanical quantification of the seemingly relevant."

"Say that again?"

"A touching faith in the mechanical quantification of the seemingly relevant."

"It's too complicated to be spontaneous. Even from you."

"What do you mean 'Even from you?'"

"You remember I told you once you were complicated compared with Robert, for instance. Don't get annoyed. I also told you it was a compliment, if you remember. But you did not answer my question. In fact, any of my questions."

"Which particular one?"

"Would you have been so much in love with Maureen if she had fallen in love with you first?"

"I can smell the pseudo-psychology clichés a mile off. Everything fits into a nice little formula. But it doesn't, not with human beings. It's the mistake all the experts make, the psychologists, the statisticians, the reformers, the people who talk blithely of sacrificing a generation for the good of humanity, the holders of all the final solutions."

"Good! I've got you worked up!"

"Would you ask why Leonardo da Vinci used a brown instead of a green in a painting? I bet you wouldn't. And yet it's a straightforward, simple, sensible question. It wouldn't occur to you to think of it, the result is so obviously right as it is, and the only possible one. And if he had used a green instead of a brown, it might still be just as right, in a picture different in consequence."

"You still haven't answered my question."

"You are incorrigible. You want a 'yes' or a 'no'?"

"Yes."

"Then I'll be generous: have both. They are both true and both false."

"In that case, put it another way. Did you love Maureen simply because she was an impossibility?"

"Why should she be an impossibility? If I made her the most beautiful woman in the world by falling in love with her, surely it was open to her to do as much for me. Don't you think I'm the most beautiful man in the world?"

"No. Only the nicest."

"Bowsie!"

"But there is a French song, a bit piggy –"

"– Cochon?"

"– Yes – which finishes up with a moral in the last line – 'Mais les femmes aiment les cochons.' What's a bowsie?"

"It's a Dublin word that can mean anything you like, according to the intonation. It can be anything from a term of affection to a challenge to a duel."

"Are you a bowsie?"

"Of course."

"In what sense?"

"Au choix. Why didn't you marry Robert? Answer yes or no!"

Her face clouded.

"I'm sorry," he said "I shouldn't have said that. 'In spite of the many subjects which exist for elegant conversation' says a Chinese proverb, 'some people can never meet a cripple without talking about feet.' I've grown particularly sensitive on that point since my operation. I shouldn't have asked that question."

"Why not? My questions to you were not very discreet."

"If you only knew how grateful I am for them, how much I needed to talk to someone for the last few days."

"Surely you know me well enough to know you can talk to me, about that or anything else?"

"I dislike boring other people with my *histoires*."

"It's not boring. Don't forget that all women love gossip about other people's affairs, especially their love affairs."

"It's what I like about you. You don't gossip."

"How do you know? With the other nurses, for example?"

"You would be too shy."

"I confided in you. About Robert, I mean."

"And I was flattered. I am flattered."

"So you see, we're quits. Except that you still haven't really told me anything. It's not that I am simply curious –"

"And it's not that I don't want to tell you, it's just that – I don't know, maybe I lack imagination. Another person is like a foreign land. You can read every book ever written about it, see every film, and it's still different from what you imagined once you put your foot on its soil. If I tell you Maureen is of medium height, but more inclined to be tall than small, has long auburn hair and eyes which I think are brown, is slim, dresses well, it might be enough to give you a blueprint of a hundred other people, any of whom I might have fallen in love with. But the person you do fall in love with is unique. If you tell me that Robert is tall, slim, well-built, with jet black hair and dark eyes, I'll believe you. But I'll find him for you, this very week, in any of half a dozen women's magazine stories you can buy down at the station bookstall."

"Alexis, please believe I'm not being just inquisitive. I remember the horrible time I went through myself. Some people thinking they were being very funny in the questions they asked. The eternal gossips, on the other hand, waiting like vultures to tear you apart. The sophisticated who think you are just being immature. I hated everybody."

"Was there no one?"

"There was Marie-Claire. And then," she said unexpectedly, "there was you."

"Me?" said Alexis.

"It all happened only a few months ago. And you were the first friend I made here, the first person I felt I could confide in."

30

What you were to me for a short time, so short a time, an anchor in the eternal flux. The time is past. What is gone is gone. But it will remain always, those few moments, days, when life stood still. You go off on a different tack. Some day, if you remember, you may remember with grief, sadness, and a nostalgia as great as I feel tonight, remembering you.

Once at school, during a football match, I shouted my head off, gave myself a sore throat. We lost just the same. Thought I had permanently ruined my voice, found I could sing better afterwards.

Retribution? Each in turn? And yours too will come when it's too late to undo the grief you caused. And so back along the umbilical chord, unbroken all the way back to Adam.

We are not prepared to try you until you have admitted your guilt. On est prié de décliner son identité. He was arrested on Sunday, 20 · October and should immediately have confessed to his crimes although he had not committed any beat your wife if you don't know why she will.

Through my fault (striking his breast), through my fault, through my most grievous fault.

A petal falls
drawing the others closer around her
the wounded rose
shivers in the wind
the variegated roofs
are sick of rain
and leprous chimney pots grow dropsical

171

will winter ne'er be over
or absence end?

Cloacal smell of a cigarette as it burns down in the ashtray to the filter.

English reserve. Spanish pride. Irish charm. French volubility. American brashness. Jewish violinists. German heaviness. Greek hospitality. Blind spots.

Who sets the symbol? Latin sensuality and Anglo-Saxon prudery.

Hey, are you still cold in that mini-skirt?

31

The ills he had brought for treatment seemed to be yielding satisfactorily despite the permanent scar they would leave, while his morale got steadily worse. Each day was as complicated as its own weather map: snow on Zermatt, cold but sunny in Geneva, scattered showers in Paris, rain in London, storms over the Atlantic, different and yet all fitting into the right seasonal pattern for the day, all covered by the same omnipresent sky. Each day had its own equilibrium of minor satisfactions and counterbalancing disagreeableness. An upset cup at breakfast was offset by the appearance of his favourite sweet at lunch... what if the same amount of joy and pain was allotted to each over the span of his life, in the same way as weather? Childhood fads, innocent, still persisting – keeping the best morsels to the end, the pith of the apple, the crust of the bread – he still did it mechanically; and then found he still had to take the soup first, although it might be what he liked best in the meal, but strangely could not be kept for savouring at the end. O Lord, let me live out my old age now and get it over. He almost wished at times for something unpleasant in the morning so as to be able to look forward to something pleasant in the afternoon; but whatever the local variations, the climate and the season remained: Maureen was irreparably lost.

He received a long amusing letter from Marie-Claire. Some people, tongue-tied in conversation are garrulous in their letters; sometimes the most witty and brilliant conversationalists have stilted pens that painfully eke out what they must write to convey with the most dismally insipid of uninspired platitudes. Marie-Claire, in her letters, was her own mirror, was Marie-Claire talking: even the rounded handwriting seemed a stylisation of her slightly plump humorous face. He had seen letters from her already which Christine had shown him. The style did not change much with the recipient,

173

and he felt warmed by the same spontaneous affection as she had shown during her visit. There was a new collection of what der Herr hat gern or hat nicht gern; she was doing part-time teaching to make some money, and was attending all the concerts she could get to.

He had decided to reply – it would be at least something positive to do – when he remembered he had not yet replied to Maureen's letter, and plunged right back into a maze of torment from which, like a child plucking at a scab, he did not want to see the end; since, outside, was the future, an unimaginable blight. If he called her name, would not the force of that bitter loneliness that seemed to curl up physically into a ball at the back of his throat not carry his cry to her? A telephone would, another, mocking voice replied – a mechanical contraption with wires. Your heart won't take you there, that superb clock smoothly operating decade after decade with never a second's rest or intermission; but the cold slab of an engine block would. An electronic brain to be as subtle in operation as mine or hers would cover the earth, they say; and yet her mind can never be persuaded to say that one simple word yes to me.

"Maureen," he called softly.

There was no reply. Naturally.

When Christine knocked, he was still sitting in the dark, listless as one who has come back from the other side of tears.

"You weren't asleep?" she asked.

"No," he said, switching on the light.

"Day-dreaming in the dark?"

"Nightmaring rather."

"The advantage of having your nightmares while awake, Alexis, is that you can control them. Did you know that?"

"I hadn't noticed."

174

"The usual?" she asked.

"As usual."

"I'm beginning to think der Herr hat das gern."

"Perhaps you're right. That reminds me – or did you know? – I had a letter from Marie-Claire."

"She told me she was writing to you."

"She writes a very amusing letter. It's there on the table, if you would like to see it."

"May I?"

"Nothing private."

"I brought you some oranges."

"How did you know? I was longing for one. Come here till I thank you."

"Shall I peel one?"

"No, give it here to me. I'll peel it while you are reading the letter."

He dug his teeth far enough into the skin to gain an opening. A little of the more tart juice of the skin got on his tongue and lip, burning slightly; a few more vapour droplets went up his nose. He sneezed, his eyes watering. Then suddenly the room was permeated with the perfume of the fruit itself.

"You would never get a job in an onion factory," said Christine.

"Ah, but watch this," he said.

The peel rolled off, unbroken. Empty of the fruit, he carefully wound it back again until the white underskin disappeared and only a breakage line remained.

"Catch," he said, throwing it to her.

She caught it expertly, so that it remained whole, then opened it out with one hand and placed it round her neck in a bizarre necklace as she continued to hold the letter she was reading with the other.

"If matron could only see you now," he said.

He pushed a piece of orange into her mouth before she could reply. He took another section himself.

"Let me concentrate," she said as soon as her mouth was free.

"Right," he answered, feeding her another slice. She grinned.

The slices alternated until the orange was gone.

"Nothing new," said Christine, putting down the letter.

"I didn't know she was teaching. Like another orange? Or a half-one I mean."

She shook her head.

"I don't know where she gets the energy from, Marie-Claire," said Christine. "All those concerts she manages to get to."

"There is a concert on the radio, I saw it in the paper. Have you time to stay?"

"Yes. I've finished for the day."

He switched on the radio. The orchestra had already started on a Rossini overture. He had a dressing-gown on over his pyjamas. He lowered himself to the ground, placing his bad leg carefully, and sat with his back against the side of the bed.

"Come and sit beside me."

She settled herself easily on the floor. He passed his arm across her shoulders.

"Wherever I hear Rossini," he said, "I feel I should be in a cinema watching cowboys and Indians. When the hero jumps on his horse and the arrows are miraculously missing him on all sides, there's nothing like the Barber of Seville to keep the nag galloping in rhythm."

She nodded, without speaking. The Brahms violin concerto started. When the soloist came in, it was almost as though they had pictured him, waiting, during the orchestral introduction to the first movement. Even on the rather poor loudspeaker, the fantastic lyrical beauty of the music came across, but just muffled enough to deny them the perfection of the original. It was pleasant to feel the warmth of her body against his shoulder. He was beginning to think: if only it were Maureen, and angrily stopped. What a fool he was. His relation with her would always have been spiky, never this easy, warm relaxed friendship. And still... He found he had lost the thread of the music; in their closeness it had become secondary.

"You were thinking again," she accused.

For answer, he kissed her on the cheek. She smiled, and they continued listening, until atmospherics began to cut in. He tried to adjust the set, but the interference got steadily worse. Exasperated, he switched it off.

"It's nearly time radio grew up," he said. "Except for a few extra knobs and buttons, there has hardly been an improvement since the old cat's whiskers went out."

"What was that?"

177

"You never saw one? The original wireless, as its name denotes. It was called a crystal set because it actually had a crystal, and you tuned in by fiddling around with a very delicate piece of wire (that was the cat's whisker) on the end of a little lever until you heard the magic sound. If it started to fade, you tried again."

"It doesn't sound very scientific."

"Well, Marie Curie worked on radium with an old cocoa tin, more or less. The cat's whisker had its poetry. For example, you had to have an enormous pole to hold up the aerial. Isn't that a beautiful word, aerial? I knew a man in Dublin who never bought another set when aerials and cat's whiskers went out. And then Rutherford nearly split the atom with a hammer and chisel. But it was all the same a great improvement when you could finally tune in a station by turning a knob, and then hold on to it, like using a self-starter on a car instead of winding it up – a great improvement until this happens. Let's try it again."

He switched on, but the interference was unabated. He looked at her helplessly.

"Science is wonderful," he said, "especially when it works."

"Try another station," she suggested.

Regretting the Brahms, he did so, and tuned in on something familiar.

"It's the Grieg," she said, "the piano concerto."

The reception was reasonably good and he left it on.

"I don't know how many times I've heard that," Christine said. "Robert played it once at a school concert. We used to listen to it with Marie-Claire on her old gramophone until we had every phrase by heart."

"Was he as good as that, good enough to play solo at a concert?"

"He was very talented. He painted too, quite well."

"You are speaking in the past tense."

"Qu'est-çe que tu veux?" she said sadly. "It's past, all that."

"You'll make me jealous," he said, smiling.

"Not much danger of that."

It was not said in a tone of reproach, but once again he felt acutely and uncomfortably conscious of his own egoism.

"He had Slav blood on his father's side. Maybe that was where he got his brilliance from, and his good looks. I remember the way other girls used to look at me, enviously, when I was out with him."

"You told me that once before."

"What I didn't tell you is that he was one of the purest, most innocent people I've ever known. It may be because he was very religious. Orthodox. He was like a child. He never kissed me on the mouth. Not even once. That evening when we lay on the bed, you remember... It was a shock to me."

"From the way you spoke, often, I thought you were very sophisticated, more, I don't know what...experienced. ...I'm sorry."

"You need not be sorry."

She was silent for a moment.

"All I know is what I've read in books," she went on. "I was utterly ignorant when I went to train as a nurse. I never really understood what I heard the other girls talking about in school. And even what I learned as a nurse is so clinical and detached, as if it had nothing to do with real flesh and blood. I would like..."

179

She stopped.

"What?"

"No, nothing."

He felt himself growing tense.

"What? Tell me."

She hesitated, then said with an embarrassed face:

"I would like to see how a man is made."

He could feel the blood rising to his face. He untied the dressing-gown and then undid the belt of his pyjamas, letting them open.

She looked uncertainly, half afraid.

"Take it in your hand," he said.

She did so, fumblingly and held it in her open palm.

"It's warm and soft," she said, closing her thumb over it.

He took a handkerchief out of his pocket.

She looked down uncertainly and whispered: "I don't know what to do" then kissed him lightly on the cheek. His hand closed over hers and he moved urgently back and forth. In a few seconds, it was over.

"It's getting small again," she whispered, and kissed him again.

They became aware of the concerto still playing. He unobtrusively fastened up his clothing again, and they sat awkwardly, in silence.

"Do you think I'm terrible?" she said at last.

He shook his head.

"Or very naive? Or maybe very awkward?"

He shook his head again.

"Strange as it may seem, I'm just as naive, if naive is the word. This is the first time this has happened to me with a girl."

They sat down on a park bench in the evening stillness on their way back from a concert a week later. It was calm and beautiful. His groping hand found its way under her dress. What happened was fumbled, hurried and unbeautiful. They got uncertainly to their feet again, and made their way back to the clinic. Her hand gripped his tightly as another of the earth's millions began in turn to make his journey to the grave under the scandalised eyes of the angels and archangels in the indifferent universe that has seen others. An echo of myself waiting to be called into life.

She became a Catholic to marry him.

PART II

32

Styx and stones will break my bones, but words will never hurt me.

My word is my Bond. If only a carriage in the Orient Express could speak.

I threw a baby grand piano out of the seventh floor window. The neighbours were having dinner and heard nothing.

Birds fluttered round like cherubs as it sailed down.

But the motorists were mad at the mess it made in the roadway, damn them. Damn them.

Mustn't say damn them. The Good Lord won't like it.

Will he not realise I'm only saying it because I know my time is getting short?

Stop asking questions. Stop it. Stop.

I am the goose that lays the golden eggs.

Suppose I found an omelette, a cold oven, a dirtied bowl, a soiled table, a yellowed fork, some remains of flour, and bits of chopped herbs and grains of fallen salt, do you think I could ever get my six beautiful eggs back again? said the hen (you can keep the baking powder).

"I'm very happy" she said to someone else present. "That's nice" I commented. She looked at me with displeasure: perhaps because we had not been introduced.

News item: a cock attacked a would-be poultry thief and so flustered him that he was easily arrested.

The puppet master took a live marionette on his knee and ventriloquated.

At the age of twenty, they are already blasé, disillusioned.

I am hazard of all I survey.

My right there is none to dispute

From the centre all round to the say

I'm a lord and a beast and a brute

Alexander

Sell Kirk

Persepolis is falling down

Falling down Shiraz Shiraz

Acropoles are burning down

For lack of oecumenication.

The cheeky Don rises in the yeast rampages through Russia and is done to death by a stone horseman and an outraged eve at the behest of a mozart in a provincial hall; such is the power of seduction, the wages of sin and the primeval urge.

33

The flame ate its way lazily along the fuse, unhurried, not caring apparently if it ever got to the other end, spurts marking little renewals of its flagging determination to get across. A flame doesn't really care. If you other humans insist, it will burn down a city for you, but it's just as happy lighting the gas for the evening meal.

The child watched, fascinated. She had been surprised when she came out of the doorway to see the man a little way down the street running away so fast. The adults she was used to were dignified and walked. When he disappeared round a corner into a side street, the flame caught her attention.

A week before, she would have chased it as surely as a kitten will chase a ball of wool. But that was before she had touched a bar of the electric fire. She gave a little whimper as the memory of that treacherous, beautiful red glow brought back the pain in her bandaged finger. But the new flame was interesting. It was blue, but instead of the monotonous blue of a gas ring, this blue was tinged with a brilliant green. She moved closer and had almost reached it when the charge exploded.

She did not have time to scream, and yet the part of the wall that fell on her seemed to detach itself leisurely before her astonished eyes as casually and clearly, in slow motion, as a wall approaches a skidding car before demolishing it. And the driver. And the passengers, if any.

34

But don't bother feeling sorry for her. Unless of course you think the abstraction you're barracking for less important than the shattered left eye driven far back into her head and the little body burned naked by the flash and a leg hanging from what remained of the hip bone (Suffer little children). Which of course, being reasonable, you don't. You didn't light the fuse or set the charge. You wouldn't. Why should I? What have we got an army and police for? (Die? Our servants will do that for us).

Can you make omelettes without breaking eggs?

35

For over a year, everything had gone wrong for her. So he was glad when the phone rang late on Friday evening and she told him she was being sent to Iceland on a week's course and leaving the following day. "I tried to ring you last night, but there was no answer." "No, I went to see Dr Zhivago." "How was it?" "Not the way I imagined it from the book." "Is anyone taking you to the airport?" "I am not going from the airport. The first part of the journey is by bus. No, don't spoil your Saturday. You know it's quite near and I shall only be taking two small cases." "It will be nice to see you anyway."

The Metro was there sooner than he calculated, and he got out at the station before her stop, crossed the road and unexpectedly ran into her. "I left a note in case you came before I got back" she said. "I absolutely must buy a pair of shoes. And then I discovered I'd forgotten to leave a key at the office yesterday." He went with her to buy the shoes. Then they took a taxi in the Place. The red Citröen had a woman driver. They collected the two cases, drove up through the city through the Saturday morning traffic, the barrows along the pavements loaded with goods, Paris at peace, along the Avenue de l'Opéra, stopped long enough for her to slip into the office, drive around to pick her up at the other end of the one-way street. The driver, seeing him look at his watch, said "An hour goes very fast when you have to catch an aeroplane." "And so slow when you are waiting for it at the airport" he answered. But they were back at the Place de la République in time to snatch a quick lunch.

It was one of those days when everyone was friendly.

"I'd like a steak," she said. "It's always the first thing I want when I get back, too." "I don't know why," he agreed, "but a steak never tastes the same anywhere as in France, even though the meat itself might be better." The waitress had the steaks along before they had time to finish a reposing cigarette. She was back again apologetically before they had finished eating. "I know you're in a hurry," she said, "perhaps you would like to order the next. A cheese, or a dessert?" In the February sun, it was cold but bright outside. "Seven hours by road. I hope the plane is on time at least." "What a fool I am," he said. She looked at him in surprise. "If I'd thought of it in time, I could have arranged to come with you on the bus." "Oh yes," she said, "oh, what a pity."

They finished the meal. Some people had already boarded the bus. Her tiny Vietnamese figure was dwarfed by a couple of Americans who would be taking the same plane on to New York. One man was photographing from the pavement a couple who were already seated; or perhaps the bus, or the Place, or Paris, or a moment in a lifetime that was an event and would remain a memory. There were not many passengers, and the bus seemed enormous. He had a kind of Jacques Tati vision of her, as she went through the door, being swallowed up in a great steel box which she would leave at the other end to get into another, small but undaunted by all the troubles she was leaving for a week, as was her country, crushed between outside forces for practically all of her twenty-five years.

She settled herself on the seat behind the driver, and then pointed to an empty place beside her. He shrugged his shoulders with a gesture of helplessness. Then she shivered in dumb show, meaning "Don't catch cold standing there." The last few moments passed of that strange premonitory limbo before departure. The bus pulled out; she waved, and he saw her hand again above the high back of the seat when she was already hidden, and then the bus itself disappeared.

That must be the way to Luxembourg, he thought.

The big store at the corner had several counters out, under the glass awning. Feeling a little lost, at half past one on a cold but sunny Saturday in Paris, he was not sure what to do with his liberty, and did not notice the crowd at the corner until he heard the cry:

"Lachez-moi, lachez-moi."

A young man was struggling desperately, securely pinioned between two policemen; a third, seeing his intervention was not necessary, turned away. But the other two had difficulty in marching him along. He advanced a few steps, then screamed again "Let me go", and wrenched in vain to free himself. His hair was now as tousled as his crumpled navy blue clothes. One of the policemen had to hold on to the iron railing along the steps down to the Metro station to steady himself. He looked the kind of man who might spend his evenings unsuccessfully trying to help his small son to do the new mathematics and wishing he could be reading his newspaper instead. The other was older and looked equally distressed, called upon to perform before a neutral and indifferently curious public, embarrassed, using force with the restraint he would have used if his brother had thrown an epileptic fit or his wife had gone hysterical, a servant caught up in mysterious abstractions, justice, law, order, and duty.

The young man continued struggling, shouting, hoarsely now, "Let me go."

A petty thief caught red-handed?

An offender anyway against society?

He resisted as if he were being dragged to his death, his almost hysterical Mediterranean face contorted like one of the prisoners before the firing squad in Goya's picture.

A little girl watching suddenly started to laugh, a frightened laugh that strung out in streaks like tagliatelle.

A Black Maria drew in to the footpath, at the spot from which the bus had departed.

The assistant behind the pavement counter grinned at the few remaining bystanders who had not gone off to complete their Saturday morning shopping.

"The performance is over for today," he said. "Who wants a bargain?"

The microcosm was complete.

The Greek chorus, detached from the action, had spoken.

I'm all right, Jack.

The microcosm is complete.

If children do get killed (on their or your side) who started the war anyway?

36

But don't be too hard on the hippies, who like to dress up too, and who don't want any hand or part in killing, and who just want to opt out: lacking your intellectual subtlety, unable to see that a child mutilated by our shrapnel is different from a child blasted by their bombs. Make love, not war (if only it were so simple).

37

Is a child a man at eighteen, that you should despise him for wanting to dress up? Are you a man or a mouse? Have you never stood there fascinated, as a military band is heard in the distance, watched it approach, your heart rising, its precision of step, a standard, our troops? Honestly, what would you have done? Would you have resisted a pair of shining top-boots, up to your knees, a proud uniform instead of a threadbare suit? The steel helmet is a bit tight, and hides my hair, gives me a low forehead. But the gun is really beautifully finished.

Mit brennenden Sorge.

His mother died of starvation and tuberculosis. His father, demobilised in 1918, had succeeded in finding work at last, thanks to a new order in Germany, almost fifteen years later, a wreck morally and physically. But now the beloved leader was speaking. Germany's shame and humiliation was ending at last. The supercilious English on their ridiculous island would learn. But first it would be the turn of the treacherous, vindictive French. They had not dared to budge when we marched into the Rhineland. The Führer stood, a godhead on his dais, and mit brennenden Sorge, delivered the New Testament, the promised land for the chosen people that would live a thousand years. Good is it in this dawn to be alive, but to be young is very heaven.

His face, as befits a warrior, frowned, but inwardly he was weeping with pride and joy and emotion. He had been born to see the day. (He would live to see Stalingrad). Not as his father, too old, or his mother, dead and as yet unavenged. He would march through a cowed Paris and up the Champs-Elysées to the Paris Triumphbogen. And who could worry if a few Jews were sacrificed when so many better men would die to create a new order in the world, a new Roman Empire that would be eternal: not even the Führer had yet made omelettes without breaking some eggs.

38

Perhaps they don't like omelettes, the hippies. For in their wisdom they say: "When an egg falls on a stone, it is the egg that breaks. When a stone falls on an egg it is still the egg that breaks."

39

Herostratos was logical. After a careful study of history, he came to the conclusion (was he wrong?) that the men who are remembered for ever are those who most destroy. And he coveted fame, but saw no way of access to the only office which enjoins it as a sacred duty to kill and plunder and destroy: military command was not for him.

So, instead, he burned down one of the seven wonders of the world, the temple of Diana at Ephesus. He was executed. And it was decreed that his name should never be mentioned, under pain of death. But here is his name, here on this page, 2,000 years later, unforgotten. Not the most glorious, perhaps, but at least unforgotten.

And the day he died, it is said, Alexander the Great was born. And the stone warriors on the broken stone stairway still standing among the pillars and the burning dust of Persepolis testify that Herostratos, though mistaken, was right. For you can see the dust of Persepolis, and carry it on your shoes afterwards for a week, through the bazaar of Shiraz and the street of the silversmiths and the temple of Saadi. And see the brown columns as the sun sets, all that Alexander left of them...

But as you burn your way into history over the carcasses and the smoking ruins, there is really only one precaution – one only – you must take: make sure you're not on the losing side. This is the only morality that endures.

40

For if (much against your will) you fought for Hitler himself and tried in spite of all to be decent you are still German and so more guilty than any English, French, American or Russian who happily raped and murdered (for even in that war, not all killing was licit). And against this law, inexorable, there is no appeal.

41

Is a Russian hippy degenerate enough even to have heard of Trotsky?

Born perhaps too long after another dawn when it was wondrous to be alive, when the people rose up in its might and anger at a misery and repression that cried to heaven for vengeance (but heaven is so far away, even when you've got sputniks to get there), determined, once and for all, to end with police and prisons and armies and governments and rank and prelates and privilege. And with that they ended, again. When the working classes first ceased power in 1917, the typewriter blandly put it.

For a new prophet rose up, and his name was Joseph, a spoiled monk. Then the prison keepers grew fat again. And the spies and the informers and the commissars. And the intellectuals of the world applauded. For what means ten million deaths so long as it will bring world happiness at last (only statistics when not one of the ten millions is yours)?

The lava settles on the desolate fields, and men pass by without noticing, for all this happened long ago and men must go on living withal.

.

42

The Russian hippy's father, own brother – even to the blond hair –
to the brave young German listening entranced to the Leader and
thinking of revenge and dreaming of imperial standards adorned with
the crooked cross planted proudly as they stand tonight in Nuremberg,
planted in the soil of Europe from the Atlantic to the Urals, gave up
the freedom he had never known and set out on the Great Patriotic
War in a country which had rendered patriotism anachronistic and saw
only one thing: the sacred soil of Holy Russia desecrated by a new
invasion of Tartar Huns, this time from the West, the hordes
advancing this time encased in iron steeds, heralded by flying demons
such as not even Gogol had imagined when the devils were abroad on
that St John's night, demons with whom no compact was possible.
For they advanced with great apocalyptic swathes deep into Russia as
if the Day of Judgement had come and time was ending and there
would be no morrow.   Except that these angels of the Apocalypse
marked none, just or unjust for saving, and the isba fell as relentlessly
destroyed as the hospital, the child as indifferently dead as the soldier,
or as hideously wounded, and occupied lands woke to the sullen
frustrated hatred of the occupied since time began.

But life was suddenly very simple. Any doubts he might ever have
had became secondary to one overriding passion – that his country
should not die, that he and his children should not live to be a
foreigner's slaves.   The hell in which his babushka had so firmly
believed and the Soviets had abolished for ever was finally installed in
Russian land.

(Every good gift comes from God, said the priest, quoting St Paul.
God is the source of all good, said he.   Then he embroidered.   But he
did not explain where, if God created all things, evil had come from,

199

or who created it. God all powerful, omniscient? Evil is from men.
You and me. You feel it of course?)

He might find himself the last of his company, or his battalion,
facing the invincible fire-power of German machine guns, but his
protesting body and shivering guts would know that there were no
prisoners in this war. For him, the Red Cross and the Geneva
Conventions did not exist. Was it eighty-six thousand that had been
massacred after Kiev? So rumour had it. And anyhow, Stalin had
decreed that there were no Russian prisoners of war, only the dead;
and traitors.

Meanwhile, Leningrad was not the only besieged Russian city
caught in the enormous pincers that lived on ice and snow and frost
and frost-laden wind or any last horse or mule or cat or dog or mouse
or rat that still remained uneaten and bread, too little, musty (but
starving, you are less fastidious), as one after another the splendid
palaces of Peter the Great's Venice were hit, damaged or destroyed,
even the great Summer Palace with the Versailles-like fountains that
spouted naturally out of the ground, embellished only by the hand of
man. He did not hear the remnants of Leningrad's Symphony
Orchestra, interrupted by the air-raids, play Shostakovich's new
symphony, but one night, when the wind was a little less bitter, a
balalaika and a Russian bass voice singing brought back to life the
Russian soul he had thought numbed for ever.

And the tide changed. Triumphant armies (what a brave sound
that makes) listened to heralds of victory at last. Radio Moskva. He
listened as he fought his bitter but now hopeful way back with his
comrades, all the way back to Berlin.

He did not see the demon in person. Few did. For the demon had
retreated permanently underground where demons have their abode,
never again to emerge to the light of day, even the day his kingdom
ended in a city lurid as a Walpurgisnacht. But he saw the bunker in
flames, and the rubble of the Chancellery of the Thousand Year
Reich.

And he took his turn in the group victoriously drunk on alcohol and victory who raped a frightened German woman, and then her daughter, her daughter of fourteen, big enough. To the victor the spoils. As the Crusaders who won Constantinople back for Christ from the Infidel. And the noble Spaniards who, more than any others, have listened to the thundering of St Paul against fornication (my sister in Christ), celebrated their victory over the infamy of human hearts torn from the living body to make sacrifice to idols, celebrated their victory on the bodies of Indian women (my sister in Christ), before finishing them off to ensure that no spawn of Satan (though of Christian father) be born to sully Our Holy Mother the Church.

For how long will gods ask sacrifice of the human heart, torn bleeding from the living breast?

How long, O Lord, how long?

43

The little girl did not die. And why feel sorry for her, for her blinded eye and leg miraculously rejoined by a surgeon's skill? Is she any worse off than millions who start life crippled? (O man, who art thou that repliest against God? Shall the thing found say to him that found it: Why hast thou made me thus?) In fifteen or perhaps twenty years, she too will be marching in protest to the Place de la République as her forbears have been marching since the first dawn in which it was good to be alive (but to be young was very heaven) to protest against whatever it may – yea will be – then.

44

The Russian could no longer feel anything except the depths of his misery. He had killed without compunction. His had been no remote war of the high-flying eagles, but a war of muck and blood and mud. He had fought the last pockets of resistance in towns which he helped to make Russian again. He had strangled a man with his hands: his life or mine. His bayonet had sunk voluptuously into German guts: one more enemy less, one more life nearer the day when I shall see home again and men can live like men.

And now, in the day of victory, the memory of a child horrified him, gave him nightmares, the memory of a horrified German child of fourteen. The Boris Godunov he had once seen in the Bolshoi came to haunt his dreams. Nights he became Boris, usurper of a kingdom which should never have been his, acquired by the murder of an innocent. The great bell tolled, the choirs already anticipating his requiem came in, heart-rending. "Death" he called out in his dreams, "My God, death, already, forgive me, forgive me," and a final shrieking "Death!" smothered in his throat.

Death had been with him as constantly as the cold, the sun, the wind, in his filthy uniform, smelling of food, his stinking feet, but it had been physical and bore no relation to this metaphysical vampire death that now settled on him.

An omnipotent planning bureaucracy can sometimes do good by stealth and cheat its own best endeavours by its own expert incompetence. The miracle of his survival was matched only by the miracle of the speed with which he got back home. The State was as far from withering away as ever: those who expected it were as quaint as Seventh Day Adventists who confidently expected the world to end on 21 June the year after next (or the year before last). That was not

203

his worry. Life was atrociously difficult. But now, at last, one could build instead of destroying.

Was there a single human being on the whole surface of the globe whose life Hitler had not changed?

People who had lived in houses now survived as best they could in cellars. Everywhere, houses, factories, schools, hospitals had to be rebuilt. The Russian land was one great wilderness: shrubs, even trees, growing out of the ruins.

And now, apparently, the Americans had invented a bomb, a new source of destruction, more terrible and hideous than any ever known – as if that were what the world needed.

People were still disappearing, enemies of the people, caught open-handed, people he had known but never suspected and who now brazenly confessed that they had been all the time working treacherously against the State, prepared to sell it to the enemy. The Revolution had, once, only barely survived. Now this war had shown how right the government had been. A second time, it had survived only through the heroism of a whole people, and vigilance must be ruthless to ensure there would never be a third time.

His mother had been crippled in a cavalry charge in 1905; it left him in no doubt as to which side he was on when the time had come. The Church had gone into the bonfire with the Tsars' imperial mummery. The priests had refused to attend the funerals of the rebels: henceforward, they would not be asked. They could add the imperial family to their icons: a few more holy corpses for the relic trade (if they could find them). Life had long since left a rotting and decomposing body dolled up in gold and brocades, and God, if there was one, could look out: he had been long enough around to manage for himself. If not, babushka would see his time out.

He threw himself into the work of rebuilding. Or at least the preparations for rebuilding. For the rubble had first to be cleared away. Bodies that had lain for years under the ruins of houses came to light. The dumps grew into small hills. The savage punishment he inflicted on his body for twelve and sometimes fourteen hours a day was at once a guilt-offering and his own contribution to a fierce love of his country, his compassion for the homeless and the even more miserable than himself; and it might have worked had it not been for Katya.

She ran to him gladly, his little daughter, when he got back, dead tired in the evening, and had to be lifted up to hug him. Her innocence twanged some nerve of his being until he felt his head must explode. He almost dreaded going home, and yet knew he needed her trust, needed it desperately. If some drunken German lout...

And yet a German would have had some excuse, or at least more excuse: brought up in a society based on the exploitation of the many by the few, in a country with only one ambition: to enslave the rest of the world. His own life had been hard, but he had never grudged the sacrifices that were asked of him, knowing he was helping to build at last a just society where all would work and all would be equal. He had been proud to be not only a Russian but a pioneer of the new race of men. Now it only seemed to underline his ignominy.

One day he turned his barrow of rubble round a corner and almost knocked down an old man. They looked at each other like two people who meet. How could the old man know that this was one of the neat urchins in a red Pioneer scarf who, fresh from learning of the counter-revolutionary Church which had tried to sell the country to enemies without and within, had flung stones after his absurd cassock and his absurd long hair, catcalling after him. But the other recognised him, recognised him from the unimaginably distant past when, now seen in retrospect, all seemed simple and idyllic; remembering too, in the eyes of this man, then already old, a look that gave him his first premonition of some ineradicable sadness in life. The eyes were sunken now, but more brilliant, the face a mixture of expressions at once so inexpressibly sad and so gentle that his mind skipped twenty years as if he had just woken from a dream.

Long immune to indifference or insult, lonely as a ghost from another century, the old man had passed on without a word before he could apologise. From a long past memory of his childhood, the thought came back of his babushka, and of her confession before the great feast days, before Easter, before what some of them still celebrate: Xristos Voskresenya, Christ is risen. The kiss of peace. The thought grew in his mind until it obsessed him: he must see this old man, this old man whose face said he bears a grief as secret and as great as my own. Unless something happened, he would go mad.

The old man's room was plain, whitewashed, with an iron bed and a few packing cases, a stove. But an unaccustomed air of distinction was lent to it by a few pieces of mahogany furniture, salvaged no doubt when his church had been shelled and had not risen from the dead. The visitor smiled involuntarily at the icon, and the old man, drying a cup he had just taken out of a basin of water, glanced anxiously at him, put the cup away, and waited.

He did not know where to start. Finally he said:

"The other day, I nearly knocked you down."

The old man looked at him in surprise.

"I had a wheelbarrow, but you hurried away so quickly I had not time to say I was sorry."

The old man smiled.

"You know," he said, "it is a little thing in the times we live in. It would hardly have killed me."

"There is more than that. I recognised you."

Again the old man looked enquiringly at him.

"Years ago, when I first got my red Pioneer scarf, and I was so proud to think that one day I would be a member of our glorious Party, we chased you in the street, and threw stones after you."

"The Arabs have a proverb," the old man said, "the dogs howl, the caravan passes. Not," he added quickly, "that I ever thought of you poor children as dogs..."

"Father," he said, wondering where he had found the word, "I am less than a dog. For even a dog does not eat a dog."

"You were in the war? You killed other men?"

"Yes, but it is not that."

The old man looked at him. "What is it, my son? What is on your mind?" he said gently.

He was silent a long time, unable to speak. Finally he blurted out his story. The old man was silent, staring at the icon or perhaps beyond it. At last he said:

"You do not believe in God?"

"No."

"You have heard of our Lord, Jesus Christ?"

"Where would I? Yes, maybe. My babushka..."

"And yet, you thirst for forgiveness? For someone to say 'your sins are forgiven you'?"

"If I do not, I do not think I can go on. I cannot face my wife. I cannot face my children, my little daughter, my little Katya."

The old man was silent a long time. Then he said:

"Adultery was a great sin among the Jews. One day they dragged before Jesus a woman taken in adultery. 'According to our law' they said, 'such a woman must be stoned.' And Jesus traced letters in the sand. And if the wind had not come, we might, perhaps even today, go and see the letters written by his hand. But the wind has passed

207

over the sand for twenty centuries. And Jesus looked up and said 'Let he who is without sin amongst you cast the first stone.' And they went silently away, starting from the oldest. And Jesus was left alone, with the woman. 'Doth no one accuse thee?' he said to her. 'No one, Lord' she answered. 'Neither do I accuse thee' he said, 'go thy way, and sin no more.' Do you understand?"

"I think I do," he answered, and then quickly added: "But do you forgive me?"

"I forgive you?" said the old man. "I, a heretic?"

"What is a heretic?"

"One cut off from the body of the Church. I'm, you might say," he said with a shy smile, "expelled from the Party".

"Did they learn that from us?"

"No," said the old man sadly. "I'm afraid they learned it from us. And when our little father, the Tsar, agreed to a pogrom of the Jews, we agreed too, forgetting it was a Jew who said 'Woe to them that call evil good, and good evil' and 'Speak to us smooth things, prophesy deceit' and 'God hath made man upright, but they have sought out many inventions.'"

"Are they your words, or another's?"

The old man stopped in surprise. After a little while he answered:

"I have read so often in that book that maybe its words have become my own."

"I think I know it. Your book, I mean."

"A book is a book, and words are words. A man can read into any book that which he wants to find in it. And men have read terrible things into that book, and out of that book, forgetting what Jesus has told them: 'Unless you be as little children you shall not enter into the kingdom of heaven.' 'In much wisdom is grief, and he that increaseth knowledge increaseth grief.' But Jesus would not have told men to be as little children if his message was not simple enough to be understood by little children. It was so simple, his message. God is love. Love God and love your neighbour. That is all the rule a man needs. For the rest, 'we spend our years as a tale that is told; for a thousand years in his sight are but yesterday when it is past, and as a watch in the night.'"

"And if a man does not believe in God?"

"Let him love his neighbour. And if he loves his neighbour he will love God. For he that says he loves God whom he cannot see and does not love his brother whom he can is a liar."

The old man's eyes closed, and he recited, half to himself:

"If I speak with the tongues of men, and of angels, and have not charity, I am become as sounding brass, or a tinkling cymbal.

"And if I should have prophecy, and should know all mysteries, and all knowledge, and if I should have all faith, so that I could move mountains, and have not charity, I am nothing.

"And if I should distribute all my goods to feed the poor, and if I should deliver my body to be burned, and have not charity, it profiteth me nothing.

"Charity is patient, is kind: charity envieth not, dealeth not perversely; is not puffed up;

"Is not ambitious, seeketh not her own, is not provoked to anger, thinketh no evil;

"Rejoiceth not in iniquity, but rejoiceth with the truth;

"Beareth all things, believeth all things, hopeth all things, endureth all things.

209

"Charity never falleth away: whether prophesy shall be made void, or tongues shall cease, or knowledge shall be destroyed.

"For we know in part and we prophesy in part.

"But when that which is perfect is come, that which is in part shall be done away.

"When I was a child, I spoke as a child, I understood as a child, I thought as a child. But, when I became a man, I put away the things of a child.

"We see now through a glass darkly; but then face to face. Now I know in part; but then I shall know even as I am known.

"And now there remain faith, hope and charity, these three: but the greatest of these is charity."

He was silent, then recited again: "For I was hungry, and you gave me to eat; I was thirsty, and you gave me to drink; I was a stranger, and you took me in. Naked, and you covered me; sick, and you visited me; I was in prison, and you came to me. And shall the just answer him, saying: Lord, when did we see you hungry, and fed thee; thirsty, and gave thee drink... ? And the king answering, shall say to them: Amen I say to you, as long as you did it to one of these my least brethren, you did it to me.

"When a man sacrifices something of his own, or something of himself, for another's good, something mysterious happens. For love is always strange and mysterious."

"What do you know of love?"

The old man was silent.

"Too little," he said at last, sadly.

"Did you ever love a woman?"

"I know all that happens in a young man's body, if that is what you mean. You have children. Does that mean you know what love is? Was it love that made your body act that night you came to tell me of?"

It was his turn to be silent.

"Are you angry with me?" the old man asked.

"Angry? No, I was curious, and I did not realise I was just being impertinent."

"No, no. Your question was right. And you are not the first to ask it. My own conscience has been asking it of me for forty years."

"If only I had as little on my conscience," the man said.

"You sacrificed a lot just in coming here."

"No, it's not true. I came because I was desperate and could think of nothing else, not since that day I almost knocked you over and then remembered you from the years before the war. I kept saying to myself 'A drowning man will clutch at a straw' because once, when I was a boy, I almost did drown. And I remember clutching, clutching desperately and feeling myself sinking. And I saw a twig, and clutched at that. I can see it now, that twig, as plain as I can see you. And it might have been the last thing I saw in this life if someone had not seen me and got me out after I had lost consciousness. There are times, now, when I wish it had."

"You don't really mean that," said the old man softly.

The man looked at him in surprise, and then slowly realised it was probably true. He realised it with a curious feeling of disappointment with himself, as if he had somehow sullied the sincerity which brought him here in the first place.

"We know nothing, nothing, until we have suffered. But if suffering were the only thing necessary in this life, we should all be

211

wise. And we are not, are we? I suppose you never thought of us as men, too, who have a life to lead?"

"No, it is true. I never thought of a priest as a man."

He remembered uncomfortably all he had learned on the subject, and not for the first time found truth changing when he saw it from a new angle.

"The greatest of these is charity," the old man repeated. "It sounds easy, but it is easy only to the pure of heart. For the heart is deceitful above all things, and desperately wicked. We were entrusted with the message and we piled up honours and titles and possessions instead, forgetting that he that maketh haste to be rich shall not be innocent, and where there is no vision, the people perish. We were wizards that peep and that mutter, saying peace, peace, when there is no peace. And God has left our house desolate and feedeth us with the bread of tears. For we sided against those who hated injustice and who hated iniquity. We spoke against them; even, God forgive us, despised them for their shabby clothes and their misery, no longer seeing Christ in his poor. And God has left our house desolate, empty and desolate, and gone where charity is living, in the fields and the factories and the market places, where men use his name only in blasphemy and do not know that God is with them because there is goodness and charity in their hearts. Those who came after Christ needed cathedrals, but he was born in a stable and preached in the open air or by the sea shore or on the mountain sides and in the desert."

He had almost forgotten his visitor. Now he looked at him shyly and said:

"I have talked too much. It is seldom I have anyone to talk to. You must forgive an old man. Yet a little sleep, a little slumber, a little folding of the hands in sleep, and I shall be here no more upon this earth. And all this does not concern you. You must forgive me."

"You have forgotten why I came. Can you, or anyone, forgive me?"

"My son, does your heart not feel lighter already? Your sin was already forgiven you when the sorrow for it entered your heart. I am not your judge. But one day I was, as it were, the ear of God, into which men could empty all the wickedness of their hearts, the evil they had done to others that they soon found was an even greater evil they had done themselves. And even that trust we perverted. For although Christ's words to all of us were 'Judge not and ye shall not be judged', we found new sins that men must confess to us. We made it a sin to hate injustice. And when men chose between disloyalty to the Tsar and disloyalty to all that Christ has taught us, we forgot Christ and condemned them too. When the book was there for all we did nothing to help the people read, preferring our own glosses; now all can read, but thanks to us, no one wants to read in it. You say you do not know God. We thought we did, and we were only presumptuous, and our sin is the greater. And God has left us no way of atoning. For we are cast out from the people, voices grown dumb in the wilderness. I even more than all my brethren, and disobedient."

"Disobedient?"

"I was told I still must follow Christ's precept and preach the gospel. But how could I? We failed. For us to preach to this new people who have grown up would be to abase Christ's word and make it as hateful, or despicable, as we had made ourselves. I know there is only one acceptable gift I can offer God now, and that is silence. Goodness will grow without us just as it survived without us. And there is so much wisdom and glory and beauty and goodness in that book that they will come back to it too, even if at first only in curiosity."

He suddenly looked very tired. The visitor rose to go.

"May I come and see you again?"

"When I was starving, it was the wife of a writer who was in Siberia for sedition against the Tsar and had not yet been released who fed me. I learned from her that Christ could also be in the heart of an

213

unbeliever, only we were too blind to see. Now he is in Siberia again. We live in strange times, and not all the State does is good, any more than the Church in its day. I do not want you to be disobedient to the State. God's love will work in you without my helping."

The old man suddenly clasped him warmly by the hand and, after what seemed a long time, said:

"You come to me like a messenger from God."

The man looked at him in astonishment.

"Like a messenger from God to say that, once before I die, he has allowed me to try to comfort another soul in trouble. All the rivers run into the sea, yet the sea is not full, and there is room for all of us in eternity, however many we be. Oh, my friend, there is still too much hate in Russia. Try to cast out hate in yourself and those around you and do what little good you can in this life. The world has so much need of good. Go in peace my son."

And the hippy's father felt that a new dimension on existence had been opened that he'd never dreamed of before, and he really did feel something like peace at last.

45

Of course a good psychiatrist will yank out a guilt complex for you nearly as easily as a dentist will a tooth; it may cost a bit more, admittedly, but then you're paid more, so what's the odds? My job is to cure you. I am not a theologian. I am a professional doctor. The reasons why you had a napalmed Vietnamese child in your arms is not my problem. It's yours. (It wasn't my child).

46

Anyhow, his troubles were far from over. Katya – he needn't really have worried so much about her. She grew up to be a lot less attractive-looking than she had been as a child. But intelligent. Reasonably intelligent that is. She became a chemist. She married a chemist. And they made their contribution to the growing population, not by alchemy, but in the most ordinary way in the world. He hated to admit it, but she was in fact dull. Good, conscientious and dull.

After Stalin's death, and the Revelations, he wondered where his eyes had been all these years. And how had the old man found in Stalin and Beria and their associates the true successors of the Apostles? Of course he had mentioned no names. The old man was not forgotten, or his strange desperate goodness. But the new revelations brought something like yet another puberty from which he despaired of ever emerging to man's estate.

He aimed a clout at Fedya, who told him where he had been keeping his eyes all those years: the answer was as unflatteringly unfilial as the suggested location was anatomically impossible. Fedya only laughed.

"What are you so peeved about?" he asked. "That's how the Chinese do their spying, and everyone knows they are more subtle than us. Did you not hear what happened last week? A crowd of Chinese came to the frontier, let down their pants, and so disguised, spied on us. It was only when someone thought of giving their backsides a portrait of Mao to admire that our forces brought the incident to a glorious conclusion."

"That's the first time I heard you make a patriotic remark since you were a child," his father said, laughing, "and even that's ambiguous. Are you studying at least?"

"Hard," said Fedya, "I found a splendid quotation last week from an Englishman called S. Johnson: 'Patriotism is the last refuge of a scoundrel'."

His son was impossible. The Soviet Union had made unbelievable progress since the war. Scarcely a trace of the war remained, and the country had gone ahead to take a spectacular lead in technology over the Americans. Schools and universities were going up everywhere. He had visited Leningrad once, and marvelled at the heroic city, splendid as if a German shell had never struck it. Young people were growing up in a paradise compared to the country of his youth, and a paradise that was yet only starting and would open immeasurable possibilities. Yet they had no word of thanks, no word of recognition for the sacrifices their parents had made. Hitler was already as remote as Napoleon.

He felt himself to be too immersed in his own past, and what he had lived through, experienced, suffered, ever to be able to escape from it. He feared for Fedya, but could not help admiring his cool detachment. He realised somewhat sadly that his own reactions to any situation could be predicted by anyone; and so could Katya's. But Fedya was quicksilver, unpredictable. And now he had taken to wearing clothes that shocked the neighbourhood, and earned for his father the commiseration of all his friends.

"Good for them," said Fedya, "do they really think that Nature, having produced them in all their glory, baggy pants and all, has now retired for good, her task completed? Do not let anyone accuse them of modesty. Like Smirnov, down the road, Smirnov, Party Secretary."

"Smirnov was wounded twice at Stalingrad; he is a brave man."

"Does that qualify him to tell me what I may read, or decide the width of my pants?"

217

"If it hadn't been for him, and people like him, you might have *Mein Kampf* to read."

"You're so square, I don't know how I ever allowed you to become my father. If Smirnov wants gratitude, let him not ask for it, and he might get it."

"But don't you see –?"

"Of course I see. But I also see, what you don't seem to, I see an ageing man who happened to get a lot of Germans before they got him, who was more expert in killing than I have any ambition to be, who was nearly as frightened as I'd be, who was silly enough to be born at a time when he had no alternative but to do just that and, as a result, thinks this entitles him to tell me how I should live. There are Generals and Marshals and Colonels and Majors walking round with medals hanging on clothes lines from their chests, all that's missing are the plumes and they'd be as good as the Tsar's. There's only one thing more ridiculous than the Napoleons and the Stalins and the Hitlers up on their pedestals, and that is the people who accept them there. The Greeks had a different way. Did you ever hear about the Greeks?"

"How could I? The Soviets had not yet been long enough in power when I was your age."

"Your point," acknowledged Fedya. "'Well, even the Greeks had to learn first. So what did they do? They invented a marvellous laboratory called the theatre where they could study a man's life from the outside and try to understand why he – and they – acted and reacted the way they did. Mark you, they were not interested in growing more food, or in becoming prosperous or exceeding their targets. And when they introduced their most deadly enemies into their plays – the Persians – they represented them too as men, men trying to live their lives and make sense of it all"

"But wasn't their civilisation based on slavery?"

218

"Your point," acknowledged Fedya again, and then added quickly: "We haven't advanced very far from them even in that, have we?"

They both fell silent. Perhaps twenty million human beings had died in slavery in as many years in the concentration camps of two dictators: a million murders a year, and not the brutal act of drunkenness, jealousy, lust or fear, but scientifically engineered in the name of social justice or racial purity. Plain bestiality. The father looked at his son and shuddered. Siberia had lost some of its terrors, but it was still there, and Fedya had said enough in ten minutes to earn spending ten years of his life, to be purged, to have sedition purged out of him, rebellion, ideals, non-conformity; and his forever irreplaceable youth.

"The Greeks had another saying," said Fedya slowly, "the unexamined life is unliveable for a man.'" As if answering his father's unspoken thought, he continued: "I will never be a good citizen in their sense. They will have plenty without me. Lots of Katyas, who will work and breed and make patriotic noises when they're told and die one day thinking they have lived. What the Smirnovs don't realise when they gave us education – how could they, they never had a thought of their own in their lives – what they did not realise is that among the docile millions they educate to make officials, and engineers, and architects, and planners, and managers out of them, there will always be a percentage, always, to whom the unexamined life is unliveable.

"And when that percentage hasn't the courage to think and act, they betray in a way the Smirnovs will never understand, even after a Stalin and a Hitler. They ask for loyalty to the State. What they really mean is loyalty to themselves and to the ideas they borrowed from others, ideas that might be true for a time, but which they never understood except as catchwords; and they are too stupid to understand that they now need changing, that life is changing all the time, and ideas must change with it. Do you really think I don't love my country?"

His father looked at him and did not answer, knowing he had more to say, and feeling closer to him in this access of confidence than he had ever done; as if this stranger he had loved only because he was his son would prolong his own battered, muddled life into something well-fashioned by the confident lucidity he would bring to it.

"I want to go to America," continued Fedya, "but I don't want to be allowed to go and I don't want to be sent: I want to go because it is my right to go. And I don't want to go because everyone there has a car and a house and is rich, so as to be like them; and I don't want to go so as to see how much worse capitalism is, or how much better, because I know without going that some things will be better and some will be worse. I want to hear jazz, not because I think I will like it better than our own music, but because it is part of the world I live in. I want to see paintings that maybe I shall despise and hate, but that I could not despise and hate more than what they fill our galleries with. I want to see the world of other men.

"And then I can come back and see my own country clearly and love it for what it is, and love it in spite of its defects. For if I ever do go, I shall certainly come back, because no Russian is happy outside Russia, and Russia is big enough for us all, and it should be also even for our opinions, and if for no other reason, because Russian is my language and what I think I have to say I can only say it in Russian. I want to love my country for what it is, not by hating others. And if that is not patriotism enough, then I don't want to be patriotic."

He stroked the long hairs that came down over his ears.

"I don't know why they so hate us, the sow-faced bullet-heads. Perhaps because they hate anything that does not suit their mean drab little minds. And yet if they had any gratitude, they should be the last to condemn us. They would not be where they are today if it were not for people like us who refused to accept the Tsar as infallible either. They would still be grovelling to the nobles and the boyars and the Tsar's police, just as they grovelled to Stalin's and Beria's. They want us to hate Americans. If they were in America, they'd be the loudest in applauding the bombing in Vietnam. And they'd be the first there, too, to say people like me were traitors, for refusing to go out murdering and inciting others to murder. It is not Americans we

220

should hate, but the spawn of Beria, wherever they may be - and especially here, where we're responsible for them.

"And if they go on, resentment will coil up inside us like a spring until one day it will either smother us from inside or force a new revolution on us, to sweep again over Russia. We have had enough of hate. I don't want to hate people, any people; but I hope I never see the day when I cease to hate injustice, and the exercise of power against the little and the helpless."

Noble words, little man. And you'll probably grow up to resent insubordination when you too become important, just as much as they do. You'll have your own personal and inviolable dogmas. Unless you happen to be one in about twenty-five million. Which is pretty long odds. But you'd never believe it, now, would you?

If you succeed in continuing your education, as opposed to your re-education, you may even get yourself sent abroad some day. You will get your bellyful then of noble words (as if you didn't get enough of them at home). You will not find many kings left to hobnob with but there will be plenty of Presidents, and Prime Ministers and Ministers and Rectors and Chancellors and Secretaries-General and Directors-General and Statesmen and Academicians and Pots generally. Hold your Slav soul and your emotions in check when the great speech is made and Man (note the capital letter) is exalted, and try instead to take a hard cool look at the great man in his relations with those who surround the great man.

It won't be easy, but it will be worth it. Presbyopic, he can confidently prescribe for humanity, gorgeously big and adequately distant; but those around him, the only ones for whom he is really responsible (for I also am subject to authority, having under me soldiers) and with whom he could show that his noble words can become everyday realities, are not really men, but his subordinates: presbyopia can coexist perfectly happily with myopia, and count yourself lucky if he hasn't got chromatopia as well. Saying peace, peace, when there is no peace. A moral squint is no handicap to the seasoned hunter, as the old Georgian proverb has it.

And if you be musical you might even compose a contrapuntal round, or a madrigal, or a four-part quartet, or a human rights oratorio, alternating 'Workers of the World Unite, Man is Born Free, You Have Nothing to Lose but Your Chains' with 'Little fleas have bigger fleas on their backs to bite them, bigger fleas have bigger fleas and so on -- for so it was in the beginning, is now and ever shall be -- ad infinitum'; perhaps borrowing the Fifth Symphony back from the BBC as well, setting Liberty, Equality, Fraternity (with a specially loud bang for Equality) to Beethoven's three hammer strokes: humanity knocking at the door. Let them knock. Dedicate it to His Presidence, the Great Flea. It's safest. And perhaps your best way of taking his place yourself one day. And getting your own back. It will be splendid training.

Numskull, dumbskull and egghead – skulls all or skulls prospective. Unless some small voice can still come to remind you out of your unimportant past

Brightness falls from the air

Queens have died young and fair

Dust hath closed Helen's eye

I am sick, I must die, Lord have mercy on us.

One in twenty-five million? How many Christians will you find between Francis of Assisi (1182 - 1226 in case you had forgotten) and John XXIII, Giovanni Ventitre, the good Pope John? You are not interested in Christians? But can't you see, it's the same side? Or that at least a little of you is that, despite your carapace of honours, can still vibrate to John Nash and his lines written in London in a Time of Pestilence?

The bombs will continue to rain down and the children to die under them; for if they didn't, it might spoil someone's chances in an election (democratic, in a democratic country). Or someone else's chances of fame. Or victory. Victory!

Children whose names will never become famous unless it be anonymous collective fame for their hapless share on the wrong side of a massacre whose infamy will quickly become part of the anonymous data of history, scientifically observed; for emotion has no place in science, emotion is not scientific, and prevents impartial observation. You are dead, you silly expendable little bastards: there will be plenty of others to replace you.

Heresy must be rooted out, by fire and the sword if necessary. For how can we advance Christ's kingdom on earth if we allow the body of the Church to grow cankered from within?

Sub speciae aeternitatis.

It is expedient that one man should die for the people.

Sub Pontio Pilato.

How can we bring them the benefits of our (superior) civilisation unless we first pacify them, we the forces of law, order and progress?

Spies and traitors (we define them, and if we don't find them, we create them) must be ruthlessly weeded out.

Communism must be contained, and the free world defended.

The kulaks must be ruthlessly weeded out.

The nobles and the aristocracy must be exterminated and the lands of the Church devoted to the common good: when we have confiscated them, the country will be rich for ever. Henceforth there will be no poor. Liberty, equality and fraternity. Vive la République!

(Ever seen a clochard?)

The power of the bourgeoisie must be broken for ever.

The means of production in the hands of the people.

223

Economics and progress.

New flowers made of plastic.

The new plastic flour.

All power to the Soviets.

More power to the Soviets.

(But when you have driven out the king or the emperor and
exterminated the nobles and the aristocracy; when you have
nationalised the land; when at the cost of millions of lives more, in
Siberia (abolished) and your concentration camps, you have wiped out
the bourgeoisie, and the traitors and (in your all-embracing love) the
counter-revolutionaries and the enemies of the people; and all power –
vested in the hands of commissars, or one, or two or how many
million fonctionnaires, for the people are not yet ripe for power – is in
the hands of the people; when you have abolished poverty, and no
man starves, and standards of living (as our statistics prove), are
rising all the time, and the family that lived five to a room now has a
room for each, and each family (at least) has that marvel once
reserved for pots and essential services, a car (and helps to kill as
many on the roads over a week-end as an old-fashioned war); what
will you then have, after all the bloodshed: a disembourgeoisied
bourgeoisie? – This earth of majesty, this seat of Mars, this other
Sweden, demi-paradise, this fortress built by Nature for herself,
against infection and the hand of war, full of hippies, harpies, cranks,
critics, ungrateful malcontents? Will your Holy Book prove wrong in
the end, and thesis cease to find antithesis and couple into higher
synthesis, and Nature, her task accomplished, retire? Will Albi, after
seven hundred years, forget at last the Albigeois and throng again to
Mass – if I forget thee, O Jerusalem, may my right hand lose its
cunning; and that great and good Pope, Innocent III, who restored the
unity of Christendom (well, a part of it at any rate); and Simon de
Montfort, servant of Christ, his strong right hand (if thy right hand
scandalise thee cut it off; but make sure first it's your own); and the
noble scion of its noblest family, Toulouse-Lautrec (shall the thing
formed say to him that formed it: why hast thou made me thus?); and

224

shalt thou drive the lapsed communist out into the wilderness with the collapsed Catholic, saying, why willst thou not forget the things that have made thy present paradise?)

47

The smell of new-mown hay was sweet on the gentle but unstable summer air. But the rain, finally, did not keep off, and the swathes, cut with such sanguine and optimistic hope in the morning, would certainly turn a different green, go musty, rot. Unable to contain his anger at the injustice of it all, Paddy Tuttle, medium small farmer (kulak perhaps to you), rushed out into his ruined field, gathered a sheaf, stuck it under his jacket, and shaking his fist at the heavens, shouted "You won't get this bit on me, at least, you up there."

But the rain continued, regardless.

PART III

48

The squad drew up, country boys to a man. It had felt strange, taking rifles into a church. And no one had remembered to tell them whether they should take their caps off or not. They had felt strangely moved when the rest of the congregation stood aside to let them pass out first. We who are about to die salute you. No, no, please: after you. No one had ever honoured them like that before.

They will be honoured again. Their memories will be enshrined in the hearts of the people for ever. Their sacrifice will be a shining example to the young of this nation. See the young man pause and reverently bow his head, before taking his girlfriend behind a bush, remembering them.

Their names will be remembered for ever. On the war memorial.

Do you know what to do with your immortality?

If only we had known.

But can you make omelettes without breaking eggs, you?

49

Myles sat on a café terrace and regarded the boulevards that led towards the Place de la République. It had been a day of missed appointments. He had intended to see Jacky and warn her to keep away from the République, but had missed her. It was not the first time that that had happened and he was beginning to feel uneasy at the repetitions.

A high-pitched blast cut in over the noise of the traffic. An ambulance approached, and with the determined nose of a speedboat cut its way swiftly through the confusion at the traffic lights. It was followed seconds after by two police cars, roof lights urgently revolving. It was not cold on the terrace, but Myles shivered.

His thoughts came back to Jacky.

What exactly was happening between her and Hassim? She had always been something of an enigma to him. Even as a child, there had been an incompatibility between her outward fragility and an unshakeable determination to have her own way. From her father's side she had inherited the dark hair and blue eyes, eyes that most of the time seemed to be accompanying her faraway thoughts and made her smile and her laugh all the more devastating when they were suddenly brought back and concentrated with full force on the person she was with. The attention of most people is as predictable as Bach; hers was rather Debussy, or Satie, vague, uncertain, and then a sudden, unexpected, luminous culmination. She could lose her temper, but usually didn't. When she did, it was almost invariably on the kind of occasion when Myles would have been extra careful not to lose his – when stopped in a car by a policeman, for example, and asked for her papers, she would get the policeman annoyed by an offhand tone that verged on the insolent, and get held up for twenty minutes by what could have been got over in two. He had learned that you cannot get the better of a policeman in that way. His own approach was to be as obsequious as if he admired them. "Sales mecs!"

There goes another load of them. There's going to be trouble tonight.

Jacky's normal reaction to something she didn't want to do was a vague smile. She was obviously listening, but could create the same kind of sensation as when the sound goes dead in a cinema and the film continues on, a smoke-screen alibi which allowed her to do exactly as she pleased but in such a way that the other felt no right to be aggrieved. Her advantage was further enhanced by the fact that she never consciously seemed to engineer the smoke screen – it just happened – and by the charm which was warm and genuine for anyone she liked.

It was more or less by accident that she had met Hassim, a fellow-student of Myles. She had been to a cinema with a friend, Monique, and they dropped into a café in the Boul' Mich'. Myles was there with Hassim and a group of other students, and an older one, Jacques. Myles saw them at the door and called them over. The discussion hung fire while places were made and the two girls were introduced.

"Jacques, here, received his calling-up papers this morning," Myles explained to the girls. "That means Algeria."

"My brother has been out in Algiers fifteen months already," said Monique, looking uncertainly at Hassim and the other Algerian student in the group, Ali.

"Don't let that worry you," said Ali, interpreting her glance, "we are all full French citizens here, Algerians included, discussing, not a war but a rebellion, and the restoring of law and order."

She said nothing, rather resenting the bitterness of his tone.

"Mademoiselle is hardly responsible for what is happening in Algeria," said Jacques quietly.

"No, of course not," said Ali. He turned to her with an apologetic smile: "Mademoiselle knows I was not being personal."

Monique, appeased by the smile, nodded.

"But," he went on, "the trouble is, no one is ever responsible. Not even the gentlemen of the Intelligence Service who have added a new chapter to the French traditional skills in making love: they are now raping Algerian women who won't talk with broken-off beer bottles."

Myles looked over at Jacky. She looked away, and caught Hassim's eye.

He looked down at the glass in front of him and said nothing.

"Psychological warfare," Ali said again, "another great breakthrough for Western civilisation, which it wants to share generously with the underdeveloped countries. And a government that calls itself socialist at that."

Whether or not the raping detail was true, they had all heard enough of torture being officially and deliberately used to feel collectively guilty, guilty by complicity by the very fact of being French and so obliged, almost unwillingly, to defend themselves.

"Horrible things were done and are being done on both sides," said Jacques. "A lot of people have had their throats slit not very prettily. And you know what happens when a bomb is pitched into a crowded café on a Sunday afternoon. It's very seldom that it gets one of the psychological warfare specialists. You know whom it gets."

"The weak have no choice of weapons. They have to defend themselves how they can," Ali retorted. "And if the others don't like it, they have only to do what the Germans were invited to do during the Occupation in France: get out. And anyhow, we are poor,

231

backward and barbarian. France is the centre of the universe. Noblesse oblige. Labourers, and street cleaners, and they hate us as they never hated the Indo-Chinese. I never saw an Indo-Chinese insulted here in Paris, even at the height of the war."

"You know how I feel about it. You know I always said Algeria should have got its independence seven or eight years ago. It would have meant seven years less useless hate and bloodshed, and saved us, and you, the longest quarter of an hour in history. For something which was bound to come in any case. But, much as I dislike Algérie Française, the others have a case."

"I have cousins," said Monique, "who are fourth generation Algerian. They regard it as their country, not France. And if it hadn't been for them and people like them, the whole of Algeria would still be one big backward *bled* today. They have earned their right to live there."

"No one is denying it," said Ali. "They are not only free to stay, but welcome in a free Algeria."

"You really believe that?" said Monique. "Because if you do, I don't."

"You can't trust the natives?"

"It's not a question of trusting or not trusting. I can see very clearly what would happen."

"All colonialists are gangsters," said Ali.

"You know the origin of Rhodesia? The African king there was foolish enough to give Rhodes a mining concession. Rhodes sent a cable to London saying that the king had sanctioned the occupation of his country. So it was then legally taken over by 200 settlers and 500 so-called police, with the connivance of the British Government. There was a little trouble of course. But the king happened to die during it. And that was that. The fact that colonial gangsters are backed by a government doesn't make them gangsters any the less, it

232

only means that the government are gangsters also. Like the Belgians in the Congo - Leopold II was one of the nastiest gangsters in history. A government is supposed to prevent crime. What do you call a government that turns a whole people into slaves, shackles them, cuts their hands and legs off if they try to escape... And you know how Algeria became a so-called part of France - another glorious conquest."

"How do you think Algeria became Arab? Perhaps you think the Berbers invited the Arabs in? If you want to rely on that argument, you can place legitimate ownership whenever it happens to suit your case. Don't get me wrong" she added, turning to Ali again, "I am as against the war as you are. I have a brother out there who may get injured, or maimed for life, or shot any minute, drafted to fight for something he never believed in. But it's no good trying to make awkward facts disappear by pretending they don't exist."

Jacky glanced over at Hassim, who seemed troubled, brooding on some problem of his own, and he made no move to join in the discussion.

Bernard, sitting farthest out of the group and importantly smoking a pipe to cover his sense of inferiority at being the youngest present, laid down the pipe and said magisterially: "The whole thing seems to me a simple question of arithmetic: eight or is it nine or ten million Algerians, one million Europeans. If you believe in democracy, there's only one answer to that. Ali's right, and..." he stopped, trying to remember what he had been making up his mind to say, then blurted out: "The army are gangsters. And if you condemn the Algerian resistance, you have also to condemn our resistance against the Germans." He stopped, blushed, and resumed his pipe.

"The Germans themselves made that one easy," Jacky put in.

"How?" said Bernard, happy to have been the first to arouse her to speak, and to have her concentrate her attention on him.

"By their race policies. They wanted to turn all Eastern Europe into a slave camp, in addition to murdering every Jew in Europe. Anyone fighting that felt he was, for once, fighting a just war."

She looked again at Hassim, who this time nodded.

"What I would like to know," said Myles, "is what Algeria is going to do with its independence when it gets it. Tunisia and Morocco don't seem to have done very much."

"That can come afterwards," Ali answered, "before anything can be done, a people has to regain its identity. It's intolerable to be a subject race in your own country."

"Agreed," said Myles. "But after? You can't afford to wait. Algérie Française or no Algérie Française, Algeria will be independent, if not this year, next. What's going to happen? Will it simply become a third bourgeois State in North Africa, with a new ruling class of army officers, university graduates and the rich, Algerian instead of French? And of course, your equivalent of the Church here. Is this really all the Algerian working class is fighting for?"

"It's curious, and a little sad, how little you French learned from the Resistance or the German Occupation. If you had, you would know there's no such thing as what you call a working class in this war. Only one thing counts: to win freedom, whatever it costs, even if it means burning down everything that has been built up – with cheap Algerian labour, and for your convenience, not ours."

"You are forgetting how much support you have here in France. Just look at the people round this table."

"How about the OAS, and the army in Algeria – and here?"

"Well you can hardly expect all the French to be on your side," said Bernard. "If they were, there would be no war, and we would be arguing about something else. Anyhow, the French are never all on one side, their own or anyone else's."

234

"The mistake the French Resistance made," Myles put in, resuming the point he was making with Ali, "was to think that there would be time afterwards. When peace came, it was the same old story all over again, the same rich, plus some new ones from the black market, the same politicians – and the same working class, the same slums, the same vast numbers of people living with just about enough to keep them alive and no more."

"You can't compare conditions in France and Algeria. There is not only social inequality, but racial."

"Well let me put it another way. Perhaps I have a better example. There is the country my father comes from, Ireland. It fought for centuries to free itself from colonial rule, and succeeded forty years ago, with the exception of one part that the British still hang on to. You will see, it will be the very last part of the Empire they will let go. But that's beside the point. After all the fighting, what did they do when they at last had the freedom to do something? Continued exactly as before, substituting some Irish for English, ministers and so on – exactly as you will do – except of course for anything in which capital could profitably be invested. The trade unions did what they could, but they represent the shabbiest working class in Europe. They have been fleeing from their liberated country in thousands; would you believe where? Yes, England. Will Algeria avoid the same thing? And of course there is another point in common. Those who don't emigrate because that's the only way to earn a living, do so to get away from the Church. Because the Church is everywhere. Nothing can be done without its approval. There are more priests to the square metre than in any country in the world, even Italy or Spain. They decide what you can eat, what you can drink, how you may dress, what you may read, what you may say, what you may think, what you may or may not do with your wife or your husband in bed – as for anybody else, don't let it be so much as mentioned amongst you."

"It sounds a terrible place," said Jacques, "but I spent a holiday there once and that wasn't at all the impression I had."

235

"You can spend a holiday on the Costa Brava and never realise you're in a police State," retorted Myles.

"I was certainly struck by the number of priests and nuns I saw," said Jacques, "but then it was explained to me that it is largely due to them that the country has had hospitals and medical care for centuries, and that they provided education when it was not alone not provided, but forbidden to the poor or the natives, which I gather meant the same thing."

"And that explains why they have an absolute stranglehold on education today. The local priest is the manager of the local primary school, and secondary education is in the hands of the Jesuits and other orders. You can imagine how much socialism will come out of that."

"Didn't Joyce go to a Jesuit school?" asked Bernard.

"Two of them, even," Myles answered, "and both of them regard him as an unexpurgable blot on their otherwise virgin copybooks. The greatest literary innovator of the twentieth century! That will show you..."

"Joyce might never have been Joyce if he hadn't gone to a Jesuit school," said Jacky. "There has been many a man irritated into writing his masterpiece, from Swift to Joyce."

"The Jesuitical ascete of the stews. Teaching languages, God help us, by the Berlitz method," she thought, "in a Svevo-visited Trieste, or lodging amongst the gnomes of Zurich. Did you pronounce them, Dublin fashion, genomes, as death came edging up the icy waters of the ever punning see?"

"It's not their fault that his genius survived them" said Myles.

"Now that I come to think of it," Jacques continued, "I remember being told that priests had their special place because they had always been with the people and against the colonialists."

"That was not because they were against the colonialist as social oppressor and exploiter, but because he was Protestant."

"Well, something the same seemed to provide a good enough reason why the Greek popes enjoy the same position in their communities. And that is a funny thing, I never thought of it before. The most marvellous people I have ever met were in the Greek islands, and in the west of Ireland. They are enough to persuade you that education is a waste of time, and all that goes for civilisation in our cities. They are really free. They work only when they feel like it – not like us, with our time-tables and the rest. They are intelligent, you can talk with them on any subject. And the hospitality – they can receive you in a two-roomed cottage with a dignity that makes the cottage absolutely irrelevant. That's what I call civilisation. And if they have religious angst, I never saw it. Even the police are affected. They have got this curious English system of closing the pubs at a certain hour. But if you want a drink, all you have to do is to get the policeman to help you get the pub door open again and, as like as not, he'll come in and have one with you."

"That's the whole trouble," said Myles, "that's how people could live everywhere. It is what capitalism has destroyed. That's what I have been trying to say to Ali, here. Independence is only the condition precedent. Leave capitalists and the generals and the bankers and the religions and other vested interests in control, and your fellahin will remain fellahin for ever – perhaps even worse off than they were under the French."

They were all silent a moment.

"We have a cousin," Jacky said, "a complete extrovert."

"Frederic?" enquired Myles, "only a second cousin, thank God."

"You would think his two years in Algeria would be enough for anyone, but after that he set off to the Congo. He is a cheerful type, in many ways even gentle, and yet he can talk of fighting, and of killing people, as if it were fiction, not real people that were involved, Indians in cowboy films I suppose…"

"No, only niggers or bicots," Ali interrupted.

"I suppose so. But he has a younger brother who was also out in Algeria, and he is a nervous wreck. He won't talk about it, or say what he saw, or did, or was made to do. He never goes out, as if he were afraid of the daylight. He hardly as much as leaves his room. And he refuses to see a doctor. No one knows what to do. Everyone is afraid that it will end in suicide."

"The other side of the story," Monique said, "is a sergeant who went out to Algeria, in the same company as my brother. He was a southerner, from Vallauris, I think, the kind who can't be with three people for three minutes without their feeling they've known him all their lives. He was stationed in a village with a squad who soon made friends with everyone. They used to mend wells, patch up walls, repair radios, give injections, and generally made themselves indispensable. The villagers on their side provided the best of everything they had: wine, chickens, couscous, fruit. It was the perfect example of what the Franco-Algerian community is still supposed to be, if you are naive enough to believe certain Ministers.

"And then, one day, the FLN began to infiltrate the area. They were ordered to relieve another post, about twenty kilometres away. The sergeant tried to find where the order had come from, to see if there was any way of getting round it; he knew what would happen if the FLN arrived. But there was nothing doing, they had to go. When they got back again, half the village was burnt down, all the animals had been slaughtered, and ten of the men had been knifed. You can't become friends with another human being; you have no right, because that is collaborating. My brother says the sergeant had to be invalided out. He was no soldier – just a man forced to put on a uniform like so many thousands of others. He would start weeping like a child. And everyone knows that that is not virile, and bad for morale."

"So what do I do?" said Jacques. "I am called to the colours. The sacred flag of the republic, one strip of blue rag, one of white, one red, vertically arranged. I know its magic. I have gone to Colombes, and shouted my head off when a man, dressed like a child

238

in a knickers and a jersey, carried an oval ball across the line and touched it down, for the greater glory of France. So I go into barracks, I exchange these clothes of an individual for a uniform, I'm taught by a series of cretins how to kill efficiently, and learn how, if I must die, it will be so that they can write decently on my tombstone, at the age of twenty-three, died for France on the field of honour. This is not Monsieur Guy Mollet or the Minister of Armies that commands, but France, eternal France.

"And before I pass out, to continue the last quarter of an hour, in which destiny strikes, they will play the Marseillaise and my soul, nurtured since I was ten years old on French logic, and Descartes, and Montaigne, and the great rotund phrases of Racine, and the healthy cynicism of Voltaire, and the heroism of Valmy when the ragged armies of the despised republic repulsed the combined armies of the dynastic kings and emperors whom history had left behind – the whole bloody lot, in fact – will suddenly realise that my friend Hassim there, who hasn't opened his mouth tonight and with whom I have spent countless evenings playing chess, is only a 'sale bicot'. And my friend Hassim, who has spent countless evenings with me playing chess, will meanwhile be transformed into a patriotic hero by a similar process while I become a 'sale colonialiste'. So, by a magical change, two civilised human beings will find it good, noble, just, patriotic and necessary to kill each other. At what point exactly this necessity occurs, I don't know. We don't have to kill each other at the moment. In any case, the State, in another form, would intervene – I mean the police wouldn't let us. But the same police will arrest me if I try to co-operate with them in not murdering Hassim, by tearing up my call-up papers. Take a good look at me: before you you see a free citizen in a free country in the twentieth century, and a typical one at that – typical of thousands of my own age. Are we all mad?"

"It was almost respectable," he continued, "until the OAS appeared. Almost a comfortable little war. I've always believed that, once Morocco and Tunisia became independent, Algeria must inevitably follow. It was only a question of when they made enough noise about it. But, with all due respect to Ali, I had a lot of sympathy with the Europeans in Algeria, who have built up the country. And not all the nastiness was on the French side. Not to mention the fact that a very large number of Algerians would prefer to go on as they have been for a hundred years now, but don't dare to say so. If I had been called upon to do my military service in Algeria – if I have to do it in any case – I would not have minded all that much.

"But now, we've got a crowd of military shits who have been costing the country millions for the last seven years. The only reason they haven't won is that we haven't supported them properly. Another few hundred thousand troops, another thousand aeroplanes, and they'll show us. 'Anybody ever hear of Dien Bien Phu? They've learned nothing from Indo-China. They need torture also, psychological warfare: they learned nothing from the German Occupation either. Even if the FLN used or are using torture, I would still say France shouldn't. Not for any reasons of moral superiority, Ali, or because I believe it never achieves its aim anyway, but because if you believe in certain things, you must inevitably go schizophrenic if you try to have it both ways. And now, after failing completely, and when the country has had more than enough of it, the same *bande de cons* are prepared not only to beat the Algerians without the country's support any more, unlimited arms, aircraft, supplies and money, but to beat Algiers and France together. Military logic. Lives don't count any more, only military objectives. Well, Bernard, you had a nice clear-cut solution a while ago. What would you recommend?"

Bernard blushed. To give himself time to think, he lit a match and put it to his extinct pipe while the others waited. Finally he said: "In view of all you've just said, the issue seems simple: either you go, or you don't."

He didn't think the answer very good, and looked hopefully in Jacky's direction. To his disappointment, she was trying to disentangle a button of her cardigan that had got caught up with the zip fastener of her dress, and did not seem to have noticed what he said.

"It may seem simple to you," said Jacques to Myles, "I don't know what your people are. I'll tell you what mine are. They have a

240

grocer's shop in Passy. You know, with the fruit and vegetables out in front. You probably don't know what it's like to serve people out in front in winter. I have a brother who is older than me, and two sisters. We have all had a good education. Do you know how? Because my parents are in that shop from seven in the morning, or earlier, until eight in the evening, or later, summer and winter. That makes about an eighty-hour week. Twice a week, my father gets up at half past five in the morning to go to the market. They are what you, Myles, would probably describe as urban kulaks. They don't think themselves extraordinary. If they try hard to make money, it isn't for themselves, but for us, so that we can have a better life than they did.

"I went to the Sorbonne on a scholarship, but if I can pay for a coffee here tonight, it is thanks to them. To me, they're the finest people in the world. You can call that petty bourgeois if you like. But be careful, if you do, you'll find yourself in the company of people you despise even more. For the customers are, for the most part, the professional bourgeoisie of Passy, who are always polite to them, but condescendingly polite. Amongst themselves they no doubt talk about 'one's grocer' as they talk about 'one's taxi-driver'. My father did his military service and finds it perfectly natural that I should do mine. For him, that's the way the world is, inexplicable maybe, but it is not for the like of him to worry about that sort of thing: he has a living to earn and a family to bring up. If I were to rebel, he would not reproach me, but it would destroy the respect he has won for himself among the good bourgeois of Passy who, like him, go to Mass every Sunday, and whose sons, or brothers, or fathers, or uncles, or cousins are lieutenants, or captains, or colonels or even generals in Algeria, in a perfectly ordained world which will always be like that."

"The same kind of people thought the same kind of thing in Tsarist Russia," said Myles.

"I am not interested at the moment in Tsarist Russia," Jacques answered. "I am only interested in the decision I have to take or maybe, have already taken."

"What's that?" asked Myles.

"What would it be in your case?" asked Jacques in return.

"After what you said a while ago, there can hardly be two answers," Myles replied.

"Your father is a doctor, if I mistake not?" asked Jacques.

Myles nodded.

"A large step up in the social scale," Jacques commented. "So naturally, better educated, more liberal and broad-minded."

"What's that got to do with it?"

"More than you probably realise. In my case, refusal would mean, to my own parents, either cowardice, or the communism which is one of the risks to which I was being exposed when I went to the university. My mother would be glad: she's a woman. But my father took the risk consciously, hoping I would have inherited his own common sense. Whereas in your case, it would be rather picturesque and fashionable. If anything, your father would regret it officially, but secretly be rather proud of you. What Brigitte Bardot can do with panache and acclaim would only earn ostracism for Madame Bovary in her native *bled*."

"You're only proving my case" said Myles impatiently. "What hope is there for a society which judges people on such idiotic grounds, which, as you said yourself, forces you to murder Hassim on patriotic grounds but exonerates you if you do it with the sanction of the bankers and the industrialists who are really running the government – they can blackmail it in any case into doing what they want – and they are making a good thing out of the war in Algeria. Probably selling arms to both sides in fact, and so patriotically helping the balance of payments. Do you really think people like that have any interest in bringing wars to an end?"

"I am not any more interested in bankers than in Tsarist Russia," said Jacques, "if I remember rightly, Hitler also never started a war. In spite of what he had written in *Mein Kampf*, when he marched into Poland, it was only to defend poor little Germany against a bankers' plot, Jewish bankers of course – in fact a Judaeo-Marxist bankers' conspiracy. If the Jews are all that clever at banking, how did they miss the greatest opportunity of all time, in German armaments? Instead, they left it all to the good old honest respectable Aryan firm of Krupp. Good Christians, no doubt. Not very bright of the Jews, you must admit. It's nearly time you grew up, Myles. It takes two sides to make a war. Whatever about ours, you don't mean to say that the bankers are also financing the Algerians?"

"My father was mixed up in the Red Cross at one time. I remember a man coming to the house once who told us he was a Red Cross delegate during the Korean war. He was in Shanghai or Hong Kong or some of these places, I don't remember exactly which. But he told us of hospital ships coming down one side, loaded with British wounded, crossing British ships going up the other side, loaded with armaments for sale to the other side. That's capitalism for you. Everyone knows where some of the Algerian arms come from – from French dumps they've captured or raided. But where do the rest come from? Perhaps they are made from dates and camel dung. I wouldn't know."

"I don't know either," said Jacques, "and I don't care."

"You don't know, and you don't care," said Myles, "you're like my father. He has his books and his practice. He loves God and honours the King. He does all the right things. He goes to Mass and he goes to confession, to rid himself of what, God only knows. The conventional sins of the Catholic Church, I suppose. But certainly not what we all ignore, our complacency about the indignities which half of the population of this earth suffer, two-thirds without as much as a bowl of rice a day. But he does his little bits of good. Sometimes he even looks after patients who can't pay. So he feels entitled to sit down at night, and take out his books. I think he even writes poetry – can you imagine anyone writing poetry in the world we live in!"

"Are you so sure," said Jacky angrily, "that you will make more, or do better with your own life?"

"No," Myles replied simply.

"Yet," Jacques said, "the money you spend tonight no doubt comes from him. If you feel like that, why don't you leave home?"

"I would have, long ago," answered Myles, "I would have, and looked for a job with real people, maybe in Renault or Citröen, if it were as easy as that."

"Well," asked Jacques, "why didn't you?"

"It is not only my father, but my mother. She is dying, of cancer."

"I am sorry," said Jacques.

"Is she old?" Bernard asked timidly.

"Forty-four, forty-five" answered Myles and looked interrogatively at Jacky.

"Forty-five, I think," said Jacky.

It was a monstrous age, which they could not imagine anyone having except parents, and yet felt it was unfairly short of the three score and ten they might reasonably expect: a death that suddenly seemed closer than all the anonymous deaths in Algeria.

"It's a splendid world we've been born into," said Jacques, "there are people working day and night to find a cure for cancer, probably grudging the time they take off to eat or sleep. And they will find a cure, as they did for tuberculosis and all the other diseases. And the same State that is subsidising them has only one design for me: to send me into a barracks, so that I can unlearn all I have learned for fourteen or fifteen years about the genius of mankind, and learn instead how to kill efficiently. Bernard is a man of simple answers.

244

Myles believes in Utopia. And you Hassim? What do you think? These others will continue here to air their theories and their cleverness. But we two poor fools risk finding ourselves face to face one bright morning as the sun comes up over your deserts, with only one alternative: to kill or be killed. You are the only one who hasn't spoken. What do you think?"

"What do you expect me to say? What have you left to say?"

"You must have something to say, just the same," said Jacky, "why not say it?"

"I have been four years in Europe," Hassim answered. "I have read all your authors. I have read all your intellectuals, all your papers, left, right and centre. There isn't a single idea I remember that you haven't brought up in the last half an hour. That is the total of all the wisdom of Europe? There is only one word I didn't hear pronounced, except by accident. Although you're all so liberal-minded, it's a word you all seem frightened of."

"What word?" asked Jacky.

"God," Hassim said, "you got close to it once, when you mentioned death. But that was all."

"No, please," said Myles, "not him again."

"You've had your say," Jacky cut in, "let Hassim speak."

"There is no room for God in your cities," Hassim continued, "you are too busy. And the result is, that there is no room for men either. But there is room for both in the desert. Only one of your writers ever understood, and that was Saint-Exupéry. But I've never met anyone here who has read that particular book of his. You think you are free. But you are a nation of slaves. The whole of Europe is a civilisation of slaves. Look at your Metro at eight in the morning or at six in the evening. Look at your mines, your factories. Look at yourselves. The best you hope for is a slightly better form of slavery than the others. And Jacques has proved it to you better than I can.

245

He is prepared to go out and die, for something he does not believe in, not because he chooses to go, but because he is sent. By a piece of paper with a stamp on it. It is not the way my people from the desert die. Yours die the way they have died in two world wars and all the other wars you have fought and inflicted on other peoples all over the world. Does it never strike you that there is something missing in your man-made civilisation?"

"You should read a little more European history," Myles retorted. "Europe was never so bloody as when armies were simply dripping with God. Even in the last war, they were praying God like mad for victory on both sides. And now there's an American Cardinal going round the world in his private aeroplane with a great open dollar cheque-book, a kind of special agent of God, blessing the showers of napalm that fall from heaven instead of the gentle rain on the just and the unjust."

"He is not God. He is only a reflection of the society he comes from. That is all I was trying to say to you. The society has gone wrong."

"Now you're talking," Myles said.

"Maybe," Hassim answered, "but I don't think we're talking the same language. I know what you mean. You think it is just a question of riches and poverty. It is the only thing Europeans can see any more, since they gave up believing in God. You have your television and your central heating and your great aeroplanes that go faster and faster. And the deeper you plunge into your materialism, the further you hide yourselves from the only things that matter: life and death. The only time you live is when death comes to visit you, or someone you love."

"What are you doing in Europe in that case?" Bernard asked.

Hassim smiled.

"You know what happened to Adam and Eve, even in the Garden of Paradise," he said. "Your civilisation has the fascination of a toy

246

for a child. The awful thing is when the child can't outgrow his toys. And your civilisation is like a poisonous drug that you have injected into our continent, Africa, both Arab and black. My own people have become addicts. They can no longer live without your cars, and your habits, and maybe most ironic of all, those clothes of yours that make them look like scarecrows. There is only one hope for Algeria, and that is that the FLN and the French and the OAS will between them destroy every vestige of Europe before the war ends."

Ali had not spoken for a long time. He was both moved and troubled by what Hassim said, as if it had touched something deeper in him than the urban gloss he had acquired. Finally he said:

"What would you do with the unemployed?"

"It is only a dream," Hassim said sadly, "too many Algerians already believe the sort of nonsense that Myles believes in. The serpent has entered the Garden of Paradise."

"It won't be any dream if this war continues much longer," said Myles grimly. "I never realised it before, Hassim, but you are a goddamn aristocrat in your soul. You wouldn't care how many unfortunates starved to nourish your dream, would you?"

"They didn't starve before you came. In a country like Algeria, there is no reason why anyone should starve. It's your urban civilisation that makes poverty. There is no poverty until there are rich. I don't want a proletariat. I want a country where everyone can be an aristocrat. And to me an aristocrat is not a man who owns land, or houses, or frigidaires, or motor cars, but one who knows what he is dying for if he has to die before his time. And every Algerian could be that if it weren't for this idea you try so desperately to bring to us that his worth is not in what he is but in what he owns of things that he could perfectly well live without – and would, if the cities you have planted everywhere hadn't corrupted him."

"Tell me one thing," Monique asked curiously, "does what Jacques said a little while ago not horrify you – the idea of you and he meeting, perhaps, and having to kill, one or the other?"

"Why should it?" Hassim replied, "perhaps it would if, like you, I had ceased to believe in any higher order, and believed that Jacques was the centre of his universe and I of mine, and that nothing existed beyond that. But if I had to kill, I would do it without hate and because it was an action in some higher order of things in which his death or mine are only incidents. I don't imagine you can understand. That is because you think you are free, and master of your own actions – in spite of the last war, in which millions of people just as free as you think you are killed one another. In your civilisation, you can see and hear nothing. From the time you are born, you are surrounded by possessions, and your only purpose in life is to get more. And that's the only solution Myles thinks will work for your poor and your oppressed. You wind yourselves round in your cocoons. If they are not material, they are intellectual which is even worse. You have never known the freedom of the desert. You may never know the presence you can feel with an empty stomach when the world is just one great empty expanse except for the stars in that immense sky above you, and the emptiness becomes a presence that even Myles might recognise as God. But then he is too full of himself ever to be able."

"So," Jacques said, "you think it is a matter of indifference whether I go or not?"

"I did not say that," Hassim answered, "you have your own ideas of right and wrong."

"And by any standards of right and wrong," said Jacques, "I should refuse to go. To go and fight, perhaps to kill, in a war which, in a few years' time people will wonder how they ever tolerated it, that is lost already, that is stupid, useless, cruel, vindictive, generating hate that it may take generations to forget."

"You can refuse to go if you feel strongly enough, and are prepared to pay the price," Hassim pointed out.

"I feel strongly enough, but the forces are too strong. I remember when I was in school reading about that American, what was his name

- Gary Davis, I think - who tore up his passport after the war, and proclaimed himself a citizen of the world. The first and only one: no one followed his example. And I think he finally had to beg his precious piece of paper back again. I can't call myself a conscientious objector - I would have gladly fought in the Resistance and, if I were an Algerian, I would probably be in the FLN. And then there are people like the brother of Mademoiselle here who have been out there - fifteen months of it already, I think you said? Should I let him get killed, and not lend a hand? Prison here doesn't seem much of an answer. No, Hassim. Another representative of a civilisation which has nevertheless produced Dante and Shakespeare and Cervantes and Goethe and Mozart and Beethoven and Paris and Florence and Rome and Plato and Michelangelo must follow in the footsteps of his ancestors and go to yet another hateful war he cannot believe in. I will try not to kill, or get killed. And may God forgive me, if there is one. In any case, I have at least as much to forgive him, if this Algeria is the best all his omnipotent and omniscient majesty can contrive."

He rose and shook hands all round.

"Before you go," said Myles, "there's one thing. I told you my father was mixed up with the Red Cross at one time. I knew a lot about it. The Swiss who founded it, Henry Dunant, had a very simple idea, that the military put out of action in a battle could be taken out of the war, and no one any the worse off, there was no need to kill them. Tolstoy had the same idea at Sebastopol, but Dunant achieved the miracle. He not only got governments to accept what was the most elementary common sense, but the generals - perhaps because it was in their own interest: you never know in a war when it will be your turn. He saved millions of lives. Perhaps..."

"It's a bit late to think that one out," said Jacques, "my papers are for tomorrow. Can you imagine, if I didn't turn up, the face of the gendarme who came to get me when I told him I was the new Henry Dunant, with a solution for the war..."

"Someone has to make a start," answered Myles, "do you think your life is less important than the face of some cretinous flic?"

"No," said Jacques. "I am not of the race of reformers or martyrs. I just wanted to continue my studies and qualify. Anyhow, we disagree on too many things to decide the future of mankind between us tonight. You remember one night when you defended your own particular orthodoxy and tried to convince me that the Russians were only saving Hungary from Americans and counter-revolutionaries in 1956. I don't know whether you still believe it, now that even Khrushchev doesn't pretend to any longer."

He stopped, and looked at Ali.

"Maybe you will realise after tonight, Ali, how at least some of those who wear French uniform in Algeria feel."

To his consternation, he found he was suddenly on the verge of tears. He muttered stupidly with a kind of twisted smile: "We who are about to die salute you" and went quickly to the door. He looked back, as if to take a last look at the simple things that make up civilisation, before going out into the night.

For the second time that evening, the others felt that the sinister world of their respectable elders had come indecently close. They all got up to leave.

Knowing she might easily be misunderstood, Jacky said to Hassim as they stood up: "I would like to meet you again some time."

"Myles has often spoken about you," Hassim answered. "Perhaps the day after tomorrow, if you are free?"

Jacky nodded. "Where?"

"Here is as simple as any," he said. "It's our home from home. Well at least we often come here."

"All right," said Jacky. "I have a lecture finishing at 6.30. I will see you here after it."

50

There was an unmistakable movement towards the République, independent of the normal homeward-bound evening traffic. There were rumours of a counter-demonstration at the Bastille. If the supporters on either side marched on the other, a pitched battle could easily develop. Jacques was already in Algeria. The war was getting progressively more vicious, with the threat of a military take-over of all government, in France as in Algeria, becoming every day more real.

Myles had taken part in student scuffles with the police in the Latin Quarter, but tonight promised to be something altogether different, and infinitely more serious. Both sides were dangerously near explosion point. The OAS believed they not only had the almost unanimous support of the army, but that they were the army, its brains, its idealism, the only force that could save the country from defeatism and the long record of humiliations it had been made to endure by an inept regime. Indochina was lost. Algeria was the test case. Now or never, France must decide if it would betray a thousand years of history and civilisation, forfeit for ever its place at the top table amongst the nations. The army still had its glamour; even those who had hated their military service looked back with a certain nostalgia to what had also been their youth, and forgot the rest. The plastic explosions were having the desired psychological effect, disrupting services, either deciding the waverers, or creating an atmosphere of doubt, uncertainty and insecurity that must inevitably tell when the decisive blow was struck. The police would stay neutral.

The union members and communists went to their demonstration in a state of sullen anger which, far from dissipating, the slogans they began to shout as the crowd coalesced into a kind of march only

251

rendered more reckless. They had had enough of a war in which they never had any interest. They did not need to be ideologically committed to resent a senseless waste of lives, and of resources which could be used to build at home. There were thousands of others to whom the republic, long forgotten except as a subject of sarcastic comment, again became a reality now that it was threatened, precious as the memory of a local bistro at home to a prisoner of war. And there were of course, Algerians and other North Africans.

Myles searched the passing crowds for a familiar face but found none. He had hoped to see Hassim, but heard that Hassim was ill. Perhaps that was where Jacky had gone... Again he felt the twinge of uneasiness. He had missed the others. Someone at a nearby table had a transistor. The news came through that the counter-demonstration had been called off. So they had thought better of it: the gallant heroes were more at home setting plastic bombs in the lodges of concierges – the fists of a workman might make a nasty mess of some of their 16th arrondissement mugs. That meant there would only be the flics and the CRS, apart from the odd fascist spoiling for a fight. Then he had the disturbing thought that there might be another reason: perhaps the OAS thought they had got beyond the need for propaganda and were not risking any losses, but just waiting for the moment to strike, decisively.

The news ended and the radio was switched off. The waiter noticed he was preparing to leave and came over.

"They and their demonstrations," the waiter said, "they can have them. I spent ten months in the Maginot line and five years in a prisoner of war camp in Germany, and that's enough wars for my lifetime. You and I have to work no matter who is in power. Am I right?"

Myles nodded, and paid. It was hardly the moment to explain the error of his ways to the waiter.

He went to the station at Richelieu-Drouot and took the Metro four stations along the line. When he emerged again, it was to find himself in the middle of a great crowd moving slowly towards the République.

He joined in, losing his identity in the corporate warmth of this one vast molten will that had formed itself out of so many elements and now was flowing sluggishly towards it knew not what mould. His first feeling was exhilaration, a feeling that he had entered into a great stream of history, these marches through which Paris had entered its protest down the centuries; it was a crowd like this who had overthrown the Bastille and set before the world a great ideal the world hadn't yet understood – not even here where it had all started.

But as he moved forward slowly, he began to be oppressed by something much less heroic. He had had only one modest glass of beer at the café. Possibly it was the excitement, the expectancy and the suppressed fears that were in the air. Anyhow, the pressure on his bladder began to mount uncomfortably. He continued for a while, hoping it would pass, but his face began to feel hot, and he knew he would never get unrelieved to the République. He hoped desperately, for a café, but in vain, and finally decided he must drop out and go down a side street. With the crowds round tonight, even that wasn't very hopeful. However, there was no alternative. He forced his way gradually towards the footpath and took the first side street that offered on the right. Never had the Ville Lumière so unfortunately lived up to is reputation. There did not seem to be an unlit corner in Paris. Finally he came to a building site. It was solidly barricaded, but one wooden door had not been fastened; it closed off a pathway which led to a completed flat that was open to inspection by prospective buyers. There seemed to be no one in sight, and he slipped inside.

He was about to leave again when he stumbled over something. He bent down to investigate and found it was a piece of wood. He picked it up to have a better look when he heard shouts and the sound of footsteps running down the street. A policeman was chasing a North African, trying to get his revolver out of its holster without at the same time slackening speed, with the risk of losing his quarry. They were a couple of yards apart when the North African passed the doorway. The policeman had got his revolver free and was raising it to fire. Myles took out the piece of wood instinctively as the policeman came level and tripped him neatly.

The policeman, taken completely by surprise, fell over heavily and crashed his head against the wooden paling. The North African stopped, came rapidly back, and whipped out a knife. Horrified, Myles struck out again hard with the piece of wood as he saw the knife descending and got the North African right across the wrist; he screamed with pain. Myles picked up the knife and flung it in far through the doorway. The North African was staring at him in hatred when a shot rang out and he doubled up, blood spouting over his clothes, and fell over. The smoking gun dropped out of the policeman's hand as he lapsed back into unconsciousness. Myles, still unable to believe what he had taken part in, looked rapidly up and down the street. By a miracle, there was still no one in sight. He ran to the next corner, turned it and walked rapidly until he got round the next, when he felt he might slow down safely.

His heart was knocking and he could not stop the trembling of his hands. To commit a murder must be something like this, or to have a heart attack alone somewhere, with no chance of help or a doctor. He was afraid of getting back into the more crowded streets, where everyone must notice his disarray, including the police, who were everywhere in the quarter tonight; and he did not dare linger in the others. He dropped all idea of going back to the République. He was almost certain that the policeman would not recognise him, but one never knew with police. The shot had probably been a reflex, in a moment of consciousness. Had he been only stunned, or was it concussion? Anyhow, his relapse had been providential. And how badly had the North African been wounded?

He must sit down somewhere and try to get things sorted out. He walked on until he had gained something like physical control over himself again, bought an evening paper, and then entered a large café with a crowded bar and a more private section with partitions, like a railway carriage. No one took any notice and he sank thankfully into a corner and ordered a cognac.

It came, and he had begun to feel a little more relaxed when a new thought struck him. He had left two inert bodies. Suppose the North African came to first, took the revolver, and finished off the policeman? He felt himself go cold, and the sweat came out on his forehead at the thought. If the law ever caught up with him, he had almost unwittingly made himself a criminal several times over that evening, and he was too aware of the law to seek any escape, even to justify himself, on ideological grounds – as far as they were concerned, he would in any case be even more guilty in a country where the police are a sacred institution, emanation of the people instead of being the hired thugs of capitalism.

It is a crime in France not to go to the help of someone in mortal danger. He thought grimly for a moment that he had at least gone to the help of the North African – Algerian no doubt – the first time, and perhaps saved his life when the policeman was about to fire. The law would hardly be impressed by that one – interfering with an officer in the execution of his duty; and at the moment, he thought bitterly, Algerian lives don't count for much in the eyes of the law – few questions asked. He was already a little vague about the sequence of events after that. Anyhow his action, however instinctive, had been prompted more by hatred of the uniform than anything else. Then the picture came back to him again, clear as if he were looking at a film: his horror at the descending knife, about to plunge into a defenceless body.

Like most Europeans, he regarded firearms, of whatever sort, as a more or less respectable agency of violence when violence is necessary, whereas a knife – perhaps because Europeans have lost their dexterity in its manipulation – is primitive, mean, sly, treacherous, cowardly, a weapon for skin savages. The Algerian, whose life he had very possibly saved a moment before, could in his fury have knifed him without compunction; his stick would have been a poor weapon if the Algerian, even with his injured hand, had got hold of the knife again. He shuddered at the thought of that horrible, ugly blade. Perhaps the policeman, whose life he had endangered, had saved him, in one moment of consciousness, from a slashed face, a nose cut off, an ear, an eye blinded, his throat slit, his heart... And now to save his own skin, he had abandoned the policeman, perhaps to be murdered in cold blood. The small circle of violence into which he had stumbled and had not escaped by escaping, seemed suddenly the epicentre of the vast upheaval and the tidal wave resulting from it that was crashing over two whole nations, wreaking destruction with all the indifference of nature itself to anything in its path.

His head was going dizzy. Circles formed before his eyes, crimson, then rainbow-coloured, advancing and receding. With an instinct of self-preservation, he fought down the dizziness, only to remember the Algerian whom he had left dying perhaps, dead maybe; if not, the best he could expect was to be picked up by a police patrol, and the casualty wards of the hospitals would have enough to do tonight with others more urgently meriting treatment than another bicot, even if he was bleeding to death from a gunshot wound... My one contribution to the liberation of Algeria. Myles hurriedly took out his handkerchief and held it over his mouth, praying he would not vomit. The crisis passed. He glanced round. Only one other booth was occupied, by a couple glued together who were much too busy to take any notice of him. They seemed to belong to a normal world he would never enter again.

51

Jacky walked up the Boul' Mich' with her bag, past the extension of the Luxembourg and the Closerie des Lilas, and round into the Boulevard du Port Royal. She took the lift up to the fourth floor and pushed the bell. Hassim came to the door in a dressing gown. He kissed her awkwardly, as he always did when they met; certain European ways would always come awkwardly to him.

"Did the doctor call?" she asked.

He nodded.

"Is it jaundice?"

"I am Algerian, not Chinese." He smiled. "Look at my wrists. And my eyes. Fortunately, it is not a very serious attack. Strict diet, no butter, no eggs and so on. Nothing to excite the liver. I feel really French, now that I've got a liver."

She looked round. "It hasn't changed. I brought you some fruit juices," she said. "I don't think any of these are forbidden. And some bread. Do you need anything else? What would you like me to make? Something with rice?"

"I have no appetite. I just want to drink. And I think all the time how wonderful it would be to be free to have a real meal again."

"It's good for the figure."

"Yes, it's another habit I got into in Paris, eating too much."

"It's bad for a horse's back?"

257

"Bad for the horse's back, and for the man's soul. Did you ever notice how, when people go flabby, their minds get enveloped in fat at the same time as their bodies?"

"Not always."

"Not always, but very often."

"Some people are born with a tendency to go to fat."

"Everyone is born with the tendency to go to fat – mentally."

"There are worse things."

"Such as?"

"Well you know what Shakespeare says – let me have men about me that are fat. Yon Cassius has a lean and hungry look, he thinks too much, such men are dangerous."

"That's *Julius Caesar* isn't it?"

"Yes. Full marks in English literature."

"But it's not Julius Caesar talking, it's Shakespeare."

"It's the best we can do. No one had tape recorders available in those days."

"But even if it was Julius Caesar, you know why he would prefer to have fat men around. Because they are compliant. They don't make trouble. That may suit a ruler very well. It doesn't mean the men themselves are worth much."

"If you were a ruler, you would prefer to have thin men round you?"

"Oh, no, fat men every time," he laughed. "But I would probably despise them."

"Isn't that dangerous?"

"Not for them."

"But it would be for you."

"How? You said: 'If I were a ruler...' On the contrary, it would be ideal. They would cause no trouble, they would be happy in their fat. I would not need to show I despise them."

"That's what I mean. Wouldn't that be dangerous? That's the way autocrats are made."

"All rulers are autocrats. If they are not, they are not rulers."

"Myles would never agree with you."

"Myles is not a ruler."

"That doesn't prevent him having ideas on the subject."

"You think Myles believes in democracy?"

"Don't you?"

"What do you think democracy is? Or what do you think Myles thinks it is?"

"I suppose the right of people to govern themselves rather than be governed."

"Can you give me one single example of where that exists?"

"Well, any parliamentary democracy."

"England, for example?"

"Yes, England."

"Was Churchill a democrat?"

"Anything but."

"Well?"

"England threw him out in 1945, even though he'd won a war that was lost years before if it hadn't been for him."

"But while he was there, he was a ruler?"

"Certainly that."

"And an autocrat?"

"As much an autocrat as Stalin. But as soon as I say that, you can see the difference. Churchill was thrown out. There was no way of getting rid of a Stalin once you've got one, except by assassination, or by natural death, if you're lucky."

"You Europeans have a way of thinking I shall never get used to. We are not talking about good or bad rulers. That's a big subject in itself, but a different one. Churchill was one of the architects of the United Nations, and yet he despised all he regarded as lesser breeds. Everything he did from the time he was a child was vainglorious. He was the sort of reactionary that Myles would hate. And yet he was the one who was essential. Compare him with the Pope who meant well, or Chamberlain, who was deliriously welcomed back to England in 1938 as the man who had saved the peace of the world. I only said that all rulers are autocrats, and that if they are not, they are not rulers. And under what you call a democracy, you admittedly have some choice. But when you have chosen, you give yourself up automatically to the rule of one man. Or if not, you have not got a ruler. And the fact that you elect him for five years doesn't alter the case. There are not so many periods of five years in an adult life. Maybe ten, on an average. So you go on for successive periods of five years, thinking always the next will be better because it can't be worse."

"You are the one who is getting away from the point now. We seem to have gone a long way from you as the ruler, surrounded by your fat men."

"No, Jacky, it's just you who lost the thread of your own argument. You are in the middle of one of your five-year periods now. Even a typical one. You think France is a democracy, don't you, because there were elections a few years ago?"

"A poor example, maybe, but still a democracy."

"And you are a free citizen of a free democracy?"

"Yes"

"Jacques - you remember that night in the café - is, like you, another free citizen, but he is nevertheless ordered to go, against his will - not alone against his will, but against all his moral convictions - to fight in a war which the country itself does not want. Do you want better proof of that, whatever you may call the regime, the ruler is autocratic, when he has the power of life and death, not only over his own people, but over those of other countries as well?"

"Is that a good thing or a bad thing?"

"There you see, you bring up the same irrelevancy again. You may think it's a good thing or a bad thing as you see best. But the important point is that it objectively exists. The fact that Jacques objected to going to Algeria doesn't prevent him from having to go. Nor does all the indignation of Myles."

"Sometimes I think your lack of emotion is much more frightening, and much more negative."

"How effective is his indignation?"

"It seems to me that generosity is a good thing in itself. And that is what his indignation springs from."

"Don't be so sure. The world is full of that sort of generosity, of people so certain they know what is good for everyone else that they're willing to kill them in order to prove it. You don't have to look very closely to see it's the most bigoted form of egoism. There's only one thing worse."

"What?"

"When your generous person realises it. Then he's a hypocrite as well."

"Oh, come," she said, "you're taking a very particular case. I don't believe anything worth while is possible without generosity. I would rather any time someone who made mistakes out of an excess of generosity than someone who had none. Wouldn't you?"

"It depends."

"It depends on what?"

"It's all right if he bears the consequences of his mistakes, and not other people."

"Everyone makes mistakes."

"That's what I mean. These people whom you call generous not only want to make their own mistakes, but make those of other people as well and they think – in fact they know – that this vague feeling they have of their own goodness and rightness entitles them to it. You will see, when Algeria becomes independent, the French intellectuals who are now in favour of it will be the first to disagree with the way Algerians run their own affairs. And, in disgust, they will go off looking for a new cause."

"Surely you're not complaining that there are people in France who believe strongly enough in justice to be prepared to go against their own country, and risk the consequences – which at the moment, may mean assassination, or having their flats blown up, or a bomb planted in their cars which goes off when they switch on the engine?"

"On the contrary. It's splendid. But your generous admiration prevents you from seeing what will inevitably happen – what I've just told you will happen."

"One thing at a time. For the moment, they are prepared to risk their lives to end what they think to be an intolerable injustice. Surely you agree that that is generous and admirable."

"In itself, yes."

"What do you mean, 'in itself, yes'? You are faced with a choice, and you do what seems to you what is right and generous. You can't foresee all the consequences of anything you do. If you try, you will never do anything."

"There are people on the other side who are convinced they are acting just as rightly and generously."

"Do you think they are?"

"That's not the point. They think they are. If I had their upbringing and was in the same circumstances, I might very easily think the same as they do."

"Sometimes I wonder if you're Algerian at all."

He smiled.

"I'm not, I'm Chinese, look at my hands."

"No, Hassim, but seriously –"

"Seriously," he answered, "I have just given you, in simple words, one of the reasons why there are wars. Paradoxical isn't it?"

"Wars may be caused by evil men, although few of them would recognise themselves in that description. Anyhow, most of the time, they are just exploiting the ground prepared for them by the people you think are generous. And they are generous, I suppose. But they can't mind their own business. And, in addition, they are convinced that what they believe to be right is infallibly right. Get enough of them on both sides, and you have a war."

"I don't agree with you. You only have to look at people who start wars. You never see a fat, jolly man start a war. They're all mean, tight-lipped, humourless fanatics, if they are not positively non-drinking, non-smoking, vegetarian puppets like Hitler, without an ounce of human feeling or generosity."

"How about Goering? He was fat and jolly."

"In a horrible way. Anyhow, he didn't actually start a war."

"He did his bit towards starting it."

"In that case, swap him for Goebbels. But you see what I mean."

"No, I think it's completely irrelevant. Stalin wasn't exactly thin, or Mussolini, or Franco, or Churchill, or – it's funny, I can't remember what Salazar looks like. You see, you always want to be true what you would like to be true."

"Come and eat," she said, putting the food on the table, "you have a lean and hungry look. You would make a horrible ruler. You would be intolerant. You would always be sure you are right. You despise nice comfortable fat men. You despise generosity. You would be a self-righteous prig."

"That's a lot to reproach me with for wanting to define the first quality of a ruler."

"What's that?"

"Not to mistake sentimentality for generosity. To try to be honest, and see clearly."

"A ruler should keep all his wits about him – in every sense. But you, alone with your fat court jesters? Too proud to seek advice from anyone else. No humility."

"A ruler may seek advice, but he must make up his own mind. You are wrong again about humility. To depend on others is not humility in a ruler, but weakness."

"You would know everything, and have no need for advice on any subject?"

"That was not what I said."

"Well, it was implied."

"Not at all. I don't have to be grateful to his plate I am eating from, for example."

"You are rapidly approaching megalomania. Your advisers aren't even human beings, they are only so many inanimate objects."

"Beware of emotion: it clouds the judgement."

"But what you just said is horrible."

"Lots of things are horrible. The way to deal with them is not to pretend they don't exist, but to see clearly that they do exist, and then decide what you're going to do. Death, for example, is horrible to most people, but they can't avoid it by saying so. But I agree with you in one thing. A ruler needs humility."

"Where is he going to find it, on your principles?"

"In the only place where it makes sense for a real ruler to find it."

"Where is that?"

"In God."

He spoke with a calm assurance, as if it had not been an academic argument they had been having, in the abstract, but as if he were in fact a ruler, or destined to be one; as if his words expressed thoughts that came so naturally to him that he did not need to think about them. She had divined some quality in him, one that seemed to set him apart, that first evening in the café with the others, and had been fascinated by it. His ruthless approach to certain subjects frightened her, and yet seemed to make most of the talk she heard from others sound flabby (a word he was fond of using to describe it).

"A man can be humble before God, for then he has something worth being humble before."

She had discovered nothing about his background or his family. He had never spoken about them to Myles either. He had been very friendly with Jacques, but probably only because Jacques had been someone who shared his passion for chess.

"You don't really care much about people, do you?" she said.

"Not the way you do," he countered.

He had a habit of disconcerting people with his abrupt references to God – so abrupt in fact that many people felt they were being unfairly treated. It never happened in a religious context, when there might be a softening-up process to ease the way. Most of his fellow-students came from homes where religion still had a place so long as the children were in school, but tended to recede like any other school subject once the necessary examinations were passed, or fade in importance like uncles, aunts or grandparents who grew older, married, died or otherwise submerged and disappeared. God remained, a kind of shadowy background figure whom no one had ever seen, but no one had ever not seen either, vaguely disturbing at all times, present at death, ceremoniously present at great affairs of State. Especially funerals. It was certainly a far cry to the almost

266

explosively present God of Hassim, who seemed to exist without benefit of religion.

Jacky knew the religious conservatism on her father's side of the family, including that of the uncle who was often at the Vatican, and was hated in the abstract with a particular virulence by Myles, who was exasperated perhaps more by his father's tolerance than by the rather naive orthodoxy of his convert mother. Both her parents were practising. She herself frankly did not know where she stood. But conservative as her convent education had been, she realised the difference between even the most conservative Catholic God and the God to whom Hassim paid allegiance with the proud humility of a mediaeval knight – not yet tired and worn out by the buffeting of the Enlightenment, the Reformation, Marxism, Leninism, Trotskyism and the social and spiritual upheavals of two world wars, completed, from beginning to end, within the record time of thirty-one years.

Hassim laid down his knife and fork.

"You'd almost think I wanted to see you fat," Jacky said, reverting to the original topic, "I don't really want to change you, you know."

He looked away, his face troubled. He had rented the studio empty, and had only his own sparse furnishing, with no pictures, but some pieces of brass work and Arab rugs and blankets. There they had come back the second evening. Their first meeting had been shy and awkward but they had nevertheless decided to meet again. The second meeting had gone altogether differently. They had a good dinner and drank rather a lot. Hassim had relaxed to an extent she would not have believed possible. They had gone back to the studio. Hassim had none of the usual social amenities, not even a radio. So, the alcohol aiding, they had lain down on the divan, and made love with abandon, Jacky in a kind of exhilarated panic. There was a certain fear of Hassim in the attitude he had had for her from the beginning: fear of something apart that was not only racial or religious, but something inherent in Hassim himself. He was not gentle with her now.

She realised she had foreseen precisely this that evening she had suggested they should meet again. The wine had loosened some of her inhibitions, but she realised that this first time was something vital in her life no matter what happened afterwards – and with a man whom she hardly knew, and didn't know if she loved or not, apart from the extraordinary fascination he exercised over her. She lay sore and exhausted afterwards. He had moved apart, and was staring at the ceiling. She thought of her father, his affection for her when she arrived home, and began to cry. Hassim looked at her in surprise, put his arm round her shoulders and drew her to him. "What is it?" he asked.

"Nothing," she said, "don't take any notice. It will pass."

She felt protected by his closeness and the warmth of his body, too grateful for it to want to think of anything else. Her sobbing subsided and she dozed off into a sleep which kept on being interrupted through the night, as one or other woke, and wondered if the other were sleeping or awake.

But they made love again twice during the night.

When morning came, the first thing that caught her eye in the room was the only ornament on the walls, apart from the rugs: a framed scroll. After a while, she realised that he too was awake, watching her staring at it. "Good morning" she said, smiling at him. "What is it?" – she nodded towards the script.

"Arabic," he answered.

"What does it say?"

"Allah. God."

That was a couple of weeks ago already.

Far from simplifying the situation between them, the night they had passed together seemed to have immensely complicated it, and the complications on her side were nothing compared to those on his. He

268

seemed to resent what had happened as an intrusion on his own almost mystic aloneness. He was too deeply engrained in his own traditions, even after four years in Europe, and a European-type education before that, to be able to accept the idea of a girl giving herself to a man, as an equal, without degrading herself by doing so. He shuddered to think of the blot on the honour of his family at home if such a thing had happened, the blow it would be to his father, his father's fury. He felt he had not alone betrayed himself, but Myles, and his friendship with Myles, as well. He liked Jacky. She was an attractive, intelligent girl and he had been flattered by her attention, but this had never reached the stage at which a European would describe himself as being in love with her. He should have had a little more sense. From any point of view, it was better to stop the affair before it went any further.

So he had seen her a few times afterwards, but briefly. He could see she did not understand and was hurt. But his reasons were not of a kind she could ever understand. Then he had suddenly felt very ill, without knowing precisely what was wrong, and realised that, if it were serious, he who had always been so self-sufficient would find himself dependent, perhaps completely dependent, on others, helpless. The thought appalled him. Except for minor ailments, he had never been ill since childhood, so that he was inclined to exaggerate the virulence of his own symptoms but was afraid to see a doctor who might confirm his fears. He had been immensely glad to see Jacky, who insisted that he should see a doctor, and said she would be along to see him the next day.

She had not dared mention a fear, forming in her own mind, that she might be pregnant. He had been in such good form when she arrived this evening. Now she noticed again that look on his face, the withdrawal, and was doubly anxious. If her fears were justified, what would happen? She did not even dare think of her parents, of her dying mother and her father who had always been so gentle with her. Thinking of him in spite of herself, she glanced at this hard impenetrable stranger before her, who was open only to a God as hard, aloof, proud and impenetrable as himself, and suddenly felt convinced she had made an irreparable mistake. His coldness, his inaccessibility, had at first been an added attraction. Now she realised that, even in the animated argument they had just had, and in which she felt she had held her own fairly well, he had been talking down to her, there was a barrier that would never be crossed over. For the first time in years, she really prayed, prayed desperately that her fears would not be justified. An unthinkable world seemed to be opening before her that would swallow up her youth and blast all her hopes in life. She was very near to tears.

Noticing the change that came over her, he was distressed and uneasy, having by then realised how sensitive she was to certain moods of his, how easily hurt; surprised that the evening that had started so well should have degenerated to this; and finally irritated with this cloying female presence that had no thought but of its own imaginary claims on one's very being.

"Is anything wrong?" he asked.

"I am not feeling so well myself," she answered.

He looked at her enquiringly.

It was an ideal opportunity to say the fears that were on her mind, but she couldn't get the words out.

"It's nothing," she said. "I am just feeling a bit tired. Perhaps it's a touch of flu. I think I shall go home shortly."

He was relieved to hear it was something outside himself that was responsible.

"You shouldn't steal my thunder like that" he said, almost gently. "You know, this is the first time I've been really ill."

"It's not from choice," she said rather sadly, and rose to go.

"I shall look in to see how you're getting on."

"Take care of yourself first," he answered. "Now that I know what is wrong, and what I have to do, there is really no problem.

Some of the others will be in to see me, and I am pretty well stocked up with everything I need."

"I see," she said.

His remorse had by now got the better of his irritation, and he had a certain sense of the loneliness that would descend on him when she had gone. He kissed her with unaccustomed warmth. She submitted rather than reacted, and he had a momentary return of anger.

She left without saying anything further.

52

Christine had been lying on her side, face to the wall. She rose on her elbows. A spasm of pain crossed her face.

"What was it?" he asked in concern.

"Nothing. It's just that my inside is as mixed up as a handbag."

"The phone didn't wake you?"

"No. At least, I was only half asleep anyway. I was supposed to be listening to the music. Disgraceful, isn't it? Such bad manners, when Beethoven comes back into the room, to play for me, and I don't even keep awake. Who was on the phone?"

"I don't know. It stopped before I got to it. Probably for Jacky."

"She's not back yet?"

"I heard her ask Myles to leave the key under the mat. That means, I suppose, she'll be late."

"I'm worried about her," Christine said.

"What can we do? She's getting to be too big a girl now to be watched over."

"You wouldn't have the heart to say anything to her anyway, would you?"

"No, I suppose not."

"I don't know what your brother the Monsignor would say."

"I do. But this is Paris, and her youth, not his, or even ours."

"Sometimes I have to ask myself which of us was born a Catholic."

"Everyone knows that there's no bigot like a convert."

"But seriously, Alexis, don't you think you should talk to her. Two nights in the last two weeks she didn't come home at all."

"She was with friends. Don't you believe her?"

"It's not that I don't believe her, it's just that I don't know what sort of friends they are."

"She has started to go out into the big world. She's got to make her own way. We can't choose her friends for her."

"And then there's all this politics. It's no concern of ours. We weren't born here."

"She was. Why, both of them almost speak broken English!"

"But why do they want to get involved in politics?"

"Maybe because they feel involved."

"All this stupid, useless killing."

"Is killing ever anything but stupid and useless? ...Was that a ring at the door?"

It rang again. Alexis got up to answer it.

"It's Frederic," he called in from the hall.

"How is everyone?"

"Come in and see," Christine called out.

"I'm not disturbing you?" he asked, bending down to kiss her. "I never saw you looking better."

"You are as good a storyteller as ever. Although I really don't know how I should take that remark. In any case, sit down."

The room was big and, the bed apart, had the air of a kind of second living room where people were used to dropping in rather than a sick room. There was an old, comfortable armchair, facing the bed, but he did not take it. Instead, sure of her affection for him, he sat familiarly on the end of the bed.

He was approaching thirty, with a small beard that gave him a buccaneering look he sedulously cultivated. Many people loathe military service, but he had revelled in his two years in Algeria, finding his place at last after the frustrations of school where he could never pass an examination. Once in uniform, he found the self-confidence that he unconsciously knew should be his. He won promotion easily, but retained the camaraderie of those he had gone out with; to them, it seemed as natural as it did to him, and there was no jealousy or resentment. He took danger with an unconcern as complete as he had for the rights and wrongs of what was happening around him. For a change of scene, instead of staying on in Algeria when his two years were up, he had gone on to the Congo, where there was more scope for initiative, and bigger pay. The rank he was given was satisfactory also, but somehow had not the same standing as a lower rank in one of the most senior armies in the world. It had been his only regret. A hasty marriage had produced three children before disastrously breaking up. He ran a smart car and always seemed to have plenty of money. Apart from his connections with the OAS, his sources of income were undisclosed.

He now took Christine's hand with a genuine tenderness.

"What are they keeping you in bed for? Anyone would think you were an invalid!"

274

"Aren't I?"

"At your age? You should be ashamed of yourself!"

Alexis looked on with mixed feelings. A man of action is a boy for ever. He must not be rotted by thought, eroded by compassion, cluttered like an old room by an accumulation of memories. His memories should only be souvenirs or, better, trophies, sterile objects clean and dusted. Disciplined, for emotion is insidious and tarnishes. Simple. If emotional tarnish there must be, let it be from the cadenced posturations of a military band.

It would be absurd to say that Alexis was jealous, but he always felt somehow excluded, almost gauche whenever Frederic dropped in like this. He was as cheerfully free of principles as his father had been obsessed by them. The charm might be superficial, but it was so effective a substitute for brain or intelligence that it often left Alexis, much to his annoyance, feeling stupid, tongue-tied; it even, for the moment, seemed to make ordinary ideas of right and wrong not only irrelevant but quaint. Frederic always seemed good-natured, good-hearted with a most engaging, boyish frankness that remained quite untroubled by such things as the heaps of corpses he had helped to make from time to time in the Congo, or the effects of plastic explosions. Alexis' instinct told him he should dislike Frederic; instead he could not help liking him and even, to his own consternation, sometimes even admiring him. What is true for me is not necessarily true for you. Morality is rules, personality is a continuous breaking of the statistical average of conduct. Perspective. Perspectives.

Christine had no such scruples. She liked Frederic, accepted him as he was without reservations, and enjoyed his flattery without being in the least taken in by it. Although he was obviously interested in Jacky, he never thought of using the mother as an approach to the daughter, but treated her as a person in her own right, one he admired and genuinely liked. It was perhaps this lack of guile, a kind of innocence, that made so many people like him who would normally have shunned him.

275

"Jacky is not in? I rang a while ago..." said Frederic.

"Oh, it was you?" said Alexis. "I was half asleep. By the time I got to the phone, it had rung off."

"I'm always afraid you might be asleep, and I might wake you up" said Frederic, turning to Christine.

"You've also got to remember my lame leg" said Alexis, "it takes me some time to get to the phone." "Although" he added to himself, "he doesn't expect to find me at the other end; if he did, he wouldn't bother to ring."

"I'm not such an invalid as all that," said Christine. "Anyhow, people have no right to be asleep before nine. It's only encouraging idleness."

Again Alexis felt uncomfortable. The reason Frederic had given was doubtless true. He was sensitive in that way, considerate. And then Alexis' thought gave another angry turn. Pilate too had been sensitive, and delicately washed his hands.

"What an ass I am," said Frederic suddenly. "I forgot something down in my car. May I leave the front door open till I come back?"

"You know the way," said Christine.

He went quickly out of the room.

"Well," said Alexis, "happy now that your boyfriend has come to see you?"

"I never understand why all of you so dislike him. I think he's charming."

"Much too charming," said Alexis.

"Surely there isn't anything wrong in that? Even Jacky. Compared with some of the people she's brought home at times..."

"Jacky has a pretty shrewd idea of people's worth."

"Not like her mother?"

"You know I didn't mean that. But..."

Frederic could be heard on the landing. He came into the room holding an enormous bunch of roses. He had opened the paper on the way up.

"Madame," he said, handing them to Christine.

"They're lovely." She turned the bouquet round slowly. The roses were between orange and red, some buds not yet open, others debutantes waiting on a threshold, a few in full bloom, the ferns delicate behind them, their scent distant as the bouquet of wine that must be coaxed from the glass. "They're really lovely," she repeated. "I think they're the most beautiful flowers I've ever seen. Thank you." She drew his face down and kissed him.

Alexis went out and came back with a large vase.

"Give it to me, Alexis," she said, "a man never knows how to arrange flowers."

She put the flowers in one by one, so that, like dancers moving in a ballet, they took on a completely new appearance, more open, spaced out.

Again, Alexis found himself wondering, meanly, why, if the flowers had been meant for Christine, Frederic had not brought them up in the first place. For Jacky, perhaps? He was rather sardonically amused to see how, with Jacky, the Don Juan was transformed back into the blushing schoolboy, unsure of himself, trying desperately to please.

It was not that Jacky actively disliked him. It was rather that, associating like Myles with those who had suddenly after school discovered the world around them, inside and outside France, the bidonvilles, the underpaid and the privileged whose greatest problem was to decide in which of their residences to reside or with which of their mistresses to sleep, the corpses lying unheeded in the streets of Algiers, wrapped in newspaper or not wrapped at all, the newspaper photos of people going about their daily affairs, stepping between bodies as if a human destiny brutally snuffed out was of no more consequence than a dustbin uncollected because the garbage man – lowest of all the underprivileged – had gone on strike, but things would return to normal in a few days and, after a few francs had been judiciously distributed, the dustbins – and the corpses – would cease to inconvenience honest citizens.

"– Would you like a drink?" Alexis asked.

"I wouldn't say no to a small Scotch, le drink des gens bien," answered Frederic.

"That's a Schweppes," said Alexis, "do you never read your theatre programmes?"

"Too intellectual for me," said Frederic. "I only go to see gangsters and Westerns. In the cinema. Anyhow, it's cheaper."

Alexis brought him a whiskey.

"You won't join me?" asked Frederic.

"If you will excuse me," said Alexis, "I'm working on a paper."

"He's been invited to read a scientific paper in Dublin," Christine said.

"Congratulations," said Frederic. "France-Soir is about the only paper I'll ever be invited to read."

Alexis left them to talk, and went back into the other room. To justify his absence, he got out various books he had been working on, and looked at them with distaste, unable to concentrate. A half-empty bottle of wine stood on the piano. He had never noticed before that the level was constantly shaking. Perhaps Terzieff was right: there are volcanoes under our feet. We have all got comfortably used to our sympathy for the victims of earthquakes in India, in Turkey, in Greece, in Yugoslavia, Sicily, South America – anywhere else, thank God but not here. The murderous Etna was a tourist attraction. But the fires underneath are always burning, and they have burst out in other places before. And been forgotten. Until one night, little dreaming of that, a sleeping Lisbon is annihilated overnight. Hiroshima before the act. And here, in the centre of this Paris emerging newly washed and furbished, everything magically rejuvenated from the grime of centuries, heartbreakingly beautiful with all the accumulation of its memories, the earth might eructate before I can rise from this chair, and reduce it all to rubble as the lunacy of man had threatened to do not so many years before.

No atomic bomb is necessary. We are all living on sufferance anyway, and the world can be destroyed without it. Each of our worlds. One city after another. A pause, repair, weariness after war, cat and mouse, start again, destroy, desolate...

The Tour Eiffel was visible, framed in the window. By moving his head slightly from side to side, the grains in the window pane made it shimmy like a dancer at an African wedding. If it fell over this way, the top would almost reach here. A black spot on the glass might have been an aeroplane in the distance. Yesterday he had gone down to the cellar, which had never been properly cleared out. He discovered a cardboard box hidden under some blocks of wood that were thick with dust, a box full of memories that had lived in the paper they were written on and, with them, a roll that might have contained a school certificate. His hands already filthy, he tried to ease out the paper with the tips of his fingers, but failed. He fished a paper handkerchief out of his pocket, wiped his hands, and tried again. The paper which finally came out was really a parchment. It had belonged to the previous occupant of the apartment, now dead: the certificate of a Grand Chancellier of the Legion d'Honneur.

279

All things have their season, and all things pass under heaven.

The cut wires on the ceiling, gelded lampshade that will never fall again as long as I am here, an occupant, for how long. Here we have no abiding place. The upright lamp will survive, pass on to other hands, as this flat over the roofs of Paris has seen the death of the Grand Chancellier whose scroll lies rolled up in my cellar, with the dusty wood that once too was his, provision against the cold of a winter he would never see.

He sat thinking of it. And the day the phone had rung, and a voice asked for the same man. Some day the phone will ring the same way, and a voice will ask for me. The books lining the walls, up to the ceiling on one side, the objects in the room. Chinese tapestry, brown, crossed by branches, blue birds in relief. Descente de la Croix. Iran, Persia, India, Costa Rica, all that mankind has built up. And that eruption, perhaps, waiting. Don Quixote, Picasso, Daumier. Abyssinian St George, miserable poor dragon, girl with come-hither eyes. Persian lamp, shapes, human, animal, merging into its brass design, just a design abstract, but shapes like shapes that clouds assume... Hard to believe that each represented a day in my life, a hesitation about the extravagance, an anticipated pleasure, a decision, a joy, a disappointment – and another day dropped into the gluttonous, never-satisfied maw. Possessions are at most a loan on which time may at any time foreclose.

Foreclose? The word raised an echo. He went over and took down a notebook. The paper had yellowed, but it was still there.

Days lengthen
the bud becomes a rose
what if, we two, loving
earth life and time
so soon foreclose?

Maureen. How much would she have changed in all these years? Perhaps he might even see her when he went to Dublin. Or maybe

280

she too, was living in some other land. Maybe even here, in Paris. Surely she must come here, sometimes.

But now the creditor was no longer a romantic spectre in an unimaginable future. He would have his pound of flesh. He'd already had instalments. And no more humane, reforming law would ever get Christine out again once she had passed into the debtor's prison. He felt lacerated, lacerated with his own, doctor's, certainty that she could not live much longer. What if we two loving. She had loved him with an unselfishness he felt no man could have merited, a tenderness that was never mawkish, a possessiveness that still never became obtrusive and recognised his need for privacy to work at times on things that interested him and that she had no interest in except in so far as she recognised them to be part of him. The only reproach which might be made her was for a touching weakness which he, for one, could scarcely feel entitled to resent – her obstinate belief in some potential greatness in him. She was proud of the reputation he had established in the medical world. But she knew he had deeper interests, the writing he had finally turned to, and which had merely resulted in a growing pile of unpublished manuscripts. And a manuscript is a terribly poor relation of a printed book.

That belief was one of the causes of trouble between her and her son. Between Jacky and her father there was a special bond of affection and understanding. But Myles resented his father with all the pure arrogance of the true reformer. He and Jacky frequented the same circles. So far as she knew of their acquaintances and their activities, their mother was terrified. Jacky took after her to the extent that people, finally, were more important to her than ideas. Her contempt for what was bourgeois remained abstract and did not cross the threshold into her own family except in arguments. Myles, on the other hand, was extreme always. He had never forgotten one occasion when he had used the word bourgeois, his favourite term of abuse, in speaking of his father, his mother had turned on him and said: "Bourgeois is just a convenient term of abuse for little snobs like you who feel superior to their betters."

The gibe struck home. Myles shared the ability of many people who are very free in their abuse of others to resent, bitterly, any that might come their own way. He resented being called a little snob because he was still young enough to regard a reference to his youth as an insult. But above all, the taunt seemed to cast doubt on both his integrity and his sincerity. Neither could be faulted. Unfortunately. If they could, if they had been less integral, it might have meant he had a sense of humour. His heart is bleeding, thought Alexis, for Chinese coolies, and it's admirable, except that he can't see his own mother is dying under his eyes, oblivious to it in his embracing love of humanity as she still was in her ignorance of her own disease. Poor Christine.

Her cancer was hopeless, but almost kind in the long respites it allowed her. A month before she had almost died, miraculously rallied, and so far recovered as to seem almost healthy again, despite the loss of weight, still apparently not suspecting what was really wrong with her. It was scarcely credible that she should go first, so young, when it was he who had always been the sickly one, her patient in fact. Perhaps I should be with her now. Who knows how long more I can be, ever? And yet that too is only an illusion.

Buying a shawl once, and the note I left with it.

The intensity of life taken on by places, things, objects, a Christmas card – emotion one blacked-out oblong in a stylised design can recapture and produce – and the sense of loss.

How everything tarnishes – the silver sugar bowl sad and yellow. After cleaning, like a woman straight from the hairdresser – not that I don't like it, but it certainly leaps to the eye.

Camargue. Arles – the car, the drive, Aigues-Mortes, the horses, the insects, the picnic, the sun, the goblets on the strand, and the inevitable packing up because there is the inevitable train. Bags left in a bistro, bistro closed, consternation. Back to hotel to which I shall never go back again...

Moments, always fleeting, always the illusion of something that may last.

No physical earthquake is necessary. No flames eructating from the middle earth. For there is nothing between us, finally, and the worms, save a small built-in machine industriously pumping blood. The heart that may go phutt et l'eau qui fait pschitt. Skulls all or skulls prospective.

He had been leaning back in the armchair with his head resting on one hand. Smoke curled up, blue through the red lampshade on the table. One knee was crossed over the other, the foot not quite touching the ground, moving in little pulsations in time with his heartbeats. He now felt his arm growing stiff. His hand had gone white as a plaster cast. He changed position, and found the pins and needles striking on the back of his palm like the heavy raindrops of an unexpected shower.

He had always refused to be dominated by his body. His tuberculosis had never become pulmonary, but had left his resistance low. Twice in his life, colds had led to pneumonia. Recently his own diagnosis of gallstones had been confirmed by a colleague. But it was not urgent, and with Christine in her condition it was hardly the time to think of an operation. On a few occasions recently he had felt other pains which might, or again might not, betoken appendicitis. Contrary to the advice he had always given others, he was in no hurry to find out. His trip to Dublin was also looming up. He felt suddenly a tremendous lassitude. Those ugly little insects with the lovely name in French – cloportes – that he had watched in the sanatorium grounds: why were there always six, or eight, or ten or eleven of them only, there invariably every morning, no matter how ruthlessly they might be cleaned away?

Do spiders ever get electrocuted?

Why not a hundred of them, a thousand, a million of them all at once? Or flies? Or ants? Who rationed their numbers? The scary lizards on the wall were friendly, but not that awful potential invasion. And crimes. Why only the two or three or twenty reported in the papers – why not some sudden outburst that would sweep away all law, order, organisation? But come to think of it, it had happened, it happened when a nation of eighty million had gone criminal almost to

283

a man. Perhaps the worms, with us in life and after, are less terrible than men after all, and Nature could be trusted to control what was merely natural, leaving the real monstrosities to be perpetrated by whatever it was in man that was supra or infranatural.

One tulip had opened under the effect of the central heating with eight enormous petals, like a Mykonos windmill. One, the lowest, was bigger than the rest, eccentric. They were deep red, the centre of the flower a large pansy, brown, yellow-flecked at the edges. The stamen looked alive. The whole thing looked live, vaguely menacing, sinister, potentially man-eating, or at least carnivorous, staring fixedly down at something. Will it do harm before it dies, or will it's petals just drop harmlessly off?

That a delicate, modest tulip should turn into this monster.

Mon coeur mis à nu.

He had taken his watch off. It was lying on the table. There were little flashes from it as the second hand, catching the light, restlessly passed a certain point.

What did I do to stop the eighty million? Nothing, uneasily glad enough to be out of it with a plausible excuse. But what could he have done? Helped to bomb women and children, or save a Jew, a Jewish father, a Jewish woman, a Jewish child from torture and ignominious death? One. One only. One even. Physically? By filling sandbags, by fire fighting, by hospital work, by curing – or by killing? All round, in this city and country tonight, people are killing again, all convinced in their variegated ways that they are right and justified. And Vietnam, that has hardly known peace for a quarter of a century. And my two children, caught up in it all, one convinced with her heart, the other with what he believes to be his reason and maybe really is his fierce, generous hatred of injustice. He's prepared to die for it. Was I? Have I any right, even in spite of Christine whose last days he is helping to poison – have I any right to stop him, to stop either of them? To stop them, maybe, helping to kill the innocent? What can I, what can any individual, do to stop all the murder that is happening in his own name – any more than I could have stopped Hitler?

He went over to the window. The Tour Eiffel was there, the beacon whirling round, the light in the pin-head the eye of some strange iron monster whose body, instead of dividing into feet, had splayed. Perhaps tonight some lunatic will succeed in setting a charge of plastic under its great sprung, concrete plinths, and it will lean over, wailing, holding itself up against some succouring, sympathetic cloud. The street lights shone down green through the branches of the trees; the top of the Arc de Triomphe, illuminated, shone over distant roofs as if made of glass. Two nuns were approaching, struggling against the wind along the path on the opposite side of the avenue, their clothes ballooning, held down by one hand as the other clung desperately to a cowl. Did they feel self-conscious in their alien black in an alien world, away from the chapel, the poor and the sick? They advanced from pool to pool of green light in a fantastic ballet.

He looked through the small prismatic circles that were set in the stained glass on either side of the window. They showed rows of Eiffel Towers, geometrically disposed vertically and horizontally, pattern for a wallpaper, but sparkling successively yellow, red, green, blue as he moved his eye from one circle to another. It was Christine who had discovered that game. It had so fascinated Jacky that he had stopped her, irrationally fearing it might give her a squint. In happier days.

His eye came back to the clear glass, the two nuns resuming their place as the unconscious stars in the ballet. They had almost reached the crossing, next to a Metro grating where a clochard had for a time set up headquarters. A large cardboard box had served him as shelter for a while. Sometimes on Sunday mornings, he would be sitting there, reading a newspaper, a little too far off for his face to be more than a blur. Crossing him one day in the street, Alexis had been surprised to see how young he was, with a roundish, kind face, hair that, receding, gave him the air of a down-at-heel musician, his trousers tucked up comically high. His cardboard house had never been kicked over by any of the recruits who passed that way from a nearby barracks. Perhaps people weren't so bad after all. The brutal

285

and licentious soldiery – victims rather of abstract forces personified in the great of the world and as little understood even by them. Alexis had been woken up one night by the unaccustomed cold in the flat, got up, and found that the window had been badly fastened, and swung open, on what proved to be one of the coldest nights of the year. Annoyed with his own carelessness, he was shutting the window when he happened to look out. The cardboard house had its occupant. He had gone back to the warmth of his bed. I was naked, and you clothed me.

He had never before noticed the little strut sticking out over the window, like a gargoyle on Notre Dame.

A droplet of water formed, gathered, and fell from the end of a drainpipe.

A car, several cars, rise to a crescendo, waves of cars breaking over a dark sea of asphalt. They flash by. A hundred and thirty deaths over the weekend, projects into eternity. Another car at the crossing, its indicator blinking, waiting until the transecting stream of traffic ends or the lights change; expecting it to swing rapidly round into its direction. Instead, it eases gently up on to the footpath to park. A flicker of lightning through the window in the blackened sky. Not sure until the thunder follows. Yet it could kill me, instantly, a twitch, unprolonged.

Unpredictability. Our only glory.

Few men literally dig their own graves, delicacy forbids it.

The two nuns had crossed over and disappeared from view. A piece of paper ran furiously across the asphalt at the crossing, stopped suddenly as the wind dropped, shambled a little, lay prostrate in the lamplight as two cars flashed over it in rapid succession. It remained there, lifeless: waiting to be insufflated into life. Life?

That crust might save a life. Can I get it to India? Shall I wrap it up, take it to the post, ask the Government of India to distribute it? Can I get the thousands of tins of food that are going into dustbins all over the continent tonight to those who starve? Or shall I pestiferate against injustice. I was hungry and you gave me to eat. Blessed are the peace-makers. If only they were let. Peace on earth to men of goodwill (if only they were let). Peace with honour. Peace with hunger. Mankind is mankind, and the worm will gnaw withal.

Mankind? I. I for one and one for all

A man with time strapped to his wrist.

He tried to rearrange his papers, so that it would seem as if he had been working. It looked unconvincing: disorder makes itself with a greater art than anyone can deliberately put into its creation. Sure enough, the door was opening.

Frederic came out, said goodnight and left. Alexis went back in to Christine.

"You are not too tired?"

"Would you do something for me?" she asked.

"Of course," he said.

"I would like to hear some Schubert. The Schnabel record, the Impromptus. No, I have changed my mind. Schubert is too sad tonight. He died too young. You know that lovely Backhaus record, the Mozart. Could you put on the second side, the one that finishes with the 'Alla Turca?' The first part of the second side is the last part of the Concerto. I can never remember their numbers. The record has got a chair on the cover, with a little music-box figure."

"Yes, I think I know the one. It's got a kind of reddish cover."

He went into the other room, and searched through the records, arranged vaguely alphabetically.

"Here it is," he said. "It's No 27. Piano Concerto No 27. There are two movements on one side."

287

"It's the other side I want," she said. "It's got that wonderful dancing start on the piano, like the beginning of a picnic on a summer's day, and then the day wears on, and sad little memories of other days and other people no longer there come and go, and all the time there is sunshine and the little stream in the background and birds, and that little tune comes back always, gets lost and comes back again. It reminds me of the first year we were married, the first time you took me to Ireland, and we went out on a picnic in the hills above Dublin, and there was heather, and brown turf, and the sea far below and just the two of us. And we stayed out until it was dusk, and the lights began to come out all along the coast, and the sky was blue and then eggshell blue and red and golden and I have never seen anything so beautiful..."

He stood with the record in his hand, listening to her, infinitely moved, realising that, whatever else happened, he had had the extraordinary good fortune to be loved for over twenty years with the same unchanging tenderness; and he was afraid to think of the time, inexorably coming, when she would be no more.

"Put it on," she said softly.

He came back and sat on the side of the bed. The gyrating disc reflected in the polished inside of the lid. Looking at it sideways almost induced a feeling of dizziness. Perhaps the mind resents movement simultaneously in too many different planes. But the music, despite its counterpoint, moved on one plane only.

They listened in silence. He remembered, distinctly, that day in the first years of their marriage. He could recall too, the small twinges of regret for Maureen, even then; somehow he would always think of her when he saw that same sea and coast. Christine, of course, had known nothing of that. It was already almost dark when they crossed the last bit of bog before getting back to the road. From a friend with whom he had made the same walk years before, he had inherited a phrase which he brought out now: "We must cross the M'bungi country before the sun goes down." She had looked at him a moment. At times the mind plays funny tricks. On this her first visit, the knowledge that she was in a strange country was always subconsciously present. When he mentioned another foreign name with all that gravity she was startled into accepting M'bungi creeping out from behind the turf ricks, spears at the ready, lions behind the bushes, elephants, tigers, orang-outangs swinging from the pathetic strands of telephone line – and then she burst out laughing. She took his arm. They clambered up the last bank on to the road. His bad leg had the limp it would always have, so he did a kind of sailor-with-a-wooden-leg hornpipe, until they had to sit down and rest before going on to where they finally caught a bus.

Did she realise it was Mozart's last piano concerto, or had it been simply a memory – perhaps of the cover? He saw at once what she had meant. The Mozart had the gaiety, but it was subdued, as their own had been by the years and what they had brought. There was always that overtone or undercurrent in Mozart. And that was the music she had chosen to symbolise their life together... This interval between a visitor's departure and the return of Jacky and Myles seemed to have organised itself without either of them knowing why into a kind of anniversary of they knew not what.

He looked at her enquiringly as the movement came to an end.

"No," she said, "I'd like to hear that part afterwards. Now I'd like to hear the whole concerto through from the beginning. I'm being difficult, aren't I?"

For answer, he bent down and kissed her.

"Do you know what I would hate to have to decide?" she asked.

He shook his head.

"What I like best in Mozart. There are times when I think I have made up my mind. But it's really not possible. There is that wonderful duo with the two women's voices in *Figaro*. There's that introduction to the serenade in *Don Giovanni* which I love so much that I am always annoyed when the singer and the actual serenade comes to interrupt it. There is that old 78 record with the dances that we've never found on any of the other records of Mozart dances you've bought."

"There was a simple solution to that."

"What?"

"It never struck me that all I had to do was to look up the number on the old record and find a new recording in the catalogue. It is what I have just done – it's ordered."

"Lovely. But there are times when this concerto is the most beautiful of them all. Especially the larghetto. If I were a composer, I mean if I were a genius, I would only write slow movements. It's when a composer really says what he wants to say. Oh yes, now I remember, I learned a word from the cover of that record. Cantilena. Do you know what it means?"

"What does it mean, Christine?"

"It means 'a little song.' Isn't it lovely? What a wonderful language. Cantilena. Andante cantabile – it goes along singing. Could anything be lovelier?"

"You want the concerto now from the beginning?"

"Please."

He watched her mentally sorting out the themes at first and then letting the music take complete control. She grew almost tense as the movement drew to a close and then listened to the opening notes of the larghetto as if those angels so often attributed to Mozart were in fact present. It was as simple as a Fra Angelico and as touching, with an innocence that no purely human being could ever have.

The needle moved into the middle. He did not attempt to turn over the record.

"You do not want to hear the third movement again," he said.

"How did you know?" she asked, surprised.

"I just felt it."

"I might like to hear the Schubert later. But not now. Not yet. Unless there is something you want to listen to yourself?"

He shook his head and sat down again. There was a sound of a key turning in the door, and Jacky came in, dropped the books she was carrying, looked in the first room and then came across the passage.

"How are you?" she asked her mother.

Alexis thought she looked more tired than usual.

"Splendid," Christine answered. "We have just been having a private concert. Have you eaten?"

"Yes, thank you." She often ate out, either at one of the student restaurants or with friends, partly for convenience, partly because, with her mother ill, it simplified the domestic arrangements at home. "I see it's becoming a real boudoir," she said, looking at the flowers. "One of your boy friends?" she said jokingly to her mother.

"I'm not sure whether yours or mine," Christine said. "Frederic."

"His widow must have let him down again."

"Widow?"

"Didn't you know? What do you think keeps him in white sports cars? The OAS?"

"Is she the latest?" asked Alexis.

"I don't know if there is an order of precedence," said Jacky.

"I hope the flowers at least are paid for out of his own pocket," put in Christine.

"A little difficult to say what that means, if anything. Anyhow, I will say one thing for him, he has taste, in flowers at any rate; they are beautiful. How is his brother?"

"You know, I completely forgot to ask him. Did you see Myles?"

"No, I've left the key under the mat for him; it was finally I who took it this morning. I think I'll go to bed, I'm feeling a bit tired."

She had just gone to her room when there was a loud imperious ring. She came back and opened the door. Policemen were standing outside, with the concierge.

53

Myles left the café and walked for a while rather aimlessly, then found he was hungry. He entered another café and ordered a cheese sandwich and a glass of beer at the counter. News had begun to filter back of baton charges, people were talking of bottles thrown, stones, but there was no mention of an isolated group of two, one Algerian and one policeman. He left the café and had an overpowering urge to get home, away from the day and all its complications. He came to a bus stop and found that none of the routes were his. Rather than go down the Metro, he picked up a taxi. The driver, fortunately, did not seem to be in any mood for conversation.

The taxi pulled up, outside a lorry parked in front of the house. He got out and paid the fare. The driver was winding up his window again, when he suddenly shouted "Watch out". The taxi pulled away fast. Myles saw three figures converging on him, two from behind one end of the lorry, one from the other. One of them said "Police". Police, or even worse? Myles dodged round one of the trees on the avenue, getting into a position slightly more advantageous strategically.

"How do I know you are police?" he said, but had the presence of mind to say it in English. It had the effect of surprise he had hoped for. The three did not advance any further for the moment. He thought quickly. If he could make it, there was a side street he could get to with a bit of luck before any of them had time to get a gun out. Anyhow, they might not risk shooting. As they were all wearing raincoats, and he had none, he might beat them to it. After that, there was a chance that some people would be about.

"Are you foreign?" asked the one who had said "Police". "Do you want to see my card?"

293

He lifted up the hem of his coat, putting his hand into an inside pocket.

For a moment, Myles was almost convinced. After all, he had his identity card, he had nothing to fear. Then he realised that if they were OAS – for whatever reason they might want him – or plain thieves, he would be acting with all the sagacity of a pigeon if he accepted the invitation to inspect the card: while he was busy looking at it, either of the other two had merely to knock him over the head. He made a quick break for it. Rather to his surprise, he heard no footsteps, and got clear away.

That solved the immediate problem. Where did he go from there? There was the tantalising nearness of his own doorway, and he felt desperately tired. He remembered there was a police station a little further on, and on a sudden impulse entered it, thinking "After all, my father pays taxes even if I don't."

Two very relaxed-looking police were behind the counter, one writing in a kind of ledger, too used to the banalities of the human comedy to be very much surprised by anything that might be told him. He addressed himself to the one who was free and explained what had happened. The other stopped writing, and looked on curiously.

"Can you describe these three men?"

"Well, you know, they came at me from two directions just as the taxi moved away. It was so unexpected, at my own doorway, that I was more interested in not getting caught than in their appearance."

"Can I see your papers?"

Myles handed over his identity card.

As he noted down the particulars, the policeman said: "Can you remember anything at all about them?"

"Two of them had fawn raincoats, and hats. The other had what looked like a navy blue raincoat."

"Their ages?"

"Fairly young. Early thirties maybe."

"All three of them?"

"As I said, what I saw is of the vaguest. There was a story in the papers last week about a false policeman down at the Champ de Mars stopping people at night. What with that, and the OAS…"

"You are not mixed up with any political groups yourself?"

Myles' heart gave an unpleasant leap.

"No."

"You are a student, I see."

Fortunately, he seemed to lose interest in Myles at that point, and turned to the other. "Ring up and see if there was anyone on special duty around that area tonight."

The other phoned, exchanged some pleasantries with his correspondent at the other end, and then waited, his hand over the mouthpiece. Then he listened again, and came back, shaking his head.

"There should be a van back in about five minutes," he said. "The best thing would be if you did a tour round me area in it and see if you can recognise anyone like your three men. Although there is little chance of it now. The fact that they are three should be a help at least."

The van was back, sure enough, in five minutes. A sergeant came in, followed by four or five police. The sergeant went first to the phone. While he was phoning, Myles looked around curiously. He had never been in a police station before. It had the deadliness of most public offices, but somehow, for better or worse, seemed more human, especially as two of the police, to his surprise, were very young and jostled each other in various forms of horseplay, like schoolboys, and very different from the sinister flics of his hatred.

The sergeant finished his telephone conversation, came over, and listened briefly. "Right," he said, "come along."

They all went out. Myles was put sitting in the back, in a seat in the middle where he could see out through the windscreen, the sides and the back. They drove back first to the house, which looked as peaceful as it normally did at that time of night, with no sign of anyone near the door. In spite of his fatigue, Myles felt himself almost enjoying the piquancy of the situation, being driven round Paris for the first time in a Black Maria, but with the flics on his side. They made a wide detour, but no one resembling the trio was visible anywhere. In a quarter of an hour, they were back at the station.

Myles felt almost as if he were entering familiar territory the second time he entered. The policeman at the counter as he came in said:

"Was your taxi a white DS?"

Myles nodded.

"Then the mystery is solved," the policeman said to the sergeant.

"They were police?" Myles asked.

"Yes, I've just had confirmation." He smiled. "You can go peacefully home."

"Well, I'm sorry to have given you so much trouble for nothing in that case," said Myles, "but I can assure you that the way they came at me from behind that lorry wasn't calculated to inspire confidence."

"As it happens, you were innocent," said the policeman. Myles again felt that unpleasant lurch in his heart. "But," the policeman went on, "I don't know if you realise there has been an average of at least one policeman a day murdered or shot at since this OAS business started, often by people who look as respectable as you. And that is as likely to happen to us from one side as from the other, often half a dozen different sides for that matter. You mustn't blame us if we value our lives as much as the rest, and have got fed up too, finally. There is no point in risking our skins unnecessarily. Goodnight," he added, holding out his hand "and safe home."

Myles shook hands with him and left.

He wasn't altogether reassured, and decided to come back from the opposite direction, which gave him a longer unobstructed view of the front of his own house. As soon as he turned the corner, he was astonished to see the door open and the light shining out on the footpath where another police van was pulled up. He could see uniforms. As he came closer, he recognised Jacky and the concierge. Jacky was the first to see him and came running up.

"Thank God you're safe," she said, "what's been happening?"

He then noticed the white taxi parked beyond the police car. The driver's first reaction when he saw the three men advancing on Myles had been to get out of the firing line. He had then driven straight to the nearest police alarm, broken the glass and alerted the police, who came rapidly, but found no one near the house. The taxi-driver was sure of the number of the house, which he had had from Myles. The police had woken up the concierge and then quickly decided rightly there was only one family to which Myles could belong. The sergeant in charge of the police car was still upstairs, with the taxi-driver.

"Come up quickly," said Jacky as soon as the first explanations had been made, "they're in a terrible way – they don't know what has happened to you."

His mother had put on a dressing gown and had insisted on getting up. She was sitting in an armchair, trembling. All eyes turned on him as he entered with Jacky.

The sergeant was a much older man. He listened quietly as Myles explained what had happened. He then got up to go, saying:

"Well, all's well that ends well."

"You'll have a little drink before you go," said Alexis.

"Madame has had a nasty shock," he said nodding towards Christine, "I had better leave you in peace. I am sorry, Madame, that the police should have been indirectly responsible."

"It could have been so much worse," she answered: "as you said yourself, all's well that ends well."

Alexis produced a bottle and some glasses.

"The country is bad enough," said the sergeant, "if the police start drinking while on duty..."

"A small one won't do you any harm," said Alexis, "it's a bottle you don't see every day – Irish whiskey..."

"If you insist –"

"I should be getting back to my taxi," demurred the driver, as Alexis poured out a second glass.

"Five minutes more or less won't make much difference," said Alexis, "we are so grateful to both of you."

"It's hard to know what to do for the best," said the driver. "I don't mind telling you", he said, turning to the sergeant, "that I never had much love for the police. In our job, we are enemies almost by the nature of things. We try to get a client to the station to catch a train, and you whistle us for trying to get across before the light changes. Or some goddamn tourist complains, because in his country, taxis don't charge extra when luggage is put in the boot, and he thinks we're trying to cheat him. Or our lights aren't right, or we are parked in the wrong place. And then, the first time I got hit over the head by a respectable young gentleman who bravely used a stick from the back seat to lay me out and stole what I had picked up in seven and a half hours driving in the snow and slush – it was in December, the year before last. And I was there, slumped over my wheel for two hours, and people passed, and no one took any notice. The second time, it was almost identical, another of these brave young men, except that this time, there was a police control, and they had him in five minutes. Then I understood. I know what the jungle is like. I swore I'd never abandon anyone again as I was abandoned the first time. And this is what happens. I cause a whole lot of unnecessary trouble to everyone, especially this poor lady, here."

"You wouldn't say that if you knew how grateful we are to you," said Christine.

"I understand you perfectly," said the sergeant. "In two years, if I live that long, I will retire to a bungalow I've bought outside Paris, and get away from it all. I don't mind admitting there was a time when I thought it wonderful to have power and be able to use it. You know, you stop a car, a big powerful car, that cost more than you will earn in a year, even if the State didn't stop half of it in taxes, and you coldly ask the driver for his papers. And you see, with a sort of voluptuousness, that although he knows everything is in order, he's still uneasy: he knows you can always get him for something. And you keep him waiting just long enough in suspense, to show your authority, and then you return his papers, enjoying his humiliation, and curtly tell him he can go. As I say, I enjoyed that during the first few years, the sense of power over people with money and influence and all sorts of advantages in life that I never had. I've been over thirty years in the police. Then the war came and the Occupation, and we no longer knew what law we were supposed to be defending. If we arrested what we thought was a black marketeer, we could never be sure we were not arresting a patriot, and playing the game of the Germans and the collaborators. I had one son only, and he fell in the Resistance in 1944, a month before the Liberation. He was eighteen

299

years old. There's a plaque to his memory in a street down near the river. I often pass by. There is a little vase attached. Sometimes the flowers have faded. Sometimes there are new flowers. I don't know who puts them there. Someone, I suppose, who has not forgotten.

"Policemen are not supposed to think, but just to serve the legitimate government. But how can we prevent ourselves from thinking, especially as we grow older, and wonder what we have lived for? Maybe in a few months, we shall have a new government, of generals, like a South American republic. In France! What do we do? Serve? Again? Without question? My wife and I had only one ambition: to retire to our little bungalow, to grow our own cabbage, and beet, and lettuce. And then, last year, she died. So she is dead. And my son is dead, died gloriously for France. So they tell me.

"So, if I live that long, I can retire, to my own solitude. The only thing I really look forward to is the time when I need no longer regard young people as juvenile delinquents or prospective enemies of society, as I must at present. The tragedy is, I don't know whether they realise how lucky they are, or how privileged. They have a freedom we never knew. Will they prove worthy of it? They are the most beautiful generation France has ever seen. They have a chance of avoiding world wars that we never had. Do they realise it? Or will they, in turn, be as stupid as we have been?"

He noticed Myles staring at him.

"Yes," he said, as he rose "I'm talking to you, young man." He slapped Myles familiarly on the shoulder. "You no doubt, think, as all the rest of your generation have always done, that we who wear uniform are 'sales flics'. It's not important. The only thing that's important is that you should do better. Only don't stay out late with your girlfriends and break your parents' hearts."

He turned to Christine, saying: "Excuse me, madame, for having inflicted this on you with all the rest. It really is a compliment."

They all stood up, except Christine.

300

"I must go," said the sergeant ironically "I have a lot of keen young men waiting downstairs, who have a career to make."

Alexis clasped him warmly by the hand.

The sergeant turned to the door.

The driver was following, when Alexis stopped him and slipped a couple of notes into his hand. The driver wanted to refuse.

"You've already wasted over an hour of your working day," said Alexis. "Surely you have done enough for us, without making a present of your time also?"

The door closed, the lift was heard descending, and the family was alone.

Christine looked at her son.

"My poor dear," she said, "you look dead." She had recovered somewhat.

"I think we have all had enough for one day," said Alexis. "Come," he said to Christine.

She allowed herself to be led off to bed. As he settled her in, she said: "Do you think God is really so jealous of a little human happiness? A little while ago, I felt as if we were having a second honeymoon."

"You know what they say in aviation?" asked Alexis. "A pilot who crashes must be taken up again immediately so as not to lose his nerve. Would you like to hear the record again?"

"Try," she answered.

Alexis put the Mozart on again.

After five minutes she said: "No, it's no good. No doubt it will come back, but not tonight."

He took off the record, and slipped in beside her in the bed. She fell asleep peacefully in his arms.

54

Much to his own surprise, Myles slept. Perhaps it was fatigue. Perhaps one experience that night temporarily cancelled out the other. At any rate, he slept.

The one member of the household who did not sleep was Jacky. Her fears were growing, not yet confirmed. She tried to consider the situation calmly, but found she could not. She had thought she was in love with Hassim but, after this evening, one thing was painfully clear, he was not in love with her. She tried to remember the warmth of his parting kiss, but knew she was deceiving herself. It meant nothing. She had just naively intruded on something which was alien to anything she had ever known, a being, a way of thinking utterly different from her own, something which resented and rejected her, even perhaps despised her in consequence. For the first time, she thought of the impossibility of ever accommodating herself to people whose minds worked like that, of living among people who thought, no doubt, like him, that awful rigidity, that self-immolation before a god whom they made in the image of their own ideals, hard, harsh, unbending; by comparison, the god of her convent school, although difficult and unreasonable at times, seemed warm, ready to forgive, merciful, human. But no, she thought for a moment, it is Hassim himself who is different from other people, even his own, hard maybe but unique, and it is that which attracted me to him in the first place. And then she thought, with a new feeling of despair, that it is not enough that I should be attracted to him if he just despises me. She had a sudden angry feeling: who is he to despise me, anyway. But that was no solution either. What if, inside me at this moment, is growing a third being who will be heir to all our incompatibilities?

Then she remembered the ring at the door, the shock of finding the policeman there with the concierge. Had Myles at last done the

303

irreparable? He was quite capable of it. Her first thought had been of her parents. Then at the sergeant's first words, it had seemed that the situation might be even worse. Had he been kidnapped, or perhaps killed? She had tried desperately to think of a way of preventing the news from getting any further, but her father had come out, and invited the others in. There had been no hiding anything, even from her mother who heard everything through her open door on to the passage and got up to come into the other room.

Seeing her condition, the sergeant had tried to choose his words, but it was already too late, and there was no alternative to hearing the truth as he knew it. No longer knowing what to do, Jacky had left them to it and gone downstairs, in the crazy hope that she would in some miraculous way be able to conjure Myles back again. She had thought first she might be going hysterical when she thought she saw him turning the corner at the top of the avenue; but it was really him.

With the unpredictability of her disease, Christine seemed to have taken the shock better than either Jacky or her father. Perhaps, to her, Myles' unexpected appearance was like one of the God-given remissions which she had several times known, and generated an analogous optimism.

In any case, Myles had proved the innocent victim of circumstances over which he had no control, and he could not be blamed for what had happened. Whereas she, who often felt the more mature of the two although he was the older, had consciously got herself into a situation from which she could see no issue – unless, she thought grimly, an unwanted child. If her mother knew, the shame might kill her, and the effect on her father was unimaginable.

And the child itself, if child there really be? Impossible in character, maybe, as its father, but born with none. Born to a mother whom, deprived of a father, it might grow up to hate, innocent cause perhaps, of its grandmother's death...

Jacky remembered Frederic with a sudden affection, wondering why she had always been so hard to him. He might be every type of adventurer, vain but, even when he sold his services for money, never really mercenary.

How many other relations visited her mother so regularly? Who had ever brought flowers like he had brought this evening? Perhaps he was stupid, irresponsible, but at least he was warm and human: it was at least better than cold, self-righteous virtue. She decided she would go and see him. Perhaps he at least could advise her. She could not bring herself to think of the advice she wanted from him. Exhausted, she at last fell asleep.

55

Myles woke at six, and was immediately awake. The final events of the evening before would have seemed comic had it not been for his mother and the shock which she seemed to have absorbed and almost digested but, in her physical condition, could not possibly have done so. That was something that must be taken as philosophically as possible. Painful as it was, it had been the result of a malignant combination of extraneous circumstances.

It was the Algerian knife that really haunted him. How long ago had it been? Nine, ten hours ago only. He could still imagine it plunging into his own side, into his heart, almost feel the coldness of the steel in his flesh, and an end to everything, including the warmth of his present bed. The knife had gone. But he had a slow motion picture of the Algerian gradually gaining consciousness first, feeling the wound – in his stomach it had seemed – and, seeing his enemy close and helpless setting out across the metre or two that separated them, and strangling the policeman, until his face went black or purple and his tongue hung out like that of a head on a butcher's block.

Myles tried to reassure himself, saying that the policeman had only been stunned. Even if he were not the first to come to, some passers-by were bound to come that way – the street was, after all, in the centre of Paris. The quarter had been full of police. The policeman had no reason to kill the Algerian – he had only to hand him over. And then Myles remembered his other fear, of the Algerian bleeding to death from his wound, and no one caring, while I lie here snug in my comfortable bed...

He knew the concierge left a newspaper at about eight – the *Figaro*, the sort of paper his father would take. He heard the lift, judged that it must be the concierge with the mail and the papers. No one else seemed to be up. He went cautiously to the door, picked up the paper and went back to his room.

As he had already gathered in his second café visit last night, the clash which had at one time been feared had not materialised. In terms of injuries to police and demonstrators, the night had been rough, but not catastrophic. A flashlight photograph showed the faces of a corner of the crowd, but it might just as well have been a photograph of a nocturnal football match, the faces startled by the flash rather than by what was happening. He went through the paper again, hoping to get some news of his own particular happening. But no. The literary box on the front page, the usual sententious editorial, the so-called revelations about the Communist Party, the supercilious theatre column... What a bloody paper. If the policeman had been killed, or picked up badly injured, there would certainly be a report. If the Arab had died – well, who would care. He threw the paper down in disgust, glad for a moment of the anger, which temporarily stifled his anxiety, and then began to wonder desperately how he could find out. He knew how careful he must be – the police would be only too anxious to interview whoever had tripped up their colleague, and they might be expected to forget to put on the kid gloves beforehand.

He decided he could not face the others that morning. To ensure they would not start worrying about a second disappearance, he left a note saying he had gone to an early lecture.

On the way to the Metro, he bought the remaining morning papers. He went first class, but even that was packed, so he had to wait until he got out at the other end and could install himself in a café. Nothing. There was a difference in presentation, but that was all. The papers had an irritating familiarity, the staleness of the already seen.

He was sitting at a table on a terrace. A policeman passed, looking as if he were searching for something to do. Myles thought he glanced suspiciously over, and had an instant's panic. He remembered reading of murderers buying all the papers available in order to read about themselves. Then he thought there were a thousand legitimate reasons why he should have bought several papers that morning. Nothing happened. The policeman merely passed on. But Myles realised that he was in a dangerous condition. People gave themselves away in the most ridiculous ways. Last night's flic might already be out on his rounds again: he would have forgotten that, even if Myles had tripped him up in the first place, he had certainly saved his life a few seconds later. That wouldn't count. And then, the Algerian?

Perhaps *France-Soir* would have something. The first edition, dated a few days hence, would be out before midday. How was he to pass the time until then? The papers were in disorder round him, the coffee had been brought already slopped into the saucer and now looked even worse, with the cup empty. He could order another coffee, but he didn't want one. There were other things in the papers, but he did not want to read them.

He might have realised he would not be too long sitting where he was without someone he knew passing. He looked up and saw Solange looking towards him, uncertain whether to join him or go to a table on her own. She smiled and came over. He hurriedly gathered up the papers and put them on a chair at the next table.

"You only need one paper to get the lottery results," she said. "It's the only thing I ever buy a paper for. I can see what's on at the cinemas around here by just looking at them. It's good exercise walking from one to the other."

Myles did not know her very well, and was rather flattered that she had joined him. She was an attractive girl who went to no trouble to hide the fact from herself. She had very dark hair that said Spain, perhaps, and eyes that immediately belied it, being of some indeterminate colour between grey-blue and green.

"I never rightly knew what you were doing," said Myles.

"You are not the only one," she answered. "Officially, I am studying English and Spanish. That happened by accident. Part of my family is Spanish – my mother is half-Spanish in fact."

"And the other half?"

"Hungarian."

"Sounds like an explosive mixture."

"How nice of you to say so."

"You must have an Irish grandmother."

"How did you guess?"

"All the best people have."

"Do you see my eyes?"

Myles looked.

"I expect to make my fortune from them," she continued. "They are Hungarian. If I hadn't got them that colour, I would have painted them in."

"But what colour do you call it?"

"Can't you see they're green?"

"Depends on the light, I think."

"How sweet of you to say so. I'd really like to have kaleidoscopic eyes. Green as a sort of foundation, but the other shades so that I could match my clothes."

"Is that very important?"

"Capital."

"Do you believe genius is an infinite capacity for taking pains?"

"Who said that? Some bore like..."

"Victor Hugo?"

"Was it?"

"Damned if I know."

"Well, in any case, he's got it all wrong: it's an infinite capacity for getting others to take pains for you."

"Are you a genius?"

"Not yet. But I think I was born one. The rest is only a matter of cultivating it."

"What makes you think you were born one – apart from what is obvious to everyone, that is?"

"Well, first of all, my mother is a genius."

"How?"

"She married a rich man, a very rich man. And then she had an only child – me."

"But that might be only chance. I believe most rich men are fools."

"It wasn't chance in her case. It's very simple, really. All you have to do is concentrate on one thing, and not bother about the rest. When you are rich enough you don't have to have an infinite capacity for... whatever it was you said. Everybody else is only too happy to look after that side of it. I understood that very young. I started off practising on my parents, and wound them round my little finger. And the nice thing, when you're rich, is that it doesn't hurt – you see, they could pay nurses, and maids and chauffeurs and governesses – and all that sort of thing and even feel virtuous about it – looking after me and giving employment. And then, last year, my father suddenly got mean. I wanted one of those adorable little Sunbeam cars. He told me I would have to get my degree first. Can you imagine? What on earth do I want with a degree? I think he's going a bit soft in the head. Does he really want me to become that sort of genius? Have you ever seen the head of a normalien or a polytechnicien? They shrivel up. I really think they must be born shrivelled. It stands to reason. The more you pack into your head, the tighter you pack the skin – look at that handbag, for example, the condition it's in, and all because I forced a couple of books and a small parcel and a pair of slippers into it – all cracked and wrinkled. But I'll get my own back. Spanish may be just an accident, but English isn't. All the richest men are Englishmen. Are you rich?" she asked suddenly.

"Do I look it?"

"I never go by externals. After all, John D. Rockefeller was no Gary Cooper. Have you not got fabulously rich parents at least?"

"They are revoltingly unrich."

"Or an uncle at death's door with a large share in a South African gold mine? Or better still, make it diamonds."

"Not one."

"Pity. Apart from that I rather like you. I might even have considered you. I suppose you think you would have to be consulted about that?"

"It is usual, isn't it?"

"Only with mediocrities."

"You mean you need both a very rich man and a genius?"

"Do you think I will settle for less?"

"But even if he is a very rich genius, he might be a bastard in every other way."

311

"If he's rich enough, that's immaterial."

"Do you never think of anything else?"

"Haven't time. Yet."

"The Algerian war for example?"

"Is it that? The solution is so simple that only a politician couldn't see it."

"What's that?"

"Give them their independence, and then dump every one of them that's come here across the other side of the Mediterranean. We can do without their labour. The only thing that would be any good – what we really need – are maids, and Algerian women are like certain wines, they don't travel. Any other problems?"

"Do you ever think of what it costs to produce your one very rich man? Have you ever seen a bidonville in your life, or visited an industrial suburb of Paris?"

"You are not going to start all that old story so early on a fine sunny morning?"

"Well, as the question is asked, answer it, and I promise not to ask any more."

"The answer is, I have been to a bidonville. It was full of Portuguese. They all arrived in the last few years. Nobody forced them to come. So presumably they came because they thought it better here. If not, nobody is stopping them from going back. And my father was rich long before they came, so it cannot be by taking anything from them that he became rich. Have I answered your question?"

"Yes and no. But a promise is a promise. Do you feel like a walk?"

312

"I do."

"Where?"

"Along the quais, where else?"

"Not many rich men there. Clochards and beatniks."

"But lots of nice houses. I'll show you the one I'm going to have. Come on."

They had got as far as St Julien-le-Pauvre when she suddenly stopped. "What a fool I am," she said, "I can't go with you. I have an appointment with the hairdresser at half past ten. I completely forgot about it."

"Couldn't you put it off?"

"Remember what I told you. You've got to concentrate on the most important things."

"But your hair is splendid as it is."

"A man knows nothing about the inner secrets of a woman's hair."

"You won't be persuaded?"

"I can't, I really am sorry."

She picked up a taxi and disappeared.

Myles felt lost. She was crazy but amusing, and for a little while he had forgotten everything else, not even bothering to contradict her outlandish statements. It wasn't the first time he had noticed that a girl who is attractive enough can say anything and get away with it. But now she'd left him as abruptly as she had appeared, to brood on his own truths. A fat woman walked in front of him. She was not even fat. Only she looked fat from behind in her black leather coat, creaking like the timbers of a ship in the wind. The great bulk of Notre-Dame looked serene as ever, sphinx of many secrets. St Julien, nearer, was small as a village church: in fact, the little surrounding green made it look like one. Churches, great and small, had a life of their own, independent of the Church. From the corner, he could see St Severin. Remembering one Sunday afternoon concert he had been to, he decided to go in. He was lucky. The sun was out, and illuminated from outside the upper stained glass windows. A sacristan was preparing the altar, and had switched on some of the lights, so that Myles could see the extraordinary pillar behind the altar which, contrasting with all the others that helped to form the nave and the curve beyond, had seemed to him one of the most beautiful objects he had ever seen. He remembered being so fascinated by it that he had scarcely heard the concert. It looked just as beautiful now. He sat down, and just looked, and for a while, forgot everything else.

Apart from the sounds made by the sacristan as he went about his work, the silence was complete. Once the siren of an ambulance – perhaps a fire engine – filtered through, but it seemed far away, from another life. He was intrigued by the oldness of churches, but found they had an insidious effect on him. He had not been brought up as he had for nothing and, unless his guard was up, he often found himself thinking thoughts that had since become heretical to him, as if his new certainties did not exist. One time he had decided to write an article attacking St Paul. It was after reading another article which argued that the communism of Christ might have inaugurated communism two thousand years earlier if it hadn't been for St Paul, the original manager, the dogmatist, the woman hater, be subject to princes and powers, obey at a word. He had decided quite firmly at the age of fifteen that he could not believe in a Church which had been guilty of the Inquisition, or a god who could have allowed the concentration camps. He had shocked his mother more than his father, refusing conformity, at any cost, to what he no longer not only did not believe in, but positively despised and hated. His sense of alienation from his home dated from then. He could see what the effect was on his mother. Things got worse when she became ill, not long afterwards, and still worse when it became known that she had cancer.

He had taken down the New Testament and turned to the Acts of the Apostles and the various epistles of St Paul, decided to search out the most damning passages. Instead, he felt anew all the urgency of the words. He read again with wonder the account of Paul's interview with the Romans, with Felix and Festus, and then Agrippa. "In a little thou persuadest me to become a Christian." "And Agrippa said to Festus: 'this man might be set at liberty, if he had not appealed to Caesar.'" It was pure Greek tragedy. The great machinery of State had been set in motion by Paul himself and would go on remorselessly to the ineluctable end. He had skipped impatiently, searching for what he wanted to find, and fell again and again on passages of a poetry which seemed to leap out of the pages as live and moving as if two thousand years had not passed meanwhile. And the extraordinary pathos of Paul's farewells, knowing that his time on this earth was coming to an end. "The night is passing and the day is at hand." "It is a more blessed thing to give, rather than to receive." "And when he had said these things, kneeling down, he prayed with them all. And there was much weeping among them all; and falling on the neck of Paul, they kissed him. Being grieved most of all for the word he had said, that they should see his face no more. And they brought him on his way to the ship."

Myles had realised he was in the presence of something bigger than he could yet understand.

He did not write his article.

Now, again, the church became something more than a conglomeration of old stones, beautiful even by their age. His thought stretched back, joined hands with memories. Latin phrases he was beginning to forget, and a whole world of fervour that had gone sour as a disappointed love but now, for a few moments, evoked all the tenderness of an old photo. The central pillar was startlingly beautiful. He could imagine it, a fossilised tree of good and evil, from some Garden of Eden in a Cranach painting, with powers that transmuted its component stone and transcended even the beauty of form and shape.

He was beginning to feel an old frustration – the mind's inability to concentrate on a thing of beauty it has been lucky enough to find, the compulsion to move on to something else and come back again later, knowing full well that the same beauty will not be there next time, but urged away just the same – when the organ began to play, very softly. Someone was practising. The thread of music was just enough, like a slight adjustment of a control, to bring his mind back on to the right wavelength, and allow his attention to concentrate again on the pillar. Outside there now were clouds, and the stained glass windows changed colour as the sun came and went. He sat watching until the organ which had re-established his mood now shattered it with a number of experimental blasts.

As he went towards the door, a sound like a distant shot, which might have been only a car backfiring, reminded him that there were other realities in Paris and in his own life at that moment. Leaving he saw the word 'Samaritan' on a notice. A man went down from Jerusalem to Jericho, and fell among thieves who also stripped him, and having wounded him went away, leaving him half dead. And a Levite passed by. And a priest. But a certain Samaritan, seeing him, was moved with compassion, and bound up his wounds, and brought him to an inn. And whatsoever thou shalt spend over and above, I, at my return, will repay thee.

I did not pass by: I ran. A man with his belly shot open, thanks to me, and I ran.

He felt suddenly angry at the injustice of everything: there was always a smug parable ready to get you in the wrong. Justice, human or eternal, poised always, waiting, ready to pounce, but never coming down to take its chance in the streets and the houses and the market places where men live; smug, superior, aloof, and finally despicable.

Nothing changes, only the actors. Notre Dame across the river, Master François Villon perhaps walked this same route, pilgrims to Compostela, Santiago, the Resistance; across the opposite side of the island, the Conciergerie, where, so many had awaited death in the first great revolution. The Hôtel-Dieu (did he put up there on visits to Paris?), the Palais de Justice, the Quai des Orfèvres, where the technicians no longer took watches to pieces, but people, their brains, their lives, their past, their crimes, their histories. Perhaps my Algerian is there at this moment.

It was not yet midday, but the first editions of the evening papers were already on sale. He bought one. Still nothing, probably. No, he was wrong. The reporters must have been working hard and late. The paper already carried a detailed report, from several contributors, on the events of the previous night. A newspaper does not live on statistics: the stories were all angled on the human interest, and he went eagerly through them. Shots had been fired, and a number of arrests made. Several people had been wounded at one point, including some Algerians, but there was not enough detail to allow Myles to identify his own particular incident. At least no deaths were announced. He had not bothered to look at the other reports, and only by chance noticed one with a large headline when he was on the point of throwing the paper away. An Algerian who had stabbed the woman he had been living with had been arrested by a policeman after a chase which had ended by the policeman firing on him. Myles went breathlessly through the report, hoping not to find the confirming detail he half expected to see. He remembered that horrible knife again. It was too awful to imagine that his bungling had gone to that extent: that far from making an already doubtful contribution to freedom in Algeria, he had only got himself mixed up with a sordid murder. From the report, it was impossible to say either way.

He began to feel that it was extraordinarily difficult to be a revolutionary. Previously, the issues had seemed simple. When it came to putting ideas into practice, a thousand complicating details cropped up to obscure the issue. Perhaps it was necessary to act mechanically, to be a machine. But a machine did not act of its own accord either. It needed direction. So the difficulty was merely shoved a stage back. Worst of all were the relations with human beings. A revolution, finally, was made with, by, on, against others, each the centre of a complex of relationships. His mother. A true revolutionary should be alone. Only alone was one free. Free to act, that is. Even then. Suppose the Algerian were in the hospital beside Notre-Dame, just across the river, some special semi-prison section of it, if one existed. Could he visit him? Myles remembered the knife again, the hatred on the Algerian's face when the knife was struck from his hand. Visit him for what? What had he to say, or to be told? How could he find out in the first place where the Algerian was? Only the police could tell, and he could not approach them without giving his own part in the incident away. He was a criminal before the law under several headings. If he dared enquire, he would be caught even before he saw the Algerian. Playing the policemen's game in fact.

He had never seen the inside of a French prison, except for a few dungeons in chateaux that had now become folklore. But he had once seen what remained of the Mathausen concentration camp in Austria. Looking at the blank walls, the remains of the ovens, he had tried to visualise what the place had been and failed. It was as hard to imagine as to relate Dumas to the stones of the dungeons he had seen; his mind would not believe that what had happened there could have been true. But all these became the prototypes of prisons in his mind – his mind, despite himself, so bourgeois in its reactions; the prototype of a horror which it was unthinkable that he should ever suffer in the flesh. He thought almost with envy, of those from poorer homes who could regard prison with a picaresque disdain, a necessary apprenticeship, inevitable as measles or whooping cough; and felt diminished by the comparison.

Perhaps it was an experience he needed.

If only he were alone.

But he was not.

His father he would not have minded. Jacky would understand, might even, in a way, be proud of him. The real difficulty was his mother. Everything he did seemed to rebound and hit or hurt her. It was not only when he had broken with religion. Even the most anodyne conversation seemed to go wrong – as on that occasion when he had referred to his father as a bourgeois. What else was he, in any case? Even last night, she had been very gentle, but he knew how much of a shock the events of the evening must have been to her – so again, he had unwittingly hurt her, not wilfully, but unwittingly, malignant circumstances in which he had been the victim much more than she. If he were sent to prison now, it might easily kill her.

He went into a cinema which opened early, came out in the late afternoon, bought another paper. He bought several papers more, but found out nothing.

The incident took on a certain nightmare quality. He transposed it in dreams. He had a dream of another German invasion, with a German army infiltrating everywhere, but only taking up position, no actual fighting. Someone said it would be better than last time, as there were only a third of them this time to do the same damage. Trying to puzzle out where the advantage lay in that, Myles found he had written a liquid play which he kept in a jam jar with the lid tightly screwed on. But his mother threw it out and washed the jam jar. He now keeps the jam jar at home, with a label, and insists that it shall never be used for anything else; he would present it to a museum when he died.

Then he felt himself coming up the stairs. There were three cats on top. How did they get in? Perhaps he might turn a hose on them. One began to come down, defiantly. The stairs were terribly steep. He tried to get a kick at it, but he knew beforehand he would miss, that his foot would not move quickly enough. It was then he saw the hole in the ceiling: he could see up, but whoever is above can certainly see down...

He woke up one morning at 3.30 and heard squealing. A lorry had stopped at the traffic lights, full of pigs, apparently. On their way to an abattoir?

He went back to sleep. Hassim brought in a small sculpted figure which he made comic by putting on a pair of his own shoes and a straw hat, and succeeded in making it stand up in the shoes. Then he laid it out flat. The arms began to move, then the head. Myles was astonished and decided he would like to have it. Hassim was absolutely nonchalant. The sergeant was present, but had somehow become de Gaulle. Myles no longer wanted the sculpture. He suggested that de Gaulle should claim it on behalf of the Republic, which he good-humouredly agreed to do. Myles realised that it wasn't very seemly to be naked during the ceremony and then, very sly, suggested that de Gaulle should note it down on a piece of paper Myles was holding (a label from a bottle?) Again he agreed, solemnly noted the accession of the sculpture to France. Myles started to grin, de Gaulle also, but his aide-de-camp wasn't at all amused. What a splendid story it would be to tell, and show the autographed copy to everyone.

But before that could happen, he was autographing copies of his own books for a stout woman and her husband. She explained that she had learned a lot from television and Reader's Digest and obviously regarded herself as her husband's intellectual superior. She explained to him that Myles would do no harm by autographing the book; that that would not reduce its value. She smiled at her husband and said: 'Culture is a thing in itself. It caught on, just like that. People realised that a book is indicative, not consultative.' Myles was trying to make out what she meant (although he knew perfectly well) when he noticed that he had forgotten his autographed label, but could find it nowhere and woke up, desperate, without his charter signed Charles de Gaulle.

He never discovered what happened to the Algerian. But the blood shed seemed to have established some sort of a kinship, of guilt perhaps. He had run away. He had been unable to face prison. A test had been proposed, and he had failed. It left him morose and miserable.

56

One war seemed to melt imperceptibly into another. The first did not so much end as peter out in an attempted assassination and a series of futile explosions. All the time, the war at the other end of the earth was growing in violence, intensity, and in the bitterness of the hatred that was radiating from it all over the world.

Jacques had been killed with three others in a jeep which was blown up by a mine shortly after he had gone to Algeria.

Christine had a good spell, so good that she was able to stay up for most of the day. The whole family had dinner together fairly often in the evenings. Alexis who, in view of the state of her health, had been undecided about his proposed trip to Dublin, felt there was no reason why he should not go. It would only be a few days in any case, so no great risk was involved. One evening at dinner, he announced that the Monsignor, his brother, was calling in, on his way back from some Commission in Rome.

"He won't find me here," said Myles. "I suppose he'd want me to kiss his ring. I'd as soon kiss his –"

He stopped as he saw his mother's expression.

"You might as well say it as think it," she said quietly.

He felt angry. Then he relaxed, and said with a grin, "Well, I don't want to kiss that either."

He so seldom smiled these days that she was disarmed by the grin.

"Why are you always so aggressive?" asked Jacky. "Anyhow, Monsignors' rings don't have to be kissed, do they?"

She looked enquiringly at Alexis.

"No," he answered, "nothing less than a bishop."

"But I thought that's what the jamboree in Rome was all about" said Myles, "that they were finally going to finish with all that mumbo-jumbo. After all, it went out even here with the aristocracy nearly two hundred years ago."

"You are forgetting one thing," said Jacky.

"What?" he asked.

"Why are you so sure he will want to see you?"

"Surely he will want to save my soul for me?"

"It never occurred to you that your uncle might be a very intelligent man?" asked Alexis.

"If he is, what's he doing in that outfit?"

"He might well ask what you were doing in some of the ones you get mixed up with."

"Everyone seems to be asking questions tonight, and no one answering," said Myles, "if I tried to answer that one, it would only seem pretentious. And anyhow, you would not understand."

"You don't think that last remark pretentious?" asked Christine, crossly.

"Let it pass," said Alexis. "Go on, tell us just the same."

"You would think two world wars were enough for anyone," said Myles. "What was it, forty million in the last one? But no. We had

322

Indochina, and then we had Algeria and before that's over, we're back in Vietnam again. I suppose it's all the fault of the communists? – Even though the Chinese, for example, walked through a large part of India and could as easily have taken the rest, but they just went home. Nevertheless, they are still causing the war, not the Americans, who are only defending the Vietnamese by bombing, burning and slaughtering them."

"What did you do to stop the war in Algeria?" asked Alexis.

Remembering his policeman episode, Myles looked suspiciously at him. But there seemed to be nothing ulterior behind the question.

"Or if you blame me, for example, for the Second World War, why did you let the war in Vietnam happen; or why don't you stop it now?"

"I don't think that question funny," Myles answered.

"It wasn't meant to be funny," said Alexis, "you don't think there is any comparison?"

"I didn't create the situation that led to the war in Algeria, or the war in Vietnam."

"You are about the age I was when Hitler started his war. All I am asking is if you have done any more to prevent or stop this war than I did to stop Hitler?"

"I have at least taken part in some demonstrations," Myles answered, and then angrily felt that his reply was absurdly lame.

"As far as I can see," said Alexis, "most demonstrations of that sort are mutual admiration societies preaching to the convinced who don't need converting, more concerned with making capital of their moral superiority than with stopping people from being senselessly slaughtered."

"You do more by sitting in your armchair and reflecting? Or maybe praying?"

"I grant you," said Alexis, "that there may be a cumulative effect on public opinion. But on one condition: that they really are spontaneous. They don't impress me very much in countries which vote ninety-nine per cent for a single list in what are called elections – as their masters order."

"No one ordered me," Myles retorted.

"That's because you happen to live in backward degenerate France."

"What's the good of arguing with you? You always get back to the same old thing."

"In other words you have no reply?" Alexis said provokingly.

"You admitted yourself that the world was rotten in 1939, that it was rotten ten years ago, and that it's still rotten. But there is nothing wrong with the world itself. There is lots for everyone, if only it were fairly distributed. And it's no good asking the rich, who control governments and armies and police, to do anything about it. It seems perfectly simple and obvious to me. The landlord lives quite happily, he has his land for free; the peasant gets his bit of land, down in the cemetery. As the peasant outnumbers the landlord a thousand or maybe fifty thousand or a hundred thousand to one, he is a mug to go on accepting it. As I say, it seems perfectly simple and obvious to me."

"Did it ever strike you that you are not the first to have found the world all wrong, and who wanted to do something about it?"

"It did, Professor."

"Don't be impertinent to your father," Christine put in.

"That's all right," Alexis said. "This is a man to man discussion. No holds barred."

"Thank you," Myles said. "Lenin not only saw the simple fact I mentioned just now, but acted on it."

"I know what comes next," said Alexis.

"And you're afraid to let me say it?"

"Not a bit of it. Except that we've had all that out before, both your arguments and mine. But if you insist..."

Myles felt a bit deflated. He shook his head.

"No, you go on," he said.

"When I was going to school," said Alexis, "we still had oil lamps. I don't know if you can imagine what a job it is, filling oil lamps, with the smell of paraffin everywhere, some of it inevitably spilling over. Small rags. Wicks that had to be trimmed and adjusted, and the sooty part got on your hands. And that dirty unpleasant job had to be done every day of your life. It seemed an impossible dream that one day, all that would be abolished, and you could have light simply by moving a switch, clean, effortless, for as long as you liked. But it happened. Soon practically every house had electricity. But people's lives were not lengthened by a beautiful gift of an extra hour of light a day and the end of a tiresome job. The hour just disappeared. It wasn't paradise yet."

No one had noticed how pale Jacky had become. She got up quickly and left the room.

"Whatever is the matter with that girl?" said Christine, "she seems to do nothing recently but get sick."

Myles had a sudden return of a suspicion he had almost forgotten.

325

57

Jacky could no longer have any doubt. She lived in constant terror, and no one in whom she could confide. As yet there were no obvious physical signs, but she was afraid her mother would guess what her sudden indispositions must mean. She did her best to keep out of sight when she felt them coming on, but last night was not the first time she had been caught unawares. And anyhow, unless she did something about it, it would only be a matter of time.

What she feared most of all for the present was that her mother would discuss it with her father. As a doctor, he must certainly reach the inevitable conclusion. With her mother, ill as she was, it was bad enough; at least she was a woman, and after the first shock, she might accept the situation. Alexis, she knew, would not behave like an outraged Victorian father – it would have been easier to face if he did. No; with that ready sympathy he had for the troubles of others, he would think first of her and of what had to be done. There would be no reproaches. Instead his pain would be hidden, and corrode within, to the measure of the enormous tenderness she knew he had for her. She had always been his favourite. She remembered how he had never been able to bring himself to say a hard word to her. She knew what an effort it already cost him to hide his anguish over Christine's illness; she could hardly bear to think what this new blow, so undeserved and from so unexpected a quarter, might mean to him.

If only she were not living at home. But, with her mother so ill, it was out of the question to think of trying to find a room somewhere else. She deliberately avoided Myles as much as possible.

She had been to see Hassim a few times since. He recovered rapidly. One evening she tensed herself to tell her secret. He was the first to know. For the first time, also, she learned something about his background, and it confirmed the impression she had originally formed. He was in fact something of a notable in his own country and, with the departure of the French from Algeria, might become something much more important. As far as she could gather there were tribal, almost dynastic issues involved. And they included a betrothal that had already taken place. Although she was by then quite sure that she was not in love with him, and realised that she had acted with almost lunatic recklessness, she could not prevent herself from feeling bitter. His coldness irritated her, the humourless sense of mission that seemed to be his only driving force. He left Paris soon after, without their ever having as much as exchanged addresses.

She had also, as she intended, arranged to see Frederic. He had been delighted by the unexpected initiative on her side. He had taken her to an excellent restaurant, where the wine had banished some of the unaccustomed shyness she always evoked in him. He grew mildly flirtatious. She was in no mood for tenderness. When she finally got round to mentioning Hassim, she found a slightly malicious pleasure in telling him of her Algerian friend, and then was rather touched to see that he had the good manners not to comment further, and then she found herself unable to tell the whole story.

In despair, she now felt he was her last resort. They met in a café, in the late afternoon. Frederic arrived, rather surprised at the seriousness of her voice when she had telephoned asking him to meet her. This time, rather than risk finding herself again unable to tell him, she went straight to the point almost as soon as they were sitting down. He listened in silence, then said:

"The black bastard."

In spite of herself, she almost smiled. She would have expected the racism but, with his marital and other backgrounds, Frederic was hardly fitted to play the role of Sir Galahad. Then she said quickly:

"He's neither one nor the other."

"If I get my hands on him, he'll be both," he said, without explaining how that surprising operation could be performed. Again

327

she had that ambiguous feeling, and felt ashamed of it. Now he was the only one she could turn to. She had never treated him seriously, or condescended to take any notice of him, although well aware of the tenderness he had for her. She knew how much in consequence he must be hurt by what she had just told him. And yet his first thought was of her, and protective, and she felt badly in need of protection. He said nothing for a while, thinking, and then asked:

"What are you going to do?"

"I don't know," she said hopelessly. "If I was the only one involved... But you know the position at home, with my mother. And I can't bear to think of my father. Apart from anything else, he is not so well either. He should have had an operation some time ago, and postponed it because of my mother."

"But your own life. You can't allow your life to be ruined. You don't want to be saddled for the rest of your life..."

He stopped suddenly, and muttered: "I'm sorry."

They were both silent. Finally he said:

"There is a doctor I know who was in the army with me. I could give him a ring. And no, on second thoughts, better not. He is sure his telephone is tapped. Come on, I'll take you there."

She followed him obediently, glad that some decision had been taken.

The doctor greeted Frederic effusively. He looked appreciatively at Jacky and then asked them to wait while he finished a consultation with a patient. Frederic managed to ask for a private word with him as he was showing them to a room away from his professional quarters. The doctor looked quizzically at him, grinned and nodded. Somewhat embarrassed, Frederic rejoined Jacky.

"Turn the television on if you feel like it," said the doctor to Frederic. "You know where the drinks are. I won't be long."

Frederic seemed quite at home. The flat was on the ground floor, with a French window opening on to a little garden at the back. Jacky did not want a drink, so Frederic did not bother either.

"It's useful at certain times to have a back door," said Frederic, and Jacky realised she was in an ex-OAS hideout that might still be operational. So that's why the phone was tapped. "You see that light over the television set?"

He went over and switched it on and off.

"A perfectly ordinary light, as you can see. Except that if it goes on or off of its own accord, it means someone has switched it from the front room, where you can see any police coming from the street."

He had hardly said the words when the light went on again. Jacky at first thought he had switched it. His face was startled for a moment. Then it broke into a grin.

"He's pulling my leg. I am sure the police are no longer on the watch."

Almost immediately there was a sharp ring at the door. Frederic grabbed her bag from the table, looked quickly round to make sure they had left nothing else, took her arm and hustled her through the door and out the back on to a different street. He had parked the car some distance from the house, and did not speak until they were safely seated in it.

"They've nothing on me, or on him either as far as I know, but it's just as well to take no chances."

Jacky was pale.

"I'm sorry," he said. "What a rotten piece of luck that that should happen this very evening. I'll try to get in touch with him tomorrow."

Still she did not speak. He looked over again and saw she was very near to tears. He drove off, to get away, without having any particular destination in mind, and finally came to a halt in a quiet square near the Champs-Elysées. She stared out of the windscreen, without looking at him, and then said:

"I've made up my mind, Frederic. What I've started I must go through with."

Misunderstanding her, he answered:

"Of course. Don't you worry. I'll see him for you tomorrow, and if he can't help, he'll send us to someone who will."

"I don't mean that," she said. "I mean that I am going to have the child, whatever happens."

He stared at her helplessly, in consternation. He knew that hard determination that so seldom showed but, when it did, was unshakeable.

"But Jacky," he began, and stopped, knowing it would be useless.

She turned towards him at last, and held out her hand.

"Thank you for everything, Frederic," she said, "you are a good friend."

"Can't I take you somewhere?"

"No, thank you. For the moment I would just like to walk, and to think things over. I don't know what I'll do next."

"Let me take you at least to where you want to begin your walk."

She shook her head.

"It doesn't matter. As well here as anywhere else."

"If there is anything I can do..."

Again she shook her head.

"I am always at the other end of a phone."

She kissed him rapidly, got out of the car and turned away. He felt a sorrow deeper than anything he had ever known. It was as if a mirage of something potentially good and beautiful that he had never realised went round a corner with her, and out of his own life.

58

The Monsignor lit a cigarette.

"It's a wonderful place, Rome," he said. "You've got the past around you anywhere your eye alights, and your own past every time you get that marvellous whiff of coffee out a doorway – and that of course is all the time. Coffee may be as good in other countries, although I doubt it, but I don't think it could anywhere have the same power of evocation as in Rome. It's not just memories of other visits that it brings back, but a kind of kaleidoscope of them all. And once you have ever been there, the mere mention of certain words – Forum, Capitol, Coliseum, Tiber, catacombs, chianti, Stazione Termini... "

"It's true," said Alexis, "as you spoke, I don't know how many images flashed across my mind, including 'and Tiber, Father Tiber, to whom the Romans pray... ' which I'm sure I haven't thought of in twenty, years – and the statue of Marcus Aurelius, the steps of Aracoeli, the Wedding Cake, Castel San Angelo and the great dome floating above the city – wasn't that the story, Michelangelo saying he would set the Pantheon floating in the sky above Rome? Some people find easier ways of becoming famous."

The visitor had arrived a couple of days later than expected, with time only to stay overnight in Paris on the way. Myles, who had never actually met him, found himself – much to his surprise and a little to his bewilderment – regretting that he had to go out that evening. He even wondered if he might not be able to get back earlier: this uncle of his was apparently nothing like the cleric he had been expecting. Christine had gone to bed shortly after they had eaten, feeling tired. Jacky too was out, leaving the two men to themselves.

332

"It is strange, too," Alexis continued, "that in spite of its size, its past, its monuments and its sophistication, it is still in many ways a village by the Tiber. Almost as provincial as Dublin. And perhaps nothing in all of it more provincial than the universal Church. It's fantastic when you think how chauvinistic all empires are – the British, the Germans – Prussian and Hitler – the French at various times, the Soviets. Perhaps an unshakeable faith in their own superiority is essential. Once they can be persuaded to take a good look and succeed in laughing at themselves the whole ridiculous edifice crumbles. And people can breathe again. Now that the British have got rid of most of their ludicrous Empire, they are becoming creative, musical, and attractive as they were supposed to have been in the time of Shakespeare."

"The economists don't seem to agree with you."

"Surely you are not going to start quoting economists to me? 'Behold the lilies of the field, how they grow, they labour not, neither do they spin...' John, do you know what's wrong with the Church?"

"Why bother to go into details? Everything."

"That's a very disarming way of putting it."

"I'd be very surprised if you could tell me anything new. For the last five or six years, I don't think there is any possible charge I cannot have heard. You remember Mao's invitation to let a hundred, or was it a thousand flowers, bloom? The difference in our case is that the gag was not put back on. I think I must have had discussions with every intellectual under the sun. And the most virulent critics of all are Catholics."

"Perhaps because they have been hurt most; the others simply don't care."

"There's nothing you can suggest, I think, that I could not embroider on. But tell me in any case what your particular theory is."

"You are very unfair."

"Why?"

"Here I was, expecting to have a good argument with you. You not only take the wind out of my sails, but made me forget what I was going to say to you. I've completely forgotten."

"Surely you are not so lacking in imagination. If you like, I will make a few suggestions." Alexis looked at him affectionately, and smiled.

"You haven't changed much, Monsignor," he said.

"Nor you either, Doctor," he replied.

Alexis had a sudden memory of his jealousy, when they were both very young, of his elder brother, and Eva, a girl of John's own age with whom Alexis was in love. Alexis had been too small for her to take any notice of, and it had made him very unhappy.

"How about the Inquisition?" John asked, "it's a nice juicy bit."

"No, it wasn't that. That comes later."

"Well, the wealth of the Church? Octaviani? Spellman? McQuaid? Pius XII not condemning the Nazis? Come on, you don't want to change roles do you, and expect me to be the devil's advocate?"

"No, I'm out of practice. You see, I had to do the dutiful father the other evening when Myles led the attack."

"Pity he had to go out in that case."

"Do you realise you're being absolutely unscrupulous? You should already be angry. Well, let me start with a story. Did you ever hear about the declaration of the Republic?"

334

"Which one? Them are so many of them nowadays."

"It was in 1937, when De Valera introduced the new Constitution, abolishing all he had objected to in the Treaty, and declaring a fully independent State. There was to be a ceremony in the Irish Legation in Rome, to which the Vatican of course was invited at, say, three in the afternoon. But no one knew then how the British would take it. And this was before the war, remember, when the British still had an enormous empire in Africa. And in that empire there were lots of Catholic schools. So that to incur British displeasure might be a very serious matter. Whereas everyone in the Vatican knows that you can't shake the loyalty of an Irish Catholic. So three o'clock came and went, with no representative of the Vatican yet arrived at the Irish Legation, where things began to get very embarrassing, since lots of other people had condescended to turn up. And then, the King of England, no less, took a hand; he sent a telegram to Dev congratulating him. News travelled fast even in those days; within ten minutes of that news reaching the Legation, the car from the Vatican arrived. Have you ever heard that story before?"

"I confess I haven't, although I thought I was pretty well up in Vatican folklore."

"Do you think it's true?"

"'Si non e vero e ben trovato.' But tell me, if you were the Vatican, what, in the words of a certain comedian, would you have done, chum?"

"If I were a politician, there is only one answer – the same thing. But that's the crux of the matter. The incident is a very minor one. Perhaps it never even happened, although I was assured it was absolutely true by the person who told it to me. But it's typical of the history of the Church for twenty centuries. And I'm not thinking of the Borgias, and nepotism, and a score of other edifying subjects."

"But my dear Alexis, the Church doesn't exist in the abstract. You cannot get away from the world so long as you are in it. I gave

335

you an opening with Pius XII, who went very definitely on record with an encyclical condemning the Nazis – Mit brennenden Sorge – and thereby laid himself open to the charge of interfering in politics. He also interfered to save the lives of thousands of Jews, and has recently been condemned in a play for not doing more. But I'll give you a simple case. One of the original Mafias was made up by beggars who monopolised church doors. It's illegal now in many countries. Suppose you're a priest who sees one of these characters, whom he knows very well to be a fraud, standing with his piteous face at his church door every Sunday. What does he do? It hardly seems the thing for him to tell the police. But if he doesn't, he may be committing an offence himself. So, again, what do you do, chum?"

"Now you're getting some place. Forgive me if I quote scripture to you –"

"Go ahead, you have a good precedent."

"Don't be frivolous. 'Be ye perfect as your Heavenly Father is perfect'; you have just given a sound instance of a case in which the Church as an institution makes it impossible."

"Isn't that a little far-fetched?"

"Well, if you want something more concrete, you can have it. A great document of the Middle Ages has recently been published, the Register of the holy man who in 1334 became Pope Benedict XII, theologian and one-time professor at the Sorbonne. It is a full record – it runs to over fifteen hundred printed pages – of the Inquisition hearings he conducted over a period of seven years. He was then a bishop and presided himself over the court, with the Papal Inquisitor always present. There is not one single case of acquittal.

"And who were the 'heretics?' Mostly simple, ignorant people. They were faced by a bench of people as subtle as the holy bishop himself, brought before them after maybe months in confinement, to answer, without any kind of legal help, questions so phrased that it would take as subtle a theologian to answer them as the one who put them. The accused was given no chance to explain what he may have meant by a statement attributed to him, sometimes dating from fifteen years previously, or to challenge hostile witnesses – examined in his absence. Against the sentence there was no appeal – and that meant death, or incarceration for life. Judging by this, Shaw was over-indulgent to the Inquisitor in *Saint Joan*; taking it on its own horrible and revolting terms, the Inquisitor took it upon himself to send a fellow human being – who, so long as he was alive, might always repent – of sending him straight to hell. And yet this gentleman became the infallible successor of St Peter and, no doubt infallibly continued the same practices. They love to be saluted in the market places, and addressed as Rabbi; the High Priest who tried Jesus was also a consecrated cleric. It terrifies me, these servants of the due processes of the law, the law become an abstraction, like death, impersonal, annihilating without pity or appeal. Just think, for what I have been saying, I could be burned at the stake, and it would be your bounden duty, O Man of God, to denounce me, to be literally burned up with Christian love and zeal."

"You are getting hot."

"I didn't know the clergy were playing it so cool."

"Perhaps you may not have noticed, or you don't remember, but a few years ago an American firm of management consultants reported that the Vatican was one of the best-run organisations in the world. You know, sometimes a surgeon has to operate to save a patient's life. He can do it better if his eyes aren't filled with tears of pity."

"You've come a long way from the original fisherman in a Roman province."

"Is that a reproach or a compliment?"

"I can give you almost the same answer as I did a moment ago: if I were a businessman it would be a compliment. But as I'm supposed to be a Christian, it appals me."

"Do you think it would be better inefficient?"

337

"The word 'efficiency' in the mouth of an American business expert sends shivers down my spine and, finally, it seldom has any meaning at all unless you accept both his premises and a particular context. You know, like the experts with their computers in Vietnam who can be shot down by a peasant – who believes – with a converted bicycle pump."

"But you are still attaching emotional connotations. Efficiency can be quite neutral – just a question of doing things well instead of doing them sloppily. Personally I hate sloppiness – like people who walk simultaneously on both sides of a footpath and I can't get past."

"The experts must have been working on you."

"Why?"

"Efficiency is the last despairing effort at self-justification in people who have sold themselves to Mammon – and realised they have made a bad bargain."

"Words. I can give you a dictionary full of them!"

"You distrust words?" asked Alexis.

"I don't either trust or distrust them. I simply use them. Although, I agree, they sometimes take on a life of their own. I have a *Shorter Oxford* which invariably opens, of its own volition, at the word 'arsy-pursy'. It always seems to me somehow anti-clerical on its part."

"There is a game I intend to invent some time with a dictionary I have here. Let me show you. It gives you the first and last word at the top of each page. I haven't worked out the details. But listen to some of these I noted down. You get combinations like 'egg-whisk elevator,' 'phlegm pigtail,' 'carriage-forward castle,' 'Capuchin carriage-paid,' 'chorister circumflex.' Did you ever send a goggle-grained circumlocution clattering? Did you ever slap slipslop in a street-door strut and sit slantwise in a plum pudding police station after a tough trajectory by tram travel, or squash a stalking-horse with

338

a spirit-level spouse? How about this for a short story: coal-black coheir, convenient cop, curt, deft, dagger, darkness, darky, deadness? Beware of the tarantula telegraphist. Do you think the Borgias used diabolical digitalis? And many an Inquisitor must have had an exterminate face (take, oh take, your pertinacious phiz away). You are, I assume atrabilious, you apple-sauce arabist. Would you grudge a guy green grub, or a heartburning helpmate in hotbed humankind his humble hydrophilia, his saturnine scarlatina, his infelicity inhibition at an irresolute jamboree? If so, you would make gibbons glimmer, you mangy marginal addle-headed adolescent, tiring, with degrading demeanour and dervish destructiveness, an arable ark under an agricultural alias to a dignified dirge in the oblivion odd of a margrave massacre.

"I remember one day when Myles was small, he came back from school all excited. He had seen two mannequins being photographed for a fashion magazine, and they were made to take up the most extraordinary poses. He said one of them looked like a butterfly getting ready to fart. Christine was shocked, but we both broke our sides laughing when she told me about it.

"Now it's sufficient to have words lined up in order, ready for service in dictionaries, but the real interest is in their own gloriously mad anarchy. Perhaps there isn't much anarchy in certain sober subjects like mathematics –"

"Don't you believe it. Look what happened when Einstein wrote his little formula $E = Mc^2$, and when he found, maybe to his own amazement, that a straight line is not the shortest distance between two points."

"True enough. But the thing is, words have a life of their own. Just put two of them together, like the ones I've just quoted, and they're off. You think you can control them, but once you try putting them down on paper, you've got to have a very tight rein indeed, or it is they who take over."

"What are you getting at?"

"Control is bad enough in one language. But when you get to translation, the difficulty increases with something approaching geometrical progression. I was reading through one of these 'What's On in Paris' guides, when I discovered a new feature: several restaurants had added in a translation of their advertisements. This is a collection of the English ones – some had added German and Spanish as well."

He handed his brother some pages, with his own sub-titles between the cuttings.

59

We Almost Speak English

Already since 3 centuries

Ruddy already received guests in the 17th century cellar, place where the attractive women of Paris and the international elite meet. The tasty grilled meat on charcoal with savouries from the province deserves the enthusiasm of connoisseurs. The troubadour atmosphere, has all the old-time charm.

Peace of mind and a contented stomach

Souvenirs of bygone days and present day renown. Here, in the heart of Paris, you will obtain peace of mind and a contented stomach. Well prepared meals by candle-light.

Who was Otero that I should eat for her?

Old French specialities are available there every day in a decor of the Belle Epoque. You can take supper there and dream of the days of hansom cabs and la belle Otero.

Or Paul Fort for that matter?

A sanctum in Montparnasse. Memories of Paul Fort, prince of poets. Terrace with flowers and shrubs. The bar of a hundred cocktails and the 'ship'.

Another non-practising ship

Seafood specialised restaurant. This is an outpost of the Ile d'Yeu, that fish paradise. Lobster 'A la nage' is the crowning glory of this ship which never sails.

A fresh air system – just drop in

The most fashionable Parisian atmosphere. Fresh air system. Acclaimed by all leading travel guides. Drop in and look around. Open every day.

A warm ambience – don't miss this

This charming restaurant, founded in 1680, full of warm ambience, in historic setting, offers a big choice of a delicious menu for 11 F, prepared with big care. Not to miss.

Those typical and unexpected mountains

An elegant setting recalls the picturesque joys of the Dolomite mountains. Delicious specialities that are as typical and unexpected as the decor.

His typically French specialities

The host, a true gourmet and connoisseur of wine, will teach you to appreciate his typically French specialities.

Know your onions

One of the best onion soups of Paris and other brasserie specialities in the picturesque surroundings of the vegetable market.

Intimate candles

Intimate candles, guitars in exile and Spanish and Latin American folklore.

Paradise for the young

Candles, a huge spit, potatoes in the ashes. Paradise for the young.

A (spicy) rite in a typical house

An Indian alcohol you can find here and the proper thing to do is to drink it according to the (spicy) rite we shall reveal to you. The sun, an Aztec god, rules over this typical house. It is to be found in the highly spiced food, in the folk songs and dances.

A few consecrated incarnations

One of the great choucroute houses of Paris, with two rooms, both consecrated to 'butterfly' oysters, draught beer, wines from Alsace and the various incarnations of that food-loving region.

A big Parade

A gourmet's rendezvous in the fine setting of Louvre and Tuileries. Famed for his sea food specialities, and his big Parade of pastries and desserts.

A royal occasion, and eternal

Her majesty the Truffle was born in Périgord; she is betrothed to Foie Gras, the noblest of her subjects. They will both welcome you at this palace of good food in the heart of Paris the eternal.

Or at least thousands of years old

One of the classic dishes of Chinese cuisine, canard laqué, reaches the heights of perfection. The time-honoured charm of Paris mingled with gastronomic traditions thousands of years old.

But are you equal to the sumptuousness?

The exceptional luxury of a table-service of Sèvres, silver-gilted cutlery, crystal glasses, placed on lace table-cloths reigns, illuminated by chandeliers of Louis XV are equal to the sumptuousness of the place.

Princely carousing

Rose-tinged sunrise over St. Petersburg – blue-toned snow over Moscow – lingering laments from the Steppes, gypsy laughter and nights of princely carousing. At the RASPOUTINE, with its dreamlike decor, you can spend an evening fit for a Russian grandee.

A great theatre lover

The St. Petersburg of bygone days brought back to life by the most Parisian of Russians, the great theatre lover. Actors love to come here to eat the chachlik and the filet Stroganoff.

Folly of inebriation, a magic carpet of Byzantine roses

SHEHERAZADE, the storyteller of a thousand and one nights, has come to Paris on a magic carpet of Byzantine roses and offers a never-ending thousand and second night devoted to nocturnal delights and pleasures. SHEHERAZADE of the hundred violins – SHERERAZADE of the languorous and plaintive laments – SHEHERAZADE of the folly of inebriation – the eternal woman, ever-mysterious – you are the champagne on which our intoxication feeds.

Good news for visiting stockbrokers

Stockbrokers' luncheons and friendly dinners take place in this bistro with its Lyons style cuisine.

Discover your own duck cooked in salt

The many Danish hors d'oeuvre hot or cold, prepare the way for the discovery of duck cooked in salt, which is so excellent. Pastel coloured pastries.

What the real people of Paris discovered

An attractive decoration, an incomparable view on the Seine River, a first-class cuisine of rare specialities, this charming restaurant, which was opened not long ago seems to only serve specialities and the real people of Paris discovered it already.

A foie gras of repute, and amply met. Just squeeze in, gourmets.

The dazzling array of hors d'oeuvres (including a foie gras of repute) and of sweets amply meet the requirements of gourmets from abroad. The guests squeeze in together happily. Lovely stemmed glasses.

Flamed kidneys until six in the morning

An extensive card, little suppers until six o'clock in the morning. Specialities: dish with bread-crumbs, flamed kidneys.

A well-established reputation (and no wonder)

A place to relax and to have fun, rendezvous of attractive women, artists and brilliant personalities, this elegant restaurant is always one of the leading restaurants in Paris. Its exceptional sea-food, the amazing specialities of its chef and his rib of beef give him a well established gastronomical reputation.

If Montmartre is still a village with the Place du Tertre as its centre, then the Cadet de Gascognes is its local inn in which the South-Western cuisine and Bordeaux wines hold sway.

60

The Monsignor handed the pages back to Alexis.

"They remind me of my favourite in Italian guide books written in English: there is invariably 'a very suggestive statue of the Virgin' somewhere."

"My own is one I found in a bilingual Mexican guide to bullfighting. After the corrida, the matador gives thanks to the Black Virgin: 'Gracias, Morena'. In English, it becomes 'Thanks, brunette.' But the interesting thing about these advertisements is that the original is perfectly acceptable French, hardly at all odd or bizarre, even when it goes the equivalent of Hollywood poetic. The English is word for word correct. And yet you see how hilarious it becomes. I suppose you haven't forgotten your catechism any more than I have. Do you remember 'He that will not hear the Church' says Christ, 'let him be to thee as the heathen and the publican'? It always made me feel very sorry for Protestants. It was only afterwards I found that the phrase was quite different, in and out of its context, that the word translated as 'Church' was simply a gathering in the original, and very different indeed from old men in ermine capes shuffling around the Vatican."

"You seem to dislike the Vatican as much as any Orangeman from Belfast."

"If the devil is the father of lies, he seems to have begotten a varied brood on our Holy Mother the Church. Truth in a very impure medium, coded into catechisms. But it all happened long ago and was kind of ossified. Now we've seen the Council, to recall how it begins. All I can say is that if the Holy Ghost inspired the proceedings at Trent, he seems to have changed his mind since.

Which would seem to be either a heretical or a blasphemous statement. But the Church has accepted nearly everything that Luther proposed, having meanwhile provoked war after war and burned and tortured countless heretics, like the holy gentleman I mentioned earlier. Not forgetting the witches. And now we find the Holy Ghost winning by a short head, very often after a bitter rearguard action by the reverentissimos who would still be burning Protestants in the market-places if they had a chance – and the power. Which represents progress of course. But why was the Holy Ghost wrong the first time? Perhaps it's these famous business management methods at the Vatican that have made the difference."

"You are beginning to make me uncomfortable."

"No more than I am myself. When do religious imperatives make contact with the lives of living people? Communists want to create the new man where Christianity has failed. My kingdom is not of this world. But if so, why was the world created? If it is impure to touch the naked body of a woman, why was it created? What is love? What do you mean by it?"

"'Love, oh love, oh careless love, you see what careless love has done' sang John. But go on. I need this – what shall I call it – anti-confession."

"I will let you off Galileo, as there are other subjects I know a little more about. I won't go into Teilhard de Chardin, who seems to me to be a kind of Catholic H.G. Wells. No, let me talk about medicine. Here you tell us, the natural law is the great yardstick. There has always been all this talk of sins and practices against nature (nature never being defined), while at the same time, nearly every natural act is sinful also. When the ideas upon which doctrine is based are proved wrong, what happens to the doctrine? The earth didn't move around the sun because that would contradict the bible, which was directly inspired by God. But if it is proved beyond doubt so to move, what happens? The ideas current at Trent about the mechanism of conception were hopelessly wrong. The alleged physical effects of masturbation were used to frighten the life out of children, and often frightened them out of religion when they did not dare go on confessing to it; and yet, it is probably as natural and as inescapable as puberty itself. The authorities are now even prepared to admit that human sexuality has a spiritual and social meaning that make it essentially different from sexuality in animals. And this of course leads quite naturally to the great question – birth control. I presume I don't have to quote figures to you, or to tell you of populations literally doubling, or poverty in India and other over-populated countries. And so on."

"Malthus did not prove right last century," said the Monsignor. "There is no knowing what way science may develop food supplies by the end of the century. Maybe from the sea-bed, where the possibilities are unlimited; maybe synthetically in ways that may abolish the need for food in the sense in which we now know it; maybe people will even be moving off to other planets. But apart from all that, can't you see the other implications? The Pope is faced with the same sort of moral dilemma as the people who found they could make an atomic bomb: a veritable sexplosion. Whatever the Church's other failings and imperfections, love has always been central to its teaching. Love has always been something more than sex. And Christian morality followed from that.

"But any morality, to be effective," said Alexis, "has to be credible and workable, and must have a strong admixture of common-sense. Apart from religious grounds, sexuality outside marriage always involved the risk of producing unwanted children, unfortunates born into the world without the protection even nature entitled them to. This is now entirely changed or soon will be. If there is no longer any risk of doing a terrible wrong to someone yet unborn, it becomes more and more like legalistic formalism to condemn the same action between two people who may be more even in love, but are not married. Especially when you consider that European ideas on monogamy are by no means universally accepted, and did not apply to Abraham for example. So why make it illegal? If the third party argument is excluded, why sex only inside marriage? If the natural law is as important as all that, what about the sexual instinct which is the most natural of all human instincts? You will remember that woman is also involved, but the legislation that applies to her, with all her physiological differences, has always been laid down by men who

348

could have no direct experience of them. It started of course from the elegant description of woman as a tub of guts. I don't know, incidentally, how the holy man who coined that phrase got round his veneration for the Blessed Virgin, who was undoubtedly a woman also. Why the prohibition?"

"The unwanted pregnancy is only the beginning. Suppose the man or the woman is already married – and you are right away into jealousy, resentment, hatred, the break-up of a family, the bewilderment and resentment of children... Nobody has ever described what happens better than Tolstoy, the irresistible, overpowering passion of Vronsky for Anna Karenina – whom he is tired of almost as soon as his object is attained, leaving her to despair and suicide under the train in which he is playing cards with his brother officers – before you know where you are into the whole stately procession of the Seven Deadly Sins – Pride, Covetousness, Lust, Anger, Gluttony, Envy and Sloth. And who told the story? Why Tolstoy, the great moral reformer who almost drove his own wife mad in the process. And the first war in Europe's history and mythology – how did it start? Over Helen of Troy; and yet Homer ends his story with the return of Ulysses – after many Circes – to the faithful Penelope. Sex is a simple matter only for people who mistake pornography for truth. The Church did not invent the morality it preaches. It was Christ himself who condemned fornication, and the Pope, sitting in the Chair of Peter, is his representative on earth."

"As far as I remember, it was precisely the legalistic formalists whom Christ was always most against, and that formalism came from an institution as legalistic as the Church."

"He still told the woman to sin no more."

The Monsignor was silent for the moment. Then he continued:

"Those who try to drag truth out into the light, like the woman taken in adultery, often find the tables turned, and the roles reversed."

"The whole world is an unending chain reaction of evil," said Alexis, "and the reaction often starts with smugness, then resentment

349

of it, leading to hostility and fighting between individuals, people, communities, nations, and finally the whole world – the great achievement of the twentieth century. With the loser hating the winner, and start all over again. Is there any point at which it can be stopped? If each could smother his own smugness and his own resentments... Christianity might have succeeded in that, but it became an organisation, and substituted theology and canon law for the simple message of the gospel. And we end up with computers in the Vatican making up the statistics of the number of hosts consumed in communion by parish, diocese, county, region, and the percentage increase or decrease worked out by statistical weighted average –"

"Don't exaggerate."

"Do I exaggerate? I've never forgotten the American Jesuit magazine talking of what would happen when modern convert-making techniques were introduced. Do you remember our mother one day at home – I think you were there too – talking about her own mother and her own childhood. That must take us back well over a hundred years. The local parish priest warned his flock against buying from Godless Jewish travelling peddlers. But, as the old lady said, these poor people had to live, the same as any one else. And she bought from them. The longer I live the more that seems to symbolise. When the overwhelming population of Irish Catholics finally won independence from the small Protestant Ascendancy, it was not they who sought revenge; there is hardly a single example of it on record. The only bitterness and sectarianism was that kept alive by a few of the more zealous churchmen who gained us a reputation even in the Vatican as being on the same level of tolerance – and intelligence – as the Daughters of the American Revolution. The wrong reasons for doing right are never as persuasive as the right reasons for doing wrong – words taken from the Devil's Book of Maxims for the Handling of Irish Bishops. There are not many John XXIIIs in the Irish episcopacy."

"There have not been many in all history, any more than there have been many Gandhis or Shakespeares or Mozarts or Dantes: except that he was God's own genius."

350

"Perhaps life is just God's design for living vicariously," said Alexis. "How can you reconcile all that bigotry with Christ's teaching? Or is the codification and the interpretation and the explanation more important than the message? Words, words, always words. Tell me that a straight line is a triangle without angles, and I have some inkling of a meaning, mathematical, philosophical, or even poetic. How many feathers has a bird to lose before it goes bald and can't fly any more?"

"It probably dies before."

"Perhaps that is a cure for baldness" said Alexis. "But how much do you think the doctrine of the Trinity or of Transubstantiation explains to a professor in the Sorbonne or a bailiff in Ballybunion? Does it really matter? Yet people have been burned as heretics for not accepting what they could not grasp, let alone understand, and were honest enough to say so."

"There is a beautiful and rather terrible story by Gogol" said the Monsignor, "called 'The Overcoat' about a poor miserable little clerk, despised by everyone, with a name as absurd as himself, Akaky Akakyevich. His overcoat grew threadbare beyond repair and he was so poor that it cost him an almost superhuman effort to replace it – but he had to if he was to continue going in the icy cold to his scrivener's job in a civil service office. Then one night he is beaten up, and the new overcoat, the only miracle in his life, is stolen. When he recovers sufficiently, he goes timidly to a General in the civil service, hoping for redress. But the great man is so incensed that Akaky has not gone through the proper channels, so shouts at him, and bellows and browbeats and frightens him, that poor Akaky goes home more dead than alive, takes to his bed, and dies, alone and forsaken as he has lived. And they took him away and buried him, and St. Petersburg went on as if Akaky Akakyevich had never existed. I confess to you that there are times when his death means more to me than the Crucifixion."

"I know that story. There is no Easter in it," said Alexis, "and no ministering angel; only an ant wriggling helplessly, caught in a hair on your arm. Loneliness amid people, dying of hunger amid surfeit,

351

born into an expanding universe, waiting for Godot in one that's all the time contracting, expanding the womb, forcing the issue and haste to the tomb, closed in again, futile and derisive dust. John," said Alexis desperately, "do you know what it's all about? Is it a kindness that thousands are dying at this moment, alone, sick, forsaken; is it God's kindness that saves them from the temptation to suicide?"

"Don't you think that a lot of the horror of the world is due to people who put dung up their noses and then complain that the world stinks? The mind is always busy, but how much fodder does it really need? Does the intellect need all that much before it will bite? Your son has probably innumerable facts à la mode to learn before he can hope to find a job and live on it afterwards. Only a few centuries ago, if you had read six books, you were learned. How far have we really got since? Any paper you pick up is full of the cleverness of intellectuals preaching, theorising, prescribing."

"But look back as far as you like, and ordinary people's preoccupations are singularly alike. And yet human liberty hangs on a thread the world over and can disappear in any country overnight. You talk about the Inquisition, and there are hundreds of new ones, from Marx to McCarthy. I saw a project recently for a new building in Moscow (although I think it's been abandoned since), like an inverted telescope shooting up into the sky, a new Tower of Babel, higher than the Empire State Building or the Tour Eiffel, with a gigantic statue of Lenin on top about a sixth of the total height, rising up into the heavens and, watch out God, we're coming after you. Saint Sartre pray for us. Saint Camus pray for us. Saint Genet, graciously hear us. The Little Father of the Peoples died at last, and his statues fell, but new gods are found. Hitler's myriads are dispersed, but Mao's millions are marching with splendid banners.

"You try to look at things objectively, from outside. You see the quarrels of others from outside, and see their absurdity – until you get involved yourself, when all your complacency disappears. You try instead to fix your mind on the great eternal things, art and beauty if you like. And you find that the suffering of others is also part of the eternal order of things. You can't get outside it, just as you can't enjoy art in the abstract any more than you can enjoy it without eating

352

and defecating. Our ideals are attained only on a horizon which is always receding and we never reach. The monstrous injustice always remains of the little man, the peasant in Vietnam, killed in the name of one of the ideologies or the other, and all our ideals and all our cleverness cannot save one of the children there who will no doubt be killed tonight –"

"– With the blessing on the engine that kills her, of the Cardinal – a rank pretty close to the heavenly throne that, and near to the Holy Ghost – who said it is holy and inevitable, a weapon in the fight for Christ. And on Christmas Day. Suffer little children to come unto me, and I will napalm them. He was right, the Irish bishop who went home and told his flock he brought them the consoling news that nothing was changed by Vatican II."

"If you have these ideas," said Alexis suddenly, "why not do something about them?"

"Because I don't want to be caught in my own trap. It's hard to be an anarchist. It is so easy to fall into the trap of rejecting dogmas and substituting your own. Ideas soon cease to vibrate in the mind in the way they do when they come to you first. Does even love last? Perhaps it's only what you can bring out of yourself that has any real reality. That is maybe what vocation means. The rest are only unconscious loans."

The stones are there for everyone, thought Alexis, but everyone assembles differently. Possessions, what a laugh, said the bones. The skull grins its toothless grin. Possession is for such a little while. And the little bits of experience accumulating, acquiring a patina, seen in different lights, changing as the setting in which they are remembered changes, and suddenly, the familiar mosaic is all wrong. Jewels in dreams that vanish with the opening eye, but leave a mark like a receding tide. Can you recapture what you have seen or experienced? Is it then artifice, artefact, or merely counterfeit? Words, poor weapons to affront the ineffable. The sun rises, immutably, every morning, and sets in the evening. But each day is different.

"I have had plenty of great ideas," continued the Monsignor, "and invariably found that their truth was relative. It has made me very wary of trying to impose them on others. And then there is another thing – what do we mean by faith?

"When has the Church, repository of the faith, ever shown faith, the faith that moves mountains? Among all the talk about the failures in love and charity, there has hardly ever been a mention of the failure of the Church as institution to trust in God; it has always preferred to rely on what it considered to be its own political and diplomatic acumen.

"And perhaps it is this that is responsible for what is so often referred to as the crisis of faith. I agree with you, Alexis. Ordinary people, with all their faults, are capable of generosity, kindness, disinterested love of their neighbours, even down to the level of emptying bedpans. In the important things, they don't need Canon Law to tell them what is right and wrong. It is not they who invented prisons, law, excommunication, inquisitors, or burning at the stake for heresy. If you believe in God, surely God can be trusted to deal with a heretic also, and it is both pretentious and blasphemous for the Church – which finally means an individual, however ecclesiastical he may be – to interfere. In other words, if God knows best, he doesn't need my advice."

"It seems elementary," said Alexis.

"Most things are just elementary common sense – when you prescribe them for others. Has there been a day since we were born when the world was wholly at peace, when people weren't killing each other in the name of some idea or ideal or another – one solitary day? People dying cruelly and stupidly. And we, living stupidly and abetting it all, with death another mechanism, the only sure one, waiting for us, another. Or Another. If people reject religious dogma, they are not happy until they find a substitute.

"I am glad of your indictment, Alexis; not glad of all these shameful things, but that the Church at last has made its own mea culpa. The difficulty is that it has had to make its confession to the world, and the world is simply not interested, or is less forgiving than the God the Church preaches.

"I no longer mind what dogmas the Church asks me to accept. I will accept them out of obedience, because God is in any case more than any dogma, and more impenetrable. Since John XXIII, the question of dogma has become irrelevant, to me at any rate. Perhaps when the Vicar of Christ was human enough to be lonely and invite his gardener to share supper with him, as one peasant to another, Christianity was once again back where it started. Material progress may be necessary, but it is not that which will save the world; there is only one hope: simplicity and goodness. Unless you be as little children you shall not enter into the kingdom of heaven. Probably, like the Church itself, I am too infected and too corrupted ever to attain that simplicity, that simple unaffected love of others. But if Christianity means anything, it is that. And for each of us, it must start with himself."

Neither spoke for a time. Then the Monsignor said:

"Suppose, as many would persuade us, we shall soon be able to increase knowledge in geometrical progression, analyse all our economic, social, financial, educational ills, work on ourselves and on our thoughts, fears, feelings, with emotional thermostats and electronic psychoanalysts, reduce all human activity to data that can be processed into some marvellously objective but indifferent machine, what will come out at the other end? A formula for immortality, the philosopher's stone, the essence of wisdom – or merely another Sphinxian riddle that has an Oedipus solution?

"Will it tell us anything more than we already know about the mystery behind every human face?

"Go to the moon if you will. What have you achieved? Is it superhuman, something beyond, transcendent, metaphysical? Or an extension only of the mechanical?

"Does it satisfy a man, bring him anywhere forward?"

355

"'The higher up the palm tree go monkey,'" quoted Alexis, "'more he show.'"

His brother continued:

"No dictator is satisfied without absolute power. But it's almost a law of nature that power corrupts, absolute power absolutely corrupts. What power could be more absolute than control over men's souls? Can you wield such power and still be uncorrupted, still be naive enough to believe that, unless you be as little children, you shall not enter into the kingdom of heaven? The answer is you can't remain uncorrupted, and you live in a practical world, so you hedge. Unless you are a John XXIII. If you live in a practical world, how can you accept the monstrous naivety, the utter childishness of a doctrine which says that there is only one enemy, hatred (when you know there are so many)? And only one thing that can vanquish it, love, and tells you to love your neighbour and, when you ask who is my neighbour, tells you my neighbour is all mankind?

"But if, living in a practical world, you don't accept it, don't accept this naive doctrine, why talk of Christianity?

"And if you can't accept it, and still call yourself Christian, where are you to find the sublime naivety of a Russian army of several million men who ended their part in a war in 1917 by simply refusing to fight, and going home?

"There are young people all over the world today who are still pure; not perhaps with the purity that was the only sort of virtue the Church could recognise for so long, but pure in heart. Sometimes I have a kind of a mad, impossible vision, not of the lilies of the field, but of the hippies in the field, of them growing older, still uncorrupted, still despising power when they inherit the earth, here, in Russia, China, America, everywhere, of them becoming the judges and rulers, and of their great bellowing Homeric and Rabelaisian laughter when some lunatics whom we accepted, until late in the twentieth century, as our most powerful, our wisest, and our most sophisticated, suggest that they should dress their children up in fancy clothes and send them out to kill one another. It's mad I suppose, and naive, but only as naive and mad as what Christ commanded us to preach."

Again both were silent. At last Alexis said:

"I am sorry Myles was not here this evening."

The Monsignor smiled, a little sadly.

"Why should your son be any more ready to accept what we may think than we were, at his age to accept the advice of others? If everything happens by God's will, it must be God's will that Myles is not here tonight. We must all learn humility enough to recognise that a human life and an individual soul is the great adventure each of us lives separately, and that perhaps nothing we know or do has any validity for another. And even our very mistakes may in the long run be more fruitful than our good intentions."

"That is what you mean by faith?" asked Alexis.

"One of the things at least."

"I had a friend once who believed in nothing, but used to go into churches in strange towns to light a candle. Is that faith?"

"Who knows from where the spark may come? The great gates of Kiev are a pile of rubble. But for anyone who has ever heard the music of Moussorgsky, they still exist. The Tour St Jacques is probably more moving than if a church were attached to it. And perhaps the only service the Turks ever did Greece was to blow up the Parthenon. For it could never be as beautiful, whole, as it is today, on its hill above the city. We are born too early or too late, but there is always so much beauty in the world, if we have eyes to see it."

Alexis asked: "What time did you say your plane is tomorrow?"

"Early. I shall have to leave the house before eight. I hope we do not disturb Christine."

357

"She usually sleeps fairly well. But she tires easily. I am sure she regrets seeing so little of you this time." He paused, and added slowly: "I say 'this time', but there will probably never be another."

His brother looked at him and did not reply, knowing it was true, that to say anything conventional would be misplaced, and yet longing to be able to utter some word of comfort.

"She is so young" he said at last.

"And 'Queens have died young and fair, dust hath closed Helen's eye, I am sick, I must die, Lord have mercy on us,'" Alexis quoted. "One last question before we go to bed. Christine became a Catholic to marry me. If you were a Protestant, now, after the Vatican Council, could you imagine yourself turning Catholic?"

The Monsignor gave him a friendly slap on the shoulder. "You mustn't forget, even if you are my brother, that I am a faithful son of the Church. There are some questions you shouldn't ask. Not yet, anyway," he added enigmatically.

"Not yet?" Alexis insisted.

"Perhaps when a generation of people too old to change has passed away, the question will cease to have any meaning."

"Perhaps by then there will be no Church left, Catholic or Protestant: only Christians?"

"God knows," he answered seriously. "Goodnight, Alexis."

61

Since he had first left it, Dublin seemed to have changed almost less than any other city he had known. Some of his contemporaries had changed, had aged shockingly; others, whom he had seen more frequently during previous visits, seemed almost exactly as he had known them. Faces reappeared which he had completely forgotten. Others he remembered, but could no longer attach a name, or recall in what circumstances he had known them. There were times when the appearance of a face he had known startled him as much as if it were the face of someone already dead, of Yeats, or Shaw, or Joyce, or of people even further back, Swift or Goldsmith, so imperceptibly had all the past from which he had been separated by his life abroad conglomerated; like the dichotomy he often experienced in a cinema or theatre, a moment almost of panic when the mind suddenly remembers a world separate and other from the one with which it has allowed itself momentarily to become absorbed, and fights for sanity, like swimming in a dream, inexplicably out of depth and far from the shore.

No hazard of a previous visit had ever brought him together with Maureen, and he had never made any attempt to see her. Many of his former colleagues were in practice in the smallish area bounded by Merrion and Fitzwilliam Squares, Stephen's Green and College Green. And it was on his second day back, just after visiting the National Library to check a reference in the paper he was to read, that he finally met her again, going up Grafton Street. She recognised him at once.

"But you haven't changed a bit," he said to her. It was true. She was astonishingly little changed. Her silhouette was dominated still by the auburn copper hair which she still wore long. Her features were as fine as ever. Only her expression seemed to have changed, to have softened. There was less of what he had once taken for haughtiness, and she greeted him with a warmth that, twenty years before, would have made his heart beat faster and now spanned the distance in time as if the bitterness of his disappointment when he lost her had never existed. Life had arranged otherwise: life was like that.

"Or you either," she answered, "except that you limp now. Was that that time in Switzerland?"

"Oh, of course," he said, "I had forgotten. I still had two normal legs the last time I saw you. Yes, I had an operation that was successful in a way, but left me with this."

He must have changed. And yet, in a way, it was true. If he had realised any of his real ambitions, if his life had been a progression instead of a steady movement away from the freedom of youth... But beyond the disappointments, the proved hollowness of so many things, do I really feel different... ?

"Have you time to come and have a drink?" he asked.

"Even if I hadn't," she smiled, "after twenty years..."

"It's not really that, is it?" he said. "Yes, I suppose it must be. Where shall we go? I am only a visitor now, you realise."

"Davy Byrne's is always there, and it's only round the corner."

When they were sitting down, he looked round, savouring his memories. They exchanged news. She had no children. He felt obscurely grateful for that without exactly knowing why; it somehow seemed to leave her less committed to another. He told her about Christine's illness. She looked at him in concern.

"Poor Alexis," she said. She took his hand, and held it for a little while. His mind was a confusion of thoughts. Christine suddenly seemed so far away, so alone, frail, forsaken and unprotected. At the same time, Maureen's presence and sympathy were very sweet to him. If only this had happened before...

After a time, she said: "You know Bill, my husband?"

"I think I remember him, in a sort of way," he answered.

"He knows you. But you must have been in Dublin in all this time. Why did you never look us up?"

He shrugged his shoulders helplessly.

"I don't know. I didn't really know your husband."

"But you knew me."

"That was different."

"How?"

"Friends are neutral, so to speak. If I had met your husband with you, accidentally, I suppose it would have been all right. But I could not bring myself to go and see you."

"But why?"

"Because I was in love with you. I always have been, in a sort of poetic, helpless way."

"But, Alexis, we hardly knew each other."

"And yet you see how it is, even after twenty years. Are we like two people who scarcely knew each other?"

"It's true," she said.

"I spent only one afternoon with you. I don't know if you remember."

"I do. We went out to Howth. And you quoted poetry to me on the top of the bus. Or was it still the tram in those days?"

"I even dared to kiss you goodnight. It was so good that I tried a second. You caught my hair in front with the most gentle violence, and disappeared."

She smiled. She had not forgotten. He felt a surge of gratitude.

"And then I had to go to London."

"And while you were away, my illness happened."

They fell silent. Did the course of life hinge on such little, almost accidental things?

"You never realised how much I was in love with you?"

"I suppose I did. To some extent at least, from your letters. There was one marvellous one. Yes, I suppose I did read between the lines. I was never much good at writing letters myself."

"Your best was the first part of your last. I've never forgotten reading it. There seemed to be something like a warmth I'd always been hoping for. And then, suddenly, the news: you were engaged."

It was her turn to shake her shoulders, hopelessly.

"I am sorry," she said.

"It all happened a long time ago, to other people in another life," he answered. "Unhappiness can be very illogical. Do you know one of the things I resented most?"

"What?"

"The fact that you would be called 'Missis'. I couldn't think of my love, beautiful and graceful, being affubulated with so utterly dull, stupid, prosaic a title. The very sight and sound of it are flat as platitude, glue on the imagination, the death of the soul."

Maureen laughed.

"It would have been the same title if I had married you."

"But then I would have had the only consolation that could have justified it."

"I'm afraid I can't stay much longer," she said, "but now that we have met, you must come and see us. Make the big sacrifice for my sake and come and see the monster. You will find he is not so terrible. In fact he is very sweet, Bill. Are you free on Thursday evening?"

"That's the day after tomorrow. Yes, I think so."

"Then I shall expect you. Come and have dinner with us. About 7.30. You promise?"

"Yes, I'll be there."

62

On his way to an appointment an hour later, Alexis felt a pain which he knew could only be one thing, the appendicitis which had been latent for so long. He rang one of his medical friends at his hospital, and arrangements were already made to receive him when he got there, after making a few further phone calls, including one to the home of the brother he was staying with, and one to Paris.

The examination confirmed his diagnosis. The case did not seem very serious and he decided that, as fate had taken a hand, he might as well have the second operation while he was still in the hospital, the one he had postponed because of Christine's condition, as it would have to be done sooner or later anyway. Both were successfully performed. As he had arranged, a telegram was sent to Paris, as soon as the second was finished, and before he was yet out of the anaesthetic.

It seemed to him he was in an enormous waiting room in which people were coming in all the time, people of all ages and conditions. They were all very orderly at first, going up to one of the five or six nurses who entered particulars in their ledgers. There were two exits, out through which people passed nervously, looking backwards as they went, as if hoping to see a friend. But there were no friends. All of a sudden one man who was being registered bolted. He got back to the door through which he had entered, shook it violently. When it did not open, he started to hammer on it. One of the nurses came over. She looked at the man, haughtily and superciliously.

"I told you," she said sternly, "the appointment is noted down in the book. It just cannot be put off." She turned to Alexis and said in a whisper: "You must be ready always to move on when the time comes, with your bags packed and ready. After all, there is so little luggage you need, except what is spoken on the wind, and hidden in the mind and in the heart."

Alexis knew that what she said was desperately important. He must at all costs not forget, and he tried to learn it by heart so that he would remember when he woke up. But to his dismay, he could not remember a single word.

He said timidly: "I admit I had to have the second operation, but you know I could have put off the first. And there are all the things, like music, I shall never do. But it doesn't matter now."

He knew there was something not right in what he said, and looked anxiously at her. To his relief, she was smiling.

"I don't know if they will accept that, but we'll see," she said.

How had he failed to see that it was Maureen? He was suddenly very happy. He would have been quite content to stay in the waiting room, but she took him gaily by the hand, out through an enormous door he had not noticed before. The sea, a mirror in the low rising sun, soon became a distant blur in the gaps between the trees. There was a large sailing boat with three red sails, taut in the wind. It was still sunny, but it had grown cloudy, tingeing the background water with black. I have never seen anything so beautiful as those three red sails. But if I had a boat, I would be afraid to have red sails in case I should grow tired of owning them. My sails would be white like everyone else's.

He turned to Maureen for confirmation, but she had vanished. He began to go down the hillside, towards the sea, because he knew that Christine was resting in a hammock, in a garden lower down.

"I have never consciously or wittingly injured another person," he said to himself as he worked his way down – his leg did not seem to cause him any difficulties in the descent – "Can God decently ask any more, considering all the potential for evil he built into me?"

But he felt uneasy just the same. He remembered Maureen, and looked round, seeking her. She was nowhere to be seen, and he resumed his way, dismally at first, thinking of Eva.

Now and at the hour of our death.

Eva, the very first (how right the name was). Her father had an old Ford, pride of the neighbourhood, into which he once packed twenty-three of the local urchins for a joy-ride. I missed that. But not another, when he took us all out to the sea. The tide was out, very far out. Channels criss-crossed the strand, where you could paddle, the water lukewarm. Sudden, frightening depths, in puddles four foot across. The strand is dangerous in spots, sand that sucks, and when the tide is in, engenders whirlpools, currents. The day was warm, the evening cooler, full of salt, seaweed smells, shells and cockles, small and large stones and the damp sand. My togs were home-made, knitted. How could I have lost them? Yet I remember nakedness sometime during that evening, so small that it did not matter to the others though it did to me.

And Eva was there. Perhaps John, too, John, Monsignor John. The one she was fond of. I was not exactly jealous, envious only. Conscious once of a smell of scent that I tried in all kinds of circumstances to recapture. And she is dead now, Eva, from that so-called delicacy in the chest they all had. Like the daughter of the tall old man next door, who passed by each morning as I tried to suck honey from the nasturtiums, and spoke to me, leaning on his walking stick. And the light in the back room at night that I could see from our kitchen. She died too. Death. What could it possibly mean? Suppose my father and mother were to die. A hole into which you fall when they put the candle out at night and there is no end to it, nothing to grip and you lose your breath and you fall and you keep falling and something rolls in waves through your head and the onset is like a cramp that gets you in the leg which you can't cheat because it's already too late.

Was she slim, Eva, or thin? I don't know. Her hair, I remember, was black and very straight I can remember her face in a kind of way, but I can't describe it. Her eyes, I think, were brown. It was no doubt the face of one marked out early for death, although she was not the first to go. It is her voice above all I remember, her voice, and a certain kindness in her face, her beautiful pale face that I saw not long before she died, when I was old enough for all those vague feelings to concentrate into something that makes you for the first time, and for days, forget everything that until then made up the world. How to describe her voice? Not hoarse, not husky, not clear either.

Their house was not far from ours, if you wanted to go by the back way. They were both on the same level. In between there was a commons, where the Ford was sometimes parked. At the other end, some steps led down to a road, upon which their house fronted. There, sometimes, the car would be parked. I often sit in it, on a Sunday morning, nonchalant at the steering wheel, hoping that the drivers of all the other cars that pass will take me for a motorist waiting for a passenger to come out.

Memory of a voice that, when she laughed, seemed to crack musically and never break. A house made of an old tea-chest, a blanket thrown over a brush, a candle fitfully burning to provide light, to make illusions, a candle butt in a cardboard box with three holes cut for windows and a slab cut on three sides with a fourth to act as hinges to a door that opened into a parallel world of normality where she never entered except in my dreams. The stars may dance for you, the violins play, and brightness fall from the air. Who but me can tell you of that brittle voice of Eva's, now that no more is left of her on this earth but what lives in the memory of my first love.

Eva? Christine? Christine with her funny English. But Christine is dying. I am sick, I must die, Lord have mercy on us. I cannot go and leave Christine. Jacky, little one, you will not let them... I see black light. Myles, what is happening?

The clot of blood killed him. When the nurse came back, his body was already growing cold.

63

Myles had still to learn the strangest lesson of all: that nothing lasts, not even despair. It was not yet possible to believe that one day again, there would be sun, carefree days, and sand and sea, that he would fall in love, and give and share the one thing that, for a while at least, brings a joy that is past all merit or understanding.

He had gone across to Dublin for his father's funeral, where everyone had been extraordinarily kind to him. The uncle he had at first avoided in Paris and then involuntarily missed, he met in different circumstances and surroundings. There had at first been a curious shyness on both sides. Then one evening they had dinner alone together, and he discovered someone altogether different from the absurd ecclesiastic of his imaginings, another such as he might have found in his father had he known in time. But now that chapter was closed for ever.

His mother, bewildered at first by the shock, had borne it with great courage, and lived in a kind of despairing loyalty that defied her grief. But her wasted body could not stand much more, and within a month, he and Jacky followed the coffin of their other parent.

Both died without ever knowing that Jacky was pregnant. His parents dead, he discovered all that underlay the apparently smooth machinery of their lives. There was no time even for the sad indulgence of a decent grief; he was caught up in the legal complications, a seemingly endless succession of papers, certificates, documents, accounts, bills. There was no immediate financial crisis, but that too was a question to be faced.

The pregnancy approached its term, and Jacky entered a clinic. He accompanied her, and went through the agonising embarrassment of having to explain that he was not the prospective father. Trying to hide his feelings from Jacky, he hoped against hope the child would not survive.

The birth was extraordinarily difficult: a forceps delivery after fourteen hours labour. The child was put in an incubator, but seemed doomed. Against all instructions, and almost by main physical force, Jacky went to see her child so that she should at least once see it alive. She stood staring at the pitiful bunch of red flesh for a long time, through the glass, telling herself it must not die, it must not die, I will not let it die. And as if some extraordinary force had passed over from her own will for it to live, it survived.

One afternoon, a month later Myles had been going through his father's papers, and found one folded in an envelope, with the rejection slip of a Sunday newspaper. He brought it in to show it to Jacky. She had the child in her arms, soothing it.

"What is it?" she asked.

"Listen," he said, and read it out to her.

369

64
To a prelate, on going to the wars
(for Catherine, who is Vietnamese)

A Viet baby
in the Orient dawn
screaming as the napalm falls
suffer little children
for the love of Mao Buddha Christ
a brief-case lifted
and another month
or year
of mangled carnage
twisted bodies
mutilated
fire knives guns blistered faces
agony
death death death
months years a quarter century
a quarter million children in five years
dead
suffer little children –
and on to total victory
for such is the Kingdom of Heaven –
and just wars end in great victories
as we all know
social escalation and a faster rise in
living standards
strategic bombing and logistic aims
a surer end to living hazards
the war is just
we have your word for it

in terms of jeans and boiler-suits respectively but
next time you lift that brief-case up
feel
with your ideological brains and
think in your mortal – for you too are mortal – guts
skulls all or skulls prospective
corpses take no bows
when the show is over in a theatre of war
and light has no meaning for the slaughtered dead
only for stage managers
leaders and thinkers and saviours of mankind
Marxist theory and Mao's thought
we love you all
Kennedy's dead smile and the live grin of Johnson
we love you all
nothing to lose but our chains
nothing to eat but our bowls
and a pox on both your houses
suffer little children
a quarter million of them
O emissary of Christ?
and on to final victory
O blasphemous Christmas Day
for such is the Kingdom of Heaven?
an orphaned universe in a stygian night
in the West bodies
thicken even without growing fat
bodies thicken
Viet bodies slender gracile
on the ground
in the jungle
at street corners bridges cafés shops
a Viet orphan
starving lost
a long knife
her first memory
a headless body spouting blood
and Catherine
O merciful Jesus

Catherine is twenty-five today

65

"Who is Catherine?" she asked.

"Didn't he talk one evening about a Vietnamese orphan adopted by a colleague of his?"

"Yes, I think you are right."

The Vietnamese war was not over yet. Since his protest days, Myles had learned in a new way what havoc death could wreak in a family. And that had been what one might almost call civilised death, not the ruthless, bloody massacre that, for a quarter of a century almost uninterruptedly, had gone relentlessly on and looked as if it might never stop.

The baby started to cry. She gave it the bottle and it was quiet again. He looked over at his sister, and her quiet confidence, her unexpected reserves of strength and moral courage, her disregard for all the conventions that he had told himself he despised and yet had so feared that he had desired the death of this unfortunate child. She held the little girl serenely, the child born fatherless into a world so libertine in its manners and so puritan in its social attitudes, so liberal in its declarations and so full of hate and racism, and began to realise, in a new way, what courage means, and the nature of love. The little girl was alive, whatever her future might hold. Before the night was out, hundreds like her might be bombed, burned or maimed in a tiny country in its twenty-fifth year of war.

Doth God exact day labour, light denied?
He doth.
Apparently.
I don't know.

373

To live one's life is not just like crossing a field.
Or so they say.
So they say.